The United Kingdom
Mathematics Trust

Title: Introductions to Number Theory and Inequalities

Author: Christopher Bradley

Editor: Geoff Smith

ISBN 0 9536823 8 2

Published by:
The United Kingdom Mathematics Trust (UKMT), an educational charity. This organization can be contacted via:

Maths Challenges Office,
School of Mathematics,
University of Leeds,
Leeds LS2 9JT (+44 113 343 2339)

e-mail: publishing@ukmt.org.uk

URL: http://www.ukmt.org.uk

Printed in the United Kingdom by Cromwell Press, Trowbridge, Wiltshire.

Contents

An Introduction to Number Theory

Introduction

The purpose of this book is to provide talented students with more challenging material than exists in secondary school syllabuses. The age range targeted is 15 to 18 years, though some who are younger would also benefit. The book is divided into 10 parts called *Weeks*. The student should work on the material in Week 1 before being reading the Commentary to Week 1. When that has been digested the material for Week 2 can be addressed and so on.

The Commentary is very full, with complete solutions to all exercises, plus additional insights. Although most readers will probably benefit from contact with an experienced expert, an exceptional student may well manage without any outside help.

A number of theorems in this book are stated without proof. They may be found in many excellent textbooks, for example, *A Friendly Introduction to Number Theory* by J. H. Silverman, Prentice Hall (1997). The other book that I heartily recommend is *An Introduction to the Theory of Numbers* by Niven, Zuckerman and Montgomery, Wiley (1991).

An alternative use for this material may be in Maths Clubs, where more guidance is available and a wider ability range is involved.

I am grateful to Prof Adam McBride of the University of Strathclyde for working through the manuscripts and making a number of corrections and suggestions for improvement. I should also like to thank Prof Jim Weigold of the University of Wales, Cardiff and Dr Brian Wilson of Royal Holloway University of London for a number of helpful comments. I am also grateful to the United Kingdom Mathematics Trust for encouragement to put what originated as a set of notes for the Bristol Regional Mathematics Circle into presentable form and in particular to Dr Geoff Smith of the University of Bath for editing the text and making a number of additions and improvements (to both books).

Christopher J Bradley, Bristol, June 2006.

Christopher Bradley

Formerly a University Lecturer in the University of Oxford and Official Fellow and Tutor at Jesus College, he was Deputy Leader of the UK Mathematical Olympiad Team from 1992-1995, and was for many years a teacher at Clifton College, Bristol. He is the author of many questions of the British Mathematical Olympiad, and plays an active part in the preparations of the British team for the annual International Mathematical Olympiad.

Editorial Remarks

These introductions are two separate books published as a single volume to provide young mathematicians with cheap and ready access to material which is particularly useful in mathematics problems competitions at secondary school level: national and regional mathematical olympiads, and the IMO itself.

Christopher Bradley is a prolific author of questions for mathematics competitions, and played an important role on the *Problem Selection Committee* of IMO 2002 in Glasgow.

This volume, and the earlier UKMT publication *Plane Euclidean Geometry: Theory and Problems* are characterized by the very large number of carefully constructed exercises which the reader is asked to do.

I hope that every secondary school will have both this book and *Plane Euclidean Geometry* in its library. The prices have been set so low that many good students will wish to purchase their own copies. Schools wishing to give out large numbers of copies of these books as prizes should note that discounts may be negotiated with the UKMT office.

Geoff Smith, University of Bath, June 2006.

Chapter 1

Number Theory: Week 1

1.1 The natural numbers, divisibility, the Euclidean algorithm and primes.

1.1.1 The natural numbers

These are sometimes called the counting numbers or the whole numbers and consist of

$$1, 2, 3, 4, 5, 6, 7, \ldots n, \ldots$$

The set of such numbers is denoted by $\mathbb{N}$.

Because the natural numbers are ordered and adjacent ones have difference 1 it follows that if $n > m$, then $n \geq m + 1$.

1.1.2 The integers

These are comprised of the natural numbers, their negatives and zero and therefore consist of

$$0, \pm 1, \pm 2, \pm 3, \pm 4, \ldots, \pm n \ldots$$

The set of such numbers is denoted by $\mathbb{Z}$. The positive integers and the natural numbers are the same set.

1.1.3   Divisibility

An integer a is said to be divisible by an integer b if there exists an integer q such that $a = bq$. A useful notation is $b \mid a$, meaning b divides a. The quantity q is sometimes called the *quotient*. Sometimes the words *dividend* and *divisor* are used for a and b respectively. Thus 21 is divisible by 7, or $7 \mid 21$, with quotient 3. We also say 7 is a *factor* of 21 and 21 is a *multiple* of 7. Note that 0 is divisible by all integers. However, you cannot divide any non-zero integer by 0.

1.1.4   Primes, irreducibles and units

We define a *prime number* p to be a positive integer bigger than 1 such that given integers m and n, if $p \mid mn$, then either $p \mid m$ or $p \mid n$. We define an *irreducible* to be an integer t which is neither 1 nor -1, and has property that t is divisible only by ± 1 and $\pm t$. The integers that divide 1 are called *units* and consist of ± 1. The primes and irreducibles have been defined so as not to include the units.

Theorem 1.1 A prime number is an irreducible.

Proof If p is prime and $p = mn$, then $p \mid mn$ and so $p \mid m$ or $p \mid n$. If $p \mid m$, then $m = cp$ and so $p = pcn$, and since $p \neq 0$, we have $cn = 1$ and so $c = n = 1$ or $c = n = -1$. A similar argument applies if $p \mid n$. Hence if m divides p, then $m = \pm 1$ or $\pm p$. ■

Later we will show that all positive irreducibles are prime. So why, you may ask, introduce two different words to define such similar objects: the irreducibles are just the positive and negative primes. The answer lies in a generalization of number systems in which 'integers' may exist, but in which primes and irreducibles are very different things.

1.1.5   An important theorem

Theorem 1.2

If $d \mid a$ and $d \mid b$ then $d \mid (xa + yb)$ for all integers x and y.

Proof   If $d \mid a$ and $d \mid b$, then $a = md$ and $b = nd$. Thus $xa + yb = xmd + ynd = (xm + yn)d$ and hence $d \mid (xa + yb)$. ∎

For example, if a and b are both multiples of 5 then so is any linear combination of a and b. It is often sensible to prove properly things that for a long time we have taken for granted.

1.1.6   The Euclidean algorithm

Suppose a and b are integers with $a > b \geq 1$. Then $(a + 1)b > ab \geq a$, so there are positive multiples of b that are greater than a. We take it as axiomatic that a non-empty subset of the positive integers has a least member. In Mathematics this is called the *principle of well ordering*. So there is a least integer $(q + 1)$ such that $(q + 1)b > a$. It follows that $qb \leq a$ and hence $a = qb + r$, where $0 \leq r$. Also $r < b$ since $(q + 1)b > a$. We may therefore write

$$a = qb + r, \quad \text{where} \quad 0 \leq r < b. \tag{1.1}$$

The ability to divide a positive integer by another one and to produce a quotient and a non-negative remainder less than the divisor is so commonplace that it is scarcely thought of as being remarkable. But in fact what we are really doing is to say that given any two positive integers a and b with $a > b \geq 1$, then there exist integers Q such that $Qb > a$ and that the set of all such integers Q has a least member namely $(q + 1)$.

Equation (1.1) is the heart of the *Euclidean algorithm* which works as follows. If $r \neq 0$, then since b and r are positive integers with $b > r \geq 1$, the Euclidean algorithm can be applied again using b and r. And the process can be repeated again and again until we get a remainder that is zero. Since the remainder is always less than the divisor, each step of the process involves a non-negative integer remainder which is less than that of the previous step. The process must therefore terminate after a finite number of steps, and consequently can be called an algorithm.

Let us apply this algorithm when $a = 893$ and $b = 705$. We have
$$
\begin{aligned}
893 &= 1 \times 705 + 188, \\
705 &= 3 \times 188 + 141, \\
188 &= 1 \times 141 + 47, \\
141 &= 3 \times 47 + 0.
\end{aligned}
$$

1.1.7 Greatest Common Divisor

The *greatest common divisor* (sometimes called the *highest common factor*) of two positive integers a and b is defined to be the positive integer d such that (i) d divides both a and b and (ii) if c is any other factor of a and b, then c divides d. The notation $d = (a, b)$ is often used. If $(a, b) = 1$ then a and b are said to be *coprime* or *relatively prime*. Hence 21 and 16 are coprime. Repeated use of the Euclidean algorithm provides the greatest common divisor as the last non-zero remainder (in almost all cases, but why is the statement not quite true)? Thus $(893, 705) = 47$. The claim that 47 is the highest common factor arises from the following argument which makes repeated use of Theorem 1.2. First 47 divides 141 and hence divides 188. It divides 141 and 188, so it divides

705. It divides 188 and 705 and so it divides 893. 47 is therefore a factor of 705 and 893. Secondly, working the other way round, if c divides both 893 and 705 it must divide 188. Since c divides both 705 and 188 it must divide 141 and hence in turn it must divide 47. Therefore 47 satisfies both property (i) and property (ii) of the above definition and is the greatest common divisor. The (slightly damaged) argument that repeated use of the Euclidean algorithm always provides the greatest common divisor as the last non-zero remainder follows precisely the same form as that used for 893 and 705. To write the argument out in detail using letters rather than numbers provides no further insight and so is omitted.

1.1.8 Least common multiple

If $a \mid m$ and $b \mid m$ them m is a common multiple of a and b. If m has the properties (i) that it is a common multiple of a and b, and (ii) $m \mid n$ whenever n is common multiple of a and b, then m is called the least common multiple of a and b.

The notation $m = [a, b]$ is often used.

The least common multiple of 893 and 705 is 13395. In the exercises below you should not express integers as products of their prime factors since we have not yet shown that such factorizations are unique. You should only use the concepts we have covered so far.

Exercises

1. Find the greatest common divisor h of 630 and 765 using the Euclidean algorithm.

2. Find the integers s and t such that $630 = hs$ and $765 = ht$ and prove that s and t such that $630 = hs$ and $765 = ht$ and

prove that s and t are coprime. Prove that $[s,t] = st$ and hence find the least common multiple of 630 and 765.

3. Verify that $630 \times 765 = (765, 630) \times [765, 630]$.

4. Is it true that $ab = (a, b) \times [a, b]$ for all positive integers a, b? If so, prove it.

5. Prove that $[893, 705] = 13395$.

Example

We prove that 75 and 34 are coprime.
    We have

$$
\begin{aligned}
75 &= 2 \times 34 + 7, \\
34 &= 4 \times 7 + 6, \\
7 &= 1 \times 6 + 1, \\
6 &= 6 \times 1.
\end{aligned}
$$

Since 1 is the last non-zero remainder 75 and 34 are coprime.

Exercises

6. Prove using the method of the example that 12 and 35 are coprime.

7. Are 430 and 259 coprime?

The working of the example above may be recast as follows:

$$
\begin{aligned}
1 &= 7 - 1 \times 6 \\
&= 7 - 1 \times (34 - 4 \times 7) \\
&= 5 \times 7 - 1 \times 34 \\
&= 5 \times (75 - 2 \times 34) - 1 \times 34 \\
&= 5 \times 75 - 11 \times 34.
\end{aligned}
$$

In terms of $a = 75$ and $b = 34$, we have $xa + yb = 1$, where $x = 5$ and $y = -11$.

Theorem 1.3

If a and b are coprime positive integers, then there exist integers x and y such that $xa + yb = 1$.

The proof is constructive, using the Euclidean algorithm in reverse, as in the example above and is therefore omitted.

Exercises

8. Use your result of Exercise 6 to find integers x and y such that $35x + 12y = 1$.

9. Write down integers x and y such that $7x + 4y = 1$.

10. Find expressions for all integers x and y such that $7x + 4y = 1$.

11. Explain why it is not possible to find integers x and y such that $133x + 84y = 1$.

12. What is the smallest positive integer h for which x and y can be found such that $133x + 84y = h$?

13. A pair of scales is provided with an arbitrarily large quantity of 7g and 4g weights. What are the weights of objects which can be accurately ascertained

    (a) if one or more weights can be placed in the pan where the object is put (with weights in the other pan) and

    (b) if the weights must be put in the pan only on the other side to that of the object being weighed?

Theorem 1.4 An irreducible integer is a prime.

Proof Suppose that t is irreducible and that $t \mid mn$. Suppose also that t does not divide m. Since the only factors of t are ± 1 and $\pm t$ this means that t and m are coprime. It follows from Theorem 1.3 that integers x and y exist such that $xt + ym = 1$. Hence $xtn + ymn = n$. Now $t \mid xtn$ and $t \mid ymn$ and hence, by Theorem 1.2, $t \mid n$. It follows that t is prime. ∎

The equivalence of positive irreducibles and primes is crucially important in the arithmetic of integers, as it allows us to prove that the factorization of a positive integer into irreducible positive integers can be done in one and only one way.

Theorem 1.5 If N a positive integer, then N is either 1, a prime, or a product of primes (positive irreducibles). Suppose that $N = p_1 p_2 \ldots p_n = q_1 q_2 q_3 \ldots q_m$, where the $p_j, j = 1$ to n and $q_k, k = 1$ to m are primes, then $n = m$ and the q_k are a permutation of the p_j. (Note that the p_j and q_k are not necessarily distinct since powers of primes may occur).

Proof The proof is technically complicated, but the ideas are simple enough. First you have to justify the first sentence. How could it fail? Only if there is at least one positive integer for which the sentence is false. Thus there is a non-empty set of positive integers for which the sentence is false. Now invoke the well-ordering principle. There must be a least positive integer M which violates the conditions. Now M is neither 1 nor a prime (i.e. a positive irreducible). Thus $M = M_1 M_2$ where both M_1 and M_2 are smaller than M. Thus for M_1 and M_2 the first sentence applies. It therefore applies to $M_1 M_2$ which is impossible because this is M. We have deduced a contradiction from the assumption that there is at least one positive integer for which the first sentence is false.

Therefore the first sentence is a true assertion about the positive integers.

Now suppose you have two rival such factorizations. Then you cancel out any common factors. If you can completely cancel out, you have proved the uniqueness of factorization. Otherwise you are not left with $1 = 1$ so there are some primes remaining on the left, and some remaining on the right, and those on the left are different from those on the right. Therefore some p_k divides a product of some of the primes q_j. Relabel the primes on the right so that the remaining ones are $q_1, q_2, \ldots, q_t$. Since the p_k is irreducible and $p_k \mid q_1 q_2 \cdots q_t$, it follows that $p_1 \mid q_1$ or $p_1 \mid q_2 \cdots q_t$. Repeating this argument again and again we establish that p_k divides some q_j. But q_j is irreducible and $p_k \neq 1$, so $p_k = q_j$ which is absurd. This contradiction establishes the result. ∎

Exercises

14. Factorize into primes 244578251 and 944578251.

15. Use the method of factorization into primes to find the greatest common divisor and the least common multiple of 4061 and 3813.

16. If p, q, r are primes and $m = p^2 q^3 r^4$ and $n = p^4 q^2 r^3$ find (m, n) and $[m, n]$ and verify that $mn = (m, n) \times [m, n]$.

Project

In Exercise 13 you had lots of 7g and 4g weights and in part (b) you should have constructed a table something like the one on the next page, where $7x + 4y = N$. You should have found that after 17 it looks as though the answer is 'Yes' for all subsequent N. Your

first task, if you have not already done it, is to **prove** that all cases
with $N > 17$ can be managed.

The abstract project is this: given any two coprime positive integers a and b, find in terms of a and b a formula for the largest positive integer N which **cannot** be expressed in the form $N = xa + yb$, where x and y are non-negative integers. You may suppose without loss of generality that $a > b$. One thing should be pretty obvious and that is the formula must be invariant under exchange of a and b. A fairly simple formula exists and is due to the English mathematician Sylvester who lived in the latter half of the nineteenth century.

N		x	y
0	Yes	0	0
1	No		
2	No		
3	No		
4	Yes	0	1
5	No		
6	No		
7	Yes	1	0
8	Yes	0	2
9	No		
10	No		
11	Yes	1	1
12	Yes	0	3
13	No		
14	Yes	2	0
15	Yes	1	2
16	Yes	0	4
17	No		

The way to set about such a project is to try other cases besides 7 and 4 for a and b and make sure you keep a catalogue of all the 'Yes' and 'No' cases, as they provide clues for the last part of the project. Try then to guess a formula that satisfies all the evidence you have. But then appreciate your work has only just begun. This is because your formula has to work for all a and b, and not for the few cases you have checked.

In other words there has to be an *algebraic proof* to cover all cases. As mentioned above the formula is fairly easy to discover, but the general proof of why it is correct is hard. You will manage only if you pick up the correct clues from the evidence you have collected. Consider it a success if you make substantial progress.

1.2 Commentary Week 1

1. $765 = 1 \times 630 + 135, 630 = 4 \times 135 + 90, 135 = 1 \times 90 + 45, 90 = 2 \times 45$, so $(765, 630) = 45$.

2. $s = 14, t = 17$, so $st = 14 \times 17 = 238$. If st/n is a common multiple of s and t where n is an integer, then both s/n and t/n must be integers. But $(s, t) = 1$, so $n = 1$ and hence $[s, t] = 238$. Now if s, t are coprime $(hs, ht) = h$ and $[hs, ht] = hst$. Putting $h = 45$ we get $[765, 630] = 45 \times 238 = 10710$.

3. $765 \times 630 = 481590 = 238 \times 10710$.

4. Yes and the proof follows exactly the steps used in the solution of Exercises 2 and 3.

5. From the text $(893, 705) = 47$. Now $893 = 47 \times 19$ and $705 = 47 \times 15$. Now $(19, 15) = 1$ and $[19, 15] = 19 \times 15 = 285$. It follows that $[893, 705] = 47 \times 285 = 13395$.

6. $35 = 2 \times 12 + 11, 12 = 1 \times 11 + 1, 11 = 11 \times 1$. The last non-zero remainder is 1, so 35 and 12 are coprime.

7. $430 = 1 \times 259 + 171, 259 = 1 \times 171 + 88, 171 = 1 \times 88 + 83, 88 = 1 \times 83 + 5$. We can shortcut the working at this point. 83 and 5 are coprime, so therefore are 430 and 259.

8. From Exercise 6 we have $1 = 12 - 1 \times 11 = 12 - 1 \times (35 - 2 \times 12) = 3 \times 12 - 1 \times 35$, so $x = -1, y = 3$ is a solution. Note that in this case you can obtain the result more quickly by observation, so do not allow a procedure get in the way of your initiative.

9. $x = -1, y = 2$ is one solution of $7x + 4y = 1$.

10. Having got one solution you can get all solutions in the following way : Put $x = -1 + X, y = 2 + Y$, then $1 = 7x + 4y = 1 + 7X + 4Y$, so $7X + 4Y = 0$. then since 7 and 4 are coprime, it follows that an integer k exists such that $X = -4k, Y = 7k$. Hence the solutions are $x = -1 - 4k$, $y = 2 + 7k$ where k can be any integer. In geometrical terms we have obtained all points on the line with equation $7x + 4y = 1$ whose coordinates are both integers.

11. It is not possible to find integers x and y such that $133x + 84y = 1$ because $7 \mid 133$ and $7 \mid 84$, so by Theorem 1.2 $7 \mid 133x + 84y$ for all integers x and y. But 7 does not divide 1.

12. By the argument in the solution to Exercise 11 h must be a multiple of 7. That $h = 7$ follows from the fact that $x = -5, y = 8$ does in fact provide a right hand side of precisely 7.

13. For part (a) from the solution to Exercise 10 note that $x = -1, y = 2$ satisfies the equation $7x + 4y = 1$, so if we wish to weigh an object of Ng one can use the result $7Nx + 4Ny = N$ to deduce one possible result. Put the object with N 7g

weights making a total of $8N$g in one pan, and then this can be balanced by $2N$ 4g weights in the other pan. This means that if weights can be put in both pans then any integer gram object can be weighed. For part (b) when weights can be put in one pan only to balance the given object in the other pan the answer is that integer gram objects of the following weights can be managed:

0g, 4g, 7g, 8g, 11g, 12g, 14g, 15g 16g and all integer weights $\geq$ 18g.

18g can be managed with 2 7g weights and 1 4g weight
19g can be managed with 1 7g weight and 3 4g weight
20g can be managed with 0 7g weight and 5 4g weights
21g can be managed with 3 7g weights and 0 4g weight.

Thereafter adding an extra 4g weight will take care of the cases 22g, 23g, 24g, 25g and so on by adding more 4g weights. Of course this will not be the most efficient way of performing the weighing, but one of the things to be learned about mathematics is that any correct method that works will do.

14. $244578251 = 23 \times 31 \times 37 \times 73 \times 127$ and $944578251 = 3^2 \times 131 \times 733 \times 1093$. If you did this without using a software package such as *DERIVE* you will have seen how difficult it is to factorize large numbers into irreducibles and how long it takes. Techniques have been developed to speed up the process that depends on trying to divide by each irreducible in turn. However, the difficulty of the task for integers having 100 or more digits enables the arithmetic of such large numbers to be used in encryption.

15. $4061 = 31 \times 131, 3813 = 3 \times 31 \times 41$, so $(4061, 3813) = 31$ and $[4061, 3813] = 499503$.

16. $(m, n) = p^2 q^2 r^3$, $[m, n] = p^4 q^3 r^4$. Both products are $p^6 q^5 r^7$.

Project

In the project you are asked to find a formula in terms of a and b for the largest positive integer N which cannot be expressed in the form $N = xa + yb$, where both x and y are non-negative integers. Here a and b are coprime positive integers and without loss of generality you may take $a > b$. Some of the evidence you might have collected is shown in the Table below.

a	b	N
5	2	3
5	3	7
5	4	11
6	5	19
7	2	5
7	3	11
7	4	17
7	5	23

It appears that a possible formula is $N = ab - a - b$. The proof is not easy, but if you have spotted the following clue you will not be surprised to know that the proof is based on it. Look at the case $a = 7, b = 4$ given in the text. In the Table you will see 0 Yes, 17 No; 1 No, 16 Yes; 2 No, 15 Yes; 3 No, 14 Yes; 4 Yes, 13 No; 5 No, 12 Yes; 6 No, 11 Yes; 7 Yes, 10 No; 8 Yes, 9 No.

Each pair has one 'Yes' and one 'No'. Tabulate some of your other evidence and you will find the same. Of course, since a and b cannot both be even the proposed value of N is always odd, so this sort of pairing off is always possible. The main part of the argument is therefore the following result.

Lemma 1.6 If m is a non-negative integer such that $0 \le m \le ab - a - b$, and $n = ab - a - b - m$, then precisely one of m, n is representable in the form $xa + yb$, where x and y are non-negative integers and the other is not so representable.

Proof Suppose in fact that $m = xa + yb$ and $n = ua + vb$. We want to disprove that all of x, y, u, v can be chosen to be non-negative. In fact we want to show that if x, y, u are non-negative then v is definitely negative. Now if x, y, u, v are non-negative then $0 \le x \le (b-1)$ and $0 \le u \le (b-1)$, otherwise m or n could get too large. Adding the two equations we get $m + n = ab - a - b = (x+u)a + (y+v)b$. That is

$$ab = (x+u+1)a + (y+v+1)b \qquad (1.2)$$

It follows from Theorem 1.2 and the fact that a and b are coprime that $b \mid (x+u+1)$. But from the above inequalities $(x+u+1) \le (2b-1) < 2b$. Hence $b = x+u+1$ and dividing Equation (1.2) by b one gets $y + v + 1 = 0$. Thus, if y is non-negative, then v is negative. ∎

If you were convinced by that argument, then wake up! There is a hole in the proof. We have shown that small m and n cannot both be representable, but we have not shown that at least one of them is. Try to mend the proof yourself, and if necessary consult the full argument in *Challenges in Geometry* by C. J. Bradley, published by Oxford University Press.

Theorem 1.7 For all integers $M > ab - a - b$ the equation $xa + ya = M$ has solutions in which x, y are non-negative.

Proof We are still assuming without loss of generality that $a > b$. Clearly none of $1, 2, 3, \ldots (b-1)$ is representable, so by the Lemma $N - 1$, $N - 2$, $N - 3$, $\ldots$, $N - b + 1$ are all representable, where $N = ab - a - b$. By adding 1 to the value of y in each of these cases we deduce that $N + b - 1, N + b - 2, N + b - 3, \ldots, N + 1$ are representable. $N + b$ is also representable, since $N + b = ab - a$ for which we may choose $x = (b-1), y = 0$. We now have a sequence of b representable consecutive integers, namely $N+1, N+2, N+3, \ldots, N+b$ and then by increasing the value of y by 1 again we get the next integers and so on. ∎

It is not an expectation that suddenly overnight you should be able to write mathematics of this level of sophistication. But it should be acknowledged that if general results are to be proved at all, then someone has to be able to do it and so it must be a reasonable aim that eventually you should be able to do so. What you should see about the above proof is that it is a generalization of the particular case $a = 7, b = 4$. For the most part this is how algebraic results are established. Algebra without the benefit of study of particular cases is very seldom constructed. The danger with modern trends in the teaching of mathematics is that emphasis is placed in framing hypotheses, but not in proving them because of their difficulty. This book will have provided a service if you appreciate that making a conjecture of a result is often a very long way from proving it, and convincing the mathematical world of its veracity. Fermat conjectured his Last Theorem, but it was 300 years before Wiles proved it. And many interesting conjectures remain as open questions.

Chapter 2

Number Theory: Week 2

2.1 Factorization, prime numbers, equations of the second degree.

2.1.1 Factorization

This is the reverse of multiplying out and collecting like terms, so the following factorizations are easily checked:

$$x^2 - y^2 = (x + y)(x - y), \tag{2.1}$$

$$xy + dx + cy + cd = (x + c)(y + d), \tag{2.2}$$

$$abx^2 + (ad + bc)x + cd = (ax + c)(bx + d) \tag{2.3}$$

Of course Equations (2.1) is a particular cases of Equation (2.2), but it is so often used that they it is quite rightly the subject of separate exercises in elementary textbooks. You should make sure you are able to complete the following Exercises before proceeding with the text. To factorize an expression such as (2.3) you multiply the coefficient of x^2 and the absolute coefficient to get $abcd$ and then this has to be factored so that the sum of the two factors is $ad + bc$.

For example, with $6x^2 - xy - 12y^2$, $abcd = -72$, then $ad = 8, bc = -9, ab = 6, cd = -12$. Hence $a = 2, b = 3, c = -3, d = 4$ and the factorization is $(2x - 3y)(3x + 4y)$.

Exercises

Factorize the following expressions:

1. $16x^2 - 25y^2$;

2. $200^2 - 1$;

3. 999991;

4. $16xy - 8x + 4y - 2$;

5. $x^4 - y^4$;

6. 9984

7. 99999919

8. $x^2 + 9x + 14$;

9. $x^2 - 9x + 14$;

10. $x^2 + 5x - 14$;

11. $x^2 - 5x - 14$;

12. $6x^2 + 25xy + 14y^2$;

13. $12x^2 + xy - 6y^2$;

14. $15x^2 - 19xy + 6y^2$;

15. $14x^2 - 3xy - 2y^2$.

Strictly speaking any factorization problem should state whether only integers are to be used, or whether other sets of numbers may be used. In the above Exercises the factorization is over the integers. The expression $x^2 + 2x + 1 - k = (x + 1)^2 - k$ factorizes over the integers if $k = a^2$, where a is an integer, for then it factors into $(x + 1 + a)(x + 1 - a)$. However, if k is not a perfect square the expression does not factorize over the integers. On the other hand if k is positive, the expression factorizes over the real numbers into $(x + 1 + \sqrt{k})(x + 1 - \sqrt{k})$. If k is negative the expression no longer factorizes over the real numbers, but it factorizes over the complex numbers.

2.1.2 The fundamental theorem of algebra

A remarkable theorem about complex numbers is that polynomial expressions always factorize into *linear factors* over the complex numbers. The proof is beyond the scope of this book, but the result should be well known.

Theorem 2.1 If $a_1, \ldots, a_n$ are any complex numbers there exist complex numbers $b_1, b_2 \ldots, b_n$ such that the expression $z^n + a_1 z^{n-1} + a_2 z^{n-2} + \ldots + a_n = (z - b_1)(z - b_2) \ldots (z - b_n)$.

A corollary of this result is that if the coefficients $a_1, a_2, \ldots, a_n$ are real numbers, then the expression factorizes over the real numbers into *linear and quadratic factors*. That is, none of the factors need be of degree higher than two. For example

$$x^3 - y^3 = (x - y)(x^2 + xy + y^2); \tag{2.4}$$

$$x^3 + y^3 = (x + y)(x^2 - xy + y^2). \tag{2.5}$$

Exercises

Factorize over the integers:

16. $x^5 - y^5$;

17. $x^5 + y^5$;

18. $x^4 + 4$;

19. $x^{2k+1} + y^{2k+1}$;

20. $x^{2k+1} - y^{2k+1}$;

21. Prove that

$$x^5 - 1 = (x-1)(x^2 + \frac{1}{2}(1+\sqrt{5})x + 1)(x^2 + \frac{1}{2}(1-\sqrt{5})x + 1).$$

2.1.3 Primes

One use of factorization is that if an integer can be thrown into an algebraic form that factorizes then it cannot be prime (unless one of the factors is 1). For example

$$973 = 1000 - 27 = 10^3 - 3^3 = (10-3)(10^2 + 10 \times 3 + 3^2) = 7 \times 139.$$

Exercises

22. Factorize 14640.

23. Factorize 10004.

24. Prove that no term in the sequence 1001, 1000001, 1000000001, ..., where the number of zeros is $(3k+2), k = 0, 1, 2, \ldots$ is prime.

25. If $N(n) = (1/3)(4^n - 1)$ prove that $N(n)$ is always an integer. Find the prime factors of $N(4), N(5), N(6)$. For what values of n does $7 \mid N(n)$? Prove that if n is not a power of 2 then $N(n)$ has a prime factor of the form $4k + 3$ (that is prime such as 3,7,11,19 ...).

Theorem 2.2 [Euclid] There are an infinite number of primes.

Proof Suppose, for contradiction, that this result is false. Thus there would be a maximum prime P. Consider Q, one more than the product of all primes up to and including P, so $Q = (2 \times 3 \times 5 \times 7 \times \ldots \times P) + 1$. Evidently Q is not divisible by any of $2,3,5,7,\ldots P$. So either Q is prime or it is divisible only by primes greater than P. In either case we have a contradiction, so there is no maximum prime. ∎

Notice that 2 is the only even prime number and apart from 2 and 3 all prime numbers are of the form $(6k - 1)$ or $(6k + 1)$.

Exercises

26. Why are there no other prime numbers besides those mentioned in the last paragraph?

27. Prove that there are an infinite number of primes of the form $6k - 1$ (that is of the form $5,11,17,23,\ldots$).

28. Prove that if p and $p^2 + 2$ are prime then $p^3 + 2$ is also a prime.

29. Prove that for all primes $p > 3$ it is the case that $24 \mid (p^2 - 1)$.

30. What can you say about p if $p, p+10$ and $p+14$ are all prime?

31. Prove that if n is odd then $2^n + 1$ is not prime unless $n = 1$.

2.1.4 Equations of the second degree

Factorization is a very useful tool in solving problems that lead to algebraic equations. You are no doubt familiar with the solution of quadratic equations by factorization, but in Number Theory we are more concerned with equations that contain two variables, but whose values are limited to be integers. These are called Diophantine equations. For example if we wish to find all positive integers x and y such that $x^2 - y^2 = 105$, we can frame the problem in factored form $(x + y)(x - y) = 3 \times 5 \times 7$. Now we can see that the following possibilities exist $x + y = 105, x - y = 1; x = y = 35, x - y = 3; x + y = 21, x - y = 5; x + y = 15, x - y = 7$. Leading to $(x, y) = (53, 52)$ or $(19, 16)$ or $(13, 8)$ or $(11, 4)$.

Exercises

32. Find all positive integer values of x and y such that $x^2 - y^2 = 60$.

33. A rectangular chessboard with m rows and n columns has the squares round the edge cut away. If only two thirds of the squares remain find all possible values of m and n.

Project

Some factorizations of $2^n + 1$ for different values of n are shown in the Table below.

n	Factors of $2^n + 1$
3	3×3
4	17
6	5×13
9	$19 \times 3 \times 3 \times 3$
16	65537
19	3×174763
24	$97 \times 673 \times 257$

If you have not completed Exercise 31 you should now be able to do so. Now investigate what happens when N is even. What do you think might be the case? What can you actually prove? But be careful not to jump to conclusions. There is one hypothesis that is still unproved and I wonder if you can detect what it might be?

2.2 Commentary   Week 2

1. $(4x + 5y)(4x - 5y)$.

2. $(200 + 1)(200 - 1) = 201 \times 199 = 3 \times 67 \times 199$.

3. $1000^2 - 3^2 = 1003 \times 997 = 17 \times 59 \times 997$.

4. $2(4x + 1)(2y - 1)$.

5. $(x^2 + y^2)(x^2 - y^2) = (x^2 + y^2)(x - y)(x + y)$.

6. By the result of the last Exercise $9984 = 10^4 - 2^4 = 104 \times 8 \times 12 = 2^8 \times 3 \times 13$.

7. Similarly $99999919 = 100^4 - 3^4 = 10009 \times 97 \times 103$.
   How much work do you have to do to show 10009 is prime? The least sophisticated and most obvious method is to divide by each prime in turn starting with 2 then 3 then 5 and so on. Can you see why it is sufficient to stop when you have tried 97?

8. $(x + 7)(x + 2)$.

9. $(x - 7)(x - 2)$.

10. $(x + 7)(x - 2)$.

11. $(x - 7)(x + 2)$.

12. $(2x + 7y)(3x + 2y)$.

13. $(3x - 2y)(4x + 3y)$.

14. $(3x - 2y)(5x - 3y)$.

15. $(2x - y)(7x + 2y)$.

16. $x^5 - y^5 = (x - y)(x^4 + x^3y + x^2y^2 + xy^3 + y^4)$.

17. $x^5 + y^5 = (x + y)(x^4 - x^3y + x^2y^2 - xy^3 + y^4)$.

18. $x^4 + 4 = (x^2 + 2x + 2)(x^2 - 2x + 2)$.

19. $x^{2k+1} + y^{2k+1} = (x + y)(x^{2k} - x^{2k-1}y + x^{2k-2}y^2 - \cdots + y^{2k})$.

20. $x^{2k+1} - y^{2k+1} = (x - y)(x^{2k} + x^{2k-1}y + x^{2k-2}y^2 + \cdots + y^{2k})$.
    Of course this may not be the complete factorization. For
    example $x^9 - y^9 = (x - y)(x^2 + xy + y^2)(x^6 + x^3y^3 + y^6)$.

21. -

22. $14640 = 11^4 - 1^4 = 10 \times 12 \times 122$.

23. $10004 = 10^4 + 4$, and by Exercise 18 this comes to $122 \times 82 = 2^2 \times 41 \times 61$.

24. The terms in the sequence $1001, 1000001, 1000000001, \ldots$ may
    be written in the form $(10^k)^3 + 1^3$, $k = 1, 2, 3 \ldots$ so by the fac-
    torization in the text they are of the form $(10^k + 1)(10^{2k} - 10k + 1)$, and hence they are not prime. For example $1001 = 11 \times 91 = 11 \times 7 \times 13$, $1000001 = 101 \times 9901$ and $1000000001 = 1001 \times 999001 = 11 \times 7 \times 13 \times 19 \times 52579$.

25. $4^n - 1$ has a factor $(4 - 1)$ so $N(n)$ is always an integer. $N(4) = 5 \times 17$, $N(5) = 11 \times 31$, $N(6) = 3 \times 5 \times 7 \times 13$. Also $N(1) = 1$, $N(2) = 5$, $N(3) = 21 = 3 \times 7$ and it is easy to show that $N(n + 2) = 5N(n + 1) - 4N(n)$, $n \geq 1$. It follows that the re-
    mainders of $N(n)$ on division by 7 are respectively $1, 5, 0, 1, 5, 0,$

...for $n = 1, 2, 3, 4, 5, 6, \ldots$ and hence $N(n)$ is divisible by 7 if and only if n is a multiple of 3. Next if n is not a power of 2, then $n = 2^s m$, where s is a non-negative integer and m is an odd number > 1. It follows that $(1/3)(4^n - 1) = (1/3)(2^n - 1)(2^n + 1)$, and $2^n - 1$ contains a factor $2^m - 1$. For example $2^{20} - 1 = (2^{10} + 1)(2^{10} - 1) = (2^{10} + 1)(2^5 + 1)(2^5 - 1)$. Now if m is odd $2^m - 1$ is never divisible by 3, but it is of the form $4t + 3$ for some integer t, and so in its prime factorization must contain an odd number of primes of the form $4k + 3$. It can be shown that if $n = 2^s$, then $N(n)$ contains only prime factors of the form $4k + 1$.

26. All integers are of the form $(6k \pm 2), (6k \pm 1), 6k$, or $6k + 3$. The latter two are divisible by 3 and the first pair by 2, so the only possible primes greater than 3 are of the form $(6k \pm 1)$. If both $6k - 1$ and $6k + 1$ are prime for the same value of k like 17 and 19, they are said to be *twin primes*. Evidence suggests that not only are primes infinite in number, but that twin primes are infinite in number. Proving this is beyond the resource of mathematics at the present time.

27. Suppose that p is the largest prime number of the form $6k - 1$. Then consider the integer $N = p! - 1$. When N is factorized into primes suppose $N = p_1 p_2 p_3 \ldots p_k$. Then each of the primes $p_j, j = 1$ to k, is greater than p for if not it would divide both N and $p!$ and hence would divide 1, which is impossible. Since p is the largest prime of the form $6k - 1$ it follows that all p_j are primes of the form $6k + 1$ and hence N, when divided by 6 leaves a remainder 1. But $N = p! - 1$, which has a remainder of 5 when divided by 6. The contradiction shows there is no largest prime number of the form $6k - 1$. A result due to Dirichlet, which is far beyond the scope of this book, is that if a and b are coprime then

there are an infinite number of primes of the form $ak + b$.

28. General results of this kind do not exist, so it must be a particular case. If p is a prime greater than 3, then $p^2 + 2$, from the result of Exercise 27, is equal to either $36k^2 - 12k + 3$ or $36k^2 + 12k + 3$ for some value of k. These are not prime. When $p = 2$ then $p^2 + 2 = 6$, which is not prime, so $p = 3$ is the only possibility, and then the three integers are 3,11,29 which are all prime.

29. Again using the result that all primes are of the form $p = 6k \pm 1$, $p^2 - 1 = 12k(3k \pm 1)$. Now if k is even there is obviously a factor of 24. And if k is odd $3k \pm 1$ is even. So in either case there is an extra factor of 2 to make $p^2 - 1$ divisible by 24. This result is true for all numbers of this form whether p is prime or not. So this result does not provide a test of whether a number is prime. We shall meet some tests for prime numbers later, but they are not very efficient.

30. Of the three integers $p, p + 10, p + 14$ if you divide them all by 3 you are bound to get one each of the remainders $0, 1, 2$(in some order). In other words one of them is divisible by 3. But they are all stated to be prime numbers. This is impossible unless $p = 3$.

31. If n is odd and greater than 1, then we may write $n = 2k + 1$ for $k > 0$ and from factorization in Exercise 17 there is a factor $2 + 1 = 3$ and so $2^n + 1$ is not prime.

32. The only possible factorizations of 60 in which both factors are even are 30×2 and 10×6 These gives two solutions $(x, y) = (16, 14)$ or $(8, 2)$.

33. If the edges are removed from the top and bottom and from both the left hand and right hand sides we are left with $m -$

2 rows and $n - 2$ columns. The data of the problem then means that $3(m - 2)(n - 2) = 2mn$. Multiplying out and rearranging this gives $mn - 6m - 6n + 12 = 0$. Factorizing we get $(m - 6)(n - 6) = 24$. Since $24 = 24 \times 1 = 12 \times 2 = 8 \times 3 = 6 \times 4$ the following possibilities occur with $m > n$: $(m, n) = (30, 7), (18, 8), (14, 9), (12, 10)$.

Project

From Exercise 31 we know that if n is odd them $2^n + 1$ is always divisible by 3. If n is even and not a power of 2, then we may write $n = (2k + 1)s$, where $s = 2^m$ for some values of $k > 0$ and $m > 0$. We then have $2^n + 1 = (2^s)^{2k+1} + 1$, which has a factor $2^s + 1$, and is therefore not prime. So $2^n + 1$ can only be prime if n is a power of 2. These numbers are called the *Fermat numbers* after Pierre de Fermat, who thought they might all be prime. He based his hypothesis on the slender evidence that they are prime for $n = 1, 2, 4, 8, 16$ when $2^n + 1 = 3, 5, 17, 257, 65537$ respectively. Later Euler showed that $2^{32} + 1 = 641 \times 6700417$, and it is now known that the next 16 are not prime. The conjecture that has not yet been proved is that only a finite number of Fermat numbers are prime. A warning is now appropriate that **you should not frame a hypothesis on a small amount of evidence**.

There is a curious and beautiful link with geometry here. If a Fermat number is prime it is possible to perform a construction with a straight edge and compass when a regular polygon has that number of sides. So, for example, it is possible to find such a construction for a regular pentagon and a regular 17-sided polygon. This is an existence theorem. It is obvious that if a Fermat number greater than 65537 is found to be prime no-one will ever perform the corresponding construction by hand.

Chapter 3

Number Theory: Week 3

3.1 More on divisibility, congruences, squares, Pythagorean triples.

3.1.1 Even and Odd

When an integer is divided by 2, the remainder is either 0 or 1. If the remainder is 0 the integer is said to be *even*, if 1 it is *odd*. Even numbers may be written as $2k$, where k is an integer and odd numbers as $2k + 1$. Even squares are therefore of the form $4k^2$ and are divisible by 4. Odd squares, on the other hand, are of the form $4k^2 + 4k + 1 = 4k(k + 1) + 1$. Now $k(k + 1)$ is the product of two consecutive integers and is therefore even. This means that an odd square must be 1 more than a multiple of 8.

3.1.2 Divisibility by 4

From these few remarks we can see that it is useful to divide integers into other categories besides even and odd. What was done for division by 2 can be done for division by 4 or indeed by any

other positive integer greater than 1. Just considering the case of 4
for the moment, when an integer is divided by 4 the remainder will
be 0,1,2 or 3. A notation has been devised for this. We write $n = 0$
(mod 4) if n is divisible by 4, $n = 1$ (mod 4) if the remainder is 1
after dividing by 4, $n = 2$ (mod 4) if the remainder is 2 and $n = 3$
(mod 4) if the remainder is 3. In this notation an even square is 0
(mod 4) and an odd square is 1 (mod 4). Indeed an odd square is
1 (mod 8). Note that some authors use the $\equiv$ symbol rather than
the $=$ symbol when dealing with modular arithmetic (mod is short
for modulo).

3.1.3   Congruences

A statement such as $a = b$ (mod m) is called a *congruence*.

It means that the integers a and b both have the same remainder after being divided by the integer m. That is, an integer k
exists such that $a = b + km$ or $m \mid (a - b)$.

Theorem 3.1 Let a, b, c, d be positive integers and m a positive integer greater than 1. The following statements about congruences
are true:

1. $a = a$ (mod m). (Reflexive).

2. $a = b$ (mod m)$\Leftrightarrow b = a$ (mod m). (Symmetric)

3. $a = b$ (mod m) & $b = c$ (mod m)$\Rightarrow a = c$ (mod m). (Transitive)

4. $a = b$ (mod m) & $c = d$ (mod m)$\Rightarrow a \pm c = b \pm d$(mod m). (Addition and Subtraction)

5. $a = b$ (mod m) & $c = d$ (mod m)$\Rightarrow ac = bd$ (mod m). (Multiplication)

6. $a = b \pmod{m}$ and $d \mid m$, where $1 < d < m \Rightarrow a = b \pmod{d}$.

7. $a = b \pmod{m}$ and $c > 0 \Leftrightarrow ac = bc \pmod{mc}$.

Proof A preliminary observation is that if such arithmetical operations as these were not true then the introduction of the notation would not serve any good purpose. The proofs of the above are very straightforward and we give only a proof of part 5 to illustrate the method. If $a = b \pmod{m}$ and $c = d \pmod{m}$ there exist integers k, l such that $a = km + b$ and $c = lm + d$. Then $ac = (km + b)(lm + d) = (klm + bl + dk)m + bd$, showing that $ac = bd \pmod{m}$. ∎

Any set of integers $a_1, a_2, a_3, \ldots a_m$ such that for every integer x there is one and only one of the a_k such that $x = a_k \pmod{m}$ is called a *complete residue system* modulo m . The most common choice of *residues* is $0, 1, 2, \ldots, (m-1)$. It requires a certain amount of practice to handle congruences, so here is a worked example, followed by a set of Exercises.

Example

We find the solution of $5x = 2 \pmod{7}$. Multiply by 3 to get $15x = 6 \pmod{7}$. But $15 = 1 \pmod{7}$, so $x = 6 \pmod{7}$.

Exercises

1. Prove part 3 of Theorem 3.1.
   In Exercises 2 -8 find all values of x satisfying the given congruence:

2. $3x = 5 \pmod{7}$.

3. $6x = 2 \pmod 8$.

4. $6x = 1 \pmod 3$.

5. $5x = 7 \pmod{11}$.

6. $4x = 0 \pmod 6$.

7. $x^2 = 2 \pmod 7$.

8. $x^2 + x + 1 = 0 \pmod{13}$.

9. If $5x = 5y \pmod{15}$ is it true that $x = y \pmod{15}$?

10. If $5x = 5y \pmod{15}$ is it true that $x = y \pmod 3$?

11. Prove that $2^{12} = 1 \pmod{13}$.

12. Prove that $8x = 8y \pmod{12}$ if, and only if, $x = y \pmod 3$. Can you generalize this?

13. Find the values of x such that $2^x = 1 \pmod 7$.

Example

We show that $x^2 = 2 \pmod 5$ and has no solutions. The only possibilities are $x = 0, 1, 2, 3, 4 \pmod 5$. The squares of these are 0,1,4,4,1 (mod 5). None of these is 2.

The allowed non-zero values of a such that solutions of $x^2 = a$ (mod 5) exist, which are $a = 1, 4$ are called the quadratic residues (mod 5). In general the allowed values of a coprime to m such that solutions exist of $x^2 = a \pmod m$ are called the quadratic residues $\pmod m$.

Exercises

14. Find the quadratic residues $(\bmod\ 7)$.

15. Find the quadratic residues $(\bmod\ 16)$.

16. Prove that if $n = 2 \pmod 3$ then it cannot be a square.

17. Prove that the sum of two odd squares cannot be a perfect square.

18. Prove that if x, y, z are integers such that $9 \mid (x^2 + y^2 + z^2)$ then $9 \mid (x^2 - y^2)$ or $9 \mid (y^2 - z^2)$ or $9 \mid (z^2 - x^2)$.

19. Find solutions, if any, of the equations $x^2 = -1 \pmod{11}$ and $x^2 = -1 \pmod{13}$. Try a few more primes besides 11 and 13 and make a conjecture from your evidence.

3.1.4 Tests for divisibility

An integer is divisible by 2 if its last digit is 0,2,4,6,8. This is because $2k = 0, 2, 4, 6, 8 \pmod{10}$, for all integers k. In fact if $k = 0$ or $5 \pmod{10}$, then $2k = 0 \pmod{10}$, if $k = 1$ or $6 \pmod{10}$, then $2k = 2 \pmod{10}$ and so on. Perhaps a better way of looking at this is to say all integers N may be written in the form $N = 10M + R$, where $0 \leq R < 10$, and since 10 is divisible by 2 it follows that $2 \mid N \Leftrightarrow 2 \mid R$.

Exercise

20. State and prove a divisibility test for when integers are divisible by (a) 4 and (b) 8.

Example

The digital sum of an integer is the sum of all its digits. We show that an integer is divisible by 9 if and only if its digital sum is divisible by 9. We write $N = 10M + R$, where $0 \leq R < 10$ and then we have $N = M + R \pmod 9$. We now observe that R is the last digit of N. Applying the same method to $M = 10P + S$, where $0 \leq S < 10$, we find $N = P + S + R \pmod 9$. We now observe that S is the second last digit of N. Continuing in this way we eventually find that N is equal to its digital sum $\pmod 9$.

Exercise

21. State and prove a divisibility test for when integers are divisible by 11.

22. Prove that $10M + R = 0 \pmod 7$ if, and only if, $M - 2R = 0 \pmod 7$.

The result of Exercise 22 can be used to devise a divisibility test for integers divisible by 7. An example should make the method clear. Take the integer 9275. Here $M = 927$ and $R = 5$ and $M - 2R = 917$. Now repeat the process. The new $M = 91$ and the new $R = 7$, then $M - 2R = 77$. Since 77 is obviously divisible by 7 it follows that 9275 is divisible by 7.

A similar method may be used to devise a divisibility test for any prime number. Take for example the prime number 31. If $10M + R = 0 \pmod{31}$ then $30M + 3R = 0 \pmod{31}$ and so $3R - M = 0 \pmod{31}$ and $M - 3R = 0 \pmod{31}$. For example 23529 leads to $2352 - 27 = 2325$ and this in turn leads to $232 - 15 = 217$. This now leads to $21 - 21 = 0$. Hence 233529 is divisible by 31.

Exercise

23. Devise a divisibility test for integers divisible by 47, and illustrate it by showing that 5802432 is divisible by 47.

3.1.5 Pythagorean triples

These are positive integers x, y, z satisfying the equation that occurs in Pythagoras's theorem.

$$x^2 + y^2 = z^2. \tag{3.1}$$

First if d divides any two of x, y, z then it divides the other. Hence, in searching for solutions, we may suppose that x, y, z are mutually coprime (and if required multiply up by a common factor afterwards, corresponding to an integer enlargement of the triangle). This means, in particular, that we may suppose that x, y, z are not all even. Also we know from the result of Exercise 17 that not both of x, y can be odd. This means that one of x, y is even and the other odd, which in turn means that z is odd. Triples of this kind, without a common factor are called *Pythagorean triples*. Almost certainly you will have encountered some of the simple cases: 3,4,5; 5,12,13; 8,15,17; 7,24,25 being often used in examination questions.

Project

Copy and complete the table below up to $u = 8$ and $v = 7$, and check that in all cases Equation (3.1) is satisfied. Here u and v are coprime positive integers of opposite parity (one even and one odd).

u	v	u^2	v^2	$x = 2uv$	$y = u^2 - v^2$	$z = u^2 + v^2$
2	1	4	1	4	3	5
3	2	9	4	12	5	13
4	1	16	1	8	15	17
4	3	16	9	24	7	25
...	...	...	...	...	...	...
...	...	...	...	...	...	...

A proof that this procedure gives all Pythagorean triples is given in the Commentary, but before looking see if you can prove it. It is the word 'all' that makes it not just a matter of verification that $(2uv)^2 + (u^2 - v^2)^2 = (u^2 + v^2)^2$. But assuming the formulae are as stated try to prove the following facts:

(1) One of x, y, z must be divisible by 3.

(2) One of x, y, z must be divisible by 5.

(3) There are an infinite number of cases in which $z = x + 1$.

(4) There are an infinite number of cases in which $y = x + 1$.

Finally find all integer-sided right-angled triangles with a total perimeter of 330 units.

3.2   Commentary   Week 3

1. $a = b + km$ and $b = c + lm$ gives $a = c + lm + km = c + (k+l)m$.

2. $x = 4 \pmod{7}$.

3. $x = 3 \pmod{4}$.

4. No solution.

5. $x = 8 \pmod{11}$.

6. $x = 0$ or 3 (mod 6).

7. $x = 3$ or 4 (mod 7).

8. $(x - 3)(x + 4) = 0(mod 13)$. Hence $x = 3$ or 9(mod 13).

9. No. $x = 3, y = 0$ is a counter-example.

10. Yes. If $5x = 5y$ (mod 15), then $5x - 5y = 15k$ and $x - y = 3k$, so $x = y$(mod 3).

11. $2^6 = 64 = -1$ (mod 13) and hence $2^{12} = 1$ (mod 13).

12. If $8x = 8y$(mod 12), then $8x - 8y = 12k$ so that $4x - 4y = 6k$ and $x - y = 0$(mod 3). Conversely, if $x = y$ (mod 3), then $x - y = 3k$ and $8x - 8y = 24k$ so $8x = 8y$ (mod 12). This generalizes as follows: If $ax = ay$ (mod m) and $(a, m) = h$, then $x = y$ (mod m/h) and conversely. For suppose $a = kh$ and $m = lh$, where k, l are coprime, then $ax = ay$ (mod m) $\Rightarrow khx - khy = tlh \Rightarrow kx - ky = tl$. But k and l are coprime so $(x - y) = sl$ and $t = sk$ for some integer s. That is $x = y$ (mod l) and $l = m/h$. The converse is straightforward.

13. $x = 0$ (mod 3).

14. 1,4,2 are the quadratic residues (mod 7).

15. 1, 9 are the quadratic residues (mod 16).

16. $(3k)^2 = 9k^2$ is divisible by 3, and $(3k \pm 1)^2 = 9k^2 \pm 6k + 1 = 1$ (mod 3), so 2(mod 3) is never a square.

17. An odd square is 1 (mod 4), so the sum of two odd squares is 2(mod 4), which is even. But all even squares are 0 (mod 4), and so the sum of two odd squares is never a square.

18. 0,1,2,3,4,5,6,7,8 (mod 9) when squared give respectively 0,1,4,0,7,7,0,4,1 (mod 9), so the only ways that three squares can be summed to give 0(mod 9) are (0,0,0); (1,4,4); (1,1,7); (4,7,7) or permutations of these triples. In all cases there is a repeat, which means that $9 \mid (x^2 - y^2)$ or $9 \mid (y^2 - z^2)$ or $9 \mid (z^2 - x^2)$.

19. There are no solutions of $x^2 = -1$ (mod 11). $x^2 = -1 = 64$ (mod 13), so $x = 5$ or 8 (mod 13). The conjecture, a proof of which is beyond our scope at present, is that $x^2 = -1$ (mod p), where p is an odd prime has solutions if and only if p is of the form $4k + 1$.

20. $N = 100M + 10P + R = 10P + R$ (mod 4). Hence N is divisible by 4 if, and only if, its last two digits are divisible by 4. Similarly, since 1000 is divisible by 8, an integer is divisible by 8 if, and only if, its last three digits are divisible by 8.

21. $10M + R = 0$ (mod 11) if, and only if, $-M + R = 0$ (mod 11). Continuing the process we discover the rule that an integer is divisible by 11 if, and only if, the sums of sets of alternate digits differ by 0 (mod 11). Thus 574904 is divisible by 11 since $5 + 4 + 0 = 7 + 9 + 4$ (mod 11).

22. $10M + R = 0$ (mod 7) $\Leftrightarrow 20M + 2R = 0$ (mod 7) $-M + 2R = 0$ (mod 7) $\Leftrightarrow M - 2R = 0$ (mod 7).

23. $10M + R = 0$ (mod 47) $\Leftrightarrow 140M + 14R = 0$ (mod 47) $\Leftrightarrow M - 14R = 0$ (mod 47). Using this relation repeatedly gives $5802432 \rightarrow 580243 - 28 = 580215 \rightarrow 58021 - 70 = 57951 \rightarrow 5795 - 14 = 5781 \rightarrow 578 - 14 = 564 \rightarrow 56 - 56 = 0$ and hence 5802432 is divisible by 47.

Project

u	v	u^2	v^2	$x = 2uv$	$y = u^2 - v^2$	$z = u^2 + v^2$
5	2	25	4	20	21	29
5	4	25	16	40	9	41
6	1	36	1	12	35	37
6	5	36	25	60	11	61
7	2	49	4	28	45	53
7	4	49	16	56	33	65
7	6	49	36	84	13	85
8	1	64	1	16	63	65
8	3	64	9	48	55	73
8	5	64	25	80	39	89
8	7	64	49	112	15	113

For proof of the necessity of the parameter system for Pythagorean triples, we start from the point in the text where we stated with proof that one of x, y must be even and the other odd. So suppose that x is even and y is odd. Then $x^2 = (z - y)(z + y)$. Now, since y and z are coprime, $z - y$ and $z + y$ have only the factor 2 in common. So each must be twice a perfect square. Writing $z + y = 2u^2$ and $z - y = 2v^2$, we find $x^2 = 4u^2v^2$ and $x = 2uv, y = u^2 - v^2, z = u^2 + v^2$. The sufficiency of the parameter system follows from the algebraic identity $(2uv)^2 + (u^2 - v^2)^2 = (u^2 + v^2)^2$.

(1) Either $u = 0$ or $v = 0$ (mod 3) in which case $3 \mid x$ or $(u, v) = (1, 1), (2, 2), (1, 2), (2, 1)$ (mod 3). In the first two cases $u - v = 0$ (mod 3) and in the second two cases $u + v = 0$ (mod 3). Then $u^2 - v^2 = 0$ (mod 3) and $3 \mid y$.

(2) If $u = 0$ or $v = 0$ (mod 5), then $5 \mid x$. If $u = v$ (mod 5), then $u - v = 0$ (mod 5) and $5 \mid y$. If $u + v = 0$ (mod 5) then $5 \mid y$. This leaves the cases $(u, v) = (1, 2), (2, 1), (1, 3), (3, 1), (2, 4), (4, 2), (3, 4), (4, 3)$ (mod 5) and in all these cases $u^2 + v^2 = 0$ (mod 5) and $5 \mid z$.

(3) If $z = x + 1$, then $u^2 + v^2 = 2uv + 1$ and so $(u - v)^2 = 1$ and $u = v + 1$. Clearly there are an infinite number of such cases.

(2) If $y = x + 1$, then $u^2 - v^2 = 2uv + 1$ and so $(u - v)^2 - 2v^2 = 1$. Putting $u - v = t$ we have $t^2 - 2v^2 = 1$. The first instance of this is $t = 3, v = 2, u = 5$, which is shown as the first entry in the Table above. Given any solution (t, v) it is easily checked that (T, V) is also a solution, where $T = 3t + 4v, V = 2t + 3v$. The next instance is therefore $T = 17, V = 12$ giving $(u, v) = (29, 12)$.

Finally you were asked to find all integer-sided right-angled triangles with perimeter 330. Now $x + y + z = 2ku(u + v)$, where k is any scale factor of enlargement. Hence $ku(u + v) = 165 = 3 \times 5 \times 11$. Also $u < u + v < 2u$. When $k = 1$ we have $u = 11, v = 4$. When $k = 3$ or 5 there are no solutions. When $k = 11$ we have $u = 3, v = 2$. The two possibilities, therefore, are $(x, y, z) = (88, 105, 137)$ or $(132, 55, 143)$.

Chapter 4

Number Theory: Week 4

4.1 Induction, arithmetic and geometric progressions, number of divisors.

4.1.1 The principle of mathematical induction

In Week 1 we stated the principle of well-ordering, which is that every subset of positive integers has a least member. It was used there to establish the Euclidean algorithm. It also has the immediate consequence that there is no integer between 0 and 1. For suppose such integers exist, then, by the principle, there is a least such integer k and $0 < k < 1$. Multiplying by k we get $0 < k^2 < k < 1$. Since k^2 is an integer less than k we have a contradiction.

The principle of well-ordering also establishes a very powerful method of proof in mathematics, called the principle of mathematical induction.

Theorem 4.1 [The principle of mathematical induction.] Suppose that you are given a sequence of propositions $P(n)$, one such proposition for each integer $n \in \mathbb{N}$, propositions which are either true or false. Then the *principle of mathematical induction* states that if $P(1)$ is true, and if the truth of $P(k)$ implies the truth of $P(k+1)$ for all k, then $P(n)$ is true for all $n \in \mathbb{N}$.

Proof Suppose there are some n for which $P(n)$ is not true. Then there is a least such n, say $n = m$. Now $m \neq 1$, since we are given that $P(1)$ is true. Thus $m - 1$ is a positive integer for which $P(m-1)$ is true. Now put $k = m - 1$ and then $P(k+1) = P(m)$ is true. This contradiction establishes the result. ∎

Example

We show that $1 + 2 + 3 + \ldots + n = \frac{1}{2}n(n+1)$. Call this proposition $P(n)$. For $n = 1$, the left-hand side $= 1$ and the right-hand side $= \frac{1}{2} \times 1 \times 2 = 1$. Hence $P(1)$ is true. If $P(k)$ is true then $1 + 2 + 3 + \ldots + k = \frac{1}{2}k(k+1)$ and hence $1 + 2 + 3 + \ldots + k + (k+1) = \frac{1}{2}k(k+1) + (k+1) = \frac{1}{2}(k+1)(k+2)$. Since this is equal to $\frac{1}{2}n(n+1)$ with $n = k + 1$, it follows that $P(k+1)$ is true. And so, by the principle of mathematical induction, $P(n)$ is true for all $n \in \mathbb{N}$.

Example

We show that $f(n) = 4^{3n-2} + 2^{3n-2} + 1$ is divisible by 7 for all positive integers n. Call this proposition $P(n)$. Now $f(1) = 4 + 2 + 1 = 7$ so $P(1)$ is true. If $P(k)$ is true then there exists an integer m such that $f(k) = 4^{3k-2} + 2^{3k-2} + 1 = 7m$. Multiplying by 64 we get $4^{3k+1} + 2^{3k+4} + 64 = 448m$ and so $f(k+1) = 4^{3k+1} + 2^{3k+1} + 1 = 448m + 2^{3k+1} - 2^{3k+4} - 63 = 448m - 2^{3k+1}(8-1) - 63 = 7(64m - 2^{3k+1} - 9)$. Since $7 \mid f(k+1)$ it follows that $P(k+1)$ is true. So, by the principle of mathematical induction, $P(n)$ is true for all $n \in \mathbb{N}$.

The importance of the principle of mathematical induction lies in the fact that it cuts short arguments that would otherwise be of infinite extent and hence not mathematics. The principle is sometimes explained by saying that it validates the sequence of steps $P(1) \Rightarrow P(2) \Rightarrow P(3) \Rightarrow P(4)$ etc. This is unfortunate because the principle of mathematical induction is designed to overcome the problems inherent in such an argument and so the principle must either be proved from the principle of well-ordering or accepted as an axiom.

The principle of mathematical induction may be extended in ways that also may be proved by the principle of well-ordering.

Theorem 4.2 Using the same notation as in Theorem 4.1.1 if $P(1)$ and $P(2)$ are true and the truth of $P(k-1)$ and $P(k)$ imply the truth of $P(k+1)$ for all k then $P(n)$ is true for all $n \in \mathbb{N}$.

Example

We show that if (u_n) is a sequence such that $u_1 = 1, u_2 = 5$ and $u_{n+1} = 5u_n - 6u_{n-1}$ for $n \geq 2$, then $u_n = 3^n - 2^n$. $P(1)$ is true since $3 - 2 = 1$, $P(2)$ is true since $9 - 4 = 5$. If $P(k-1)$ and $P(k)$ are true then $u_{k-1} = 3^{k-1} - 2^{k-1}$ and $u_k = 3^k - 2^k$ and from the recurrence relation we have $u_{k+1} = 5 \times 3^k - 5 \times 2^k - 6 \times 3^{k-1} + 6 \times 2^{k-1} = 3^{k-1}(15-6) + 2^{k-1}(6-10) = 3^{k+1} - 2^{k+1}$ and hence $P(k+1)$ is true. It follows that $P(n)$ is true for all $n \in \mathbb{N}$.

Theorem 4.3 [Second (or Strong) principle of mathematical induction.] Using the same notation, if $P(1)$ is true and the truth of all $P(n)$ for $n = 1, 2, 3, \ldots k$ imply the truth of $P(k+1)$ then $P(n)$ is true for all $n \in \mathbb{N}$.

It should also be noted that there is no reason why the start of an induction should be the case $n = 1$. If the start is $n = 3$, for example, then an induction only proves $P(n)$ to be true for integers $n \geq 3$. Quite often it is convenient to start at $n = 0$. The following questions should be answered using the principle of mathematical induction.

Exercises

1. Prove that $1^2 + 2^2 + 3^2 + \ldots + n^2 = n(n+1)(2n+1)/6$.

2. Prove that $1/(1 \times 2) + 1/(2 \times 3) + 1/(3 \times 4) + \ldots + 1/\{n(n+1)\} = n/(n+1)$.

3. Prove that $n^3 - 25n$ is divisible by 6 for all positive integers n .

4. Consider the sequence (u_n) defined by $u_1 = 3, u_2 = 5, u_{n+2} = 3u_{n+1} - 2u_n, n \geq 1$. Make a conjecture about the value of u_n and establish its truth by induction.

4.1.2 Arithmetic progressions

The word 'progression' in this context has been used for a long time, but only means the same as the word 'sequence'. An *arithmetic progression* is defined as the sequence (u_n) such that $u_1 = a, u_2 = a + d, u_3 = a + 2d, \ldots, u_n = a + (n-1)d$, where a and d are constants. The *first term* is a and since the difference between any two consecutive terms is constant and equal to d it is called the *common difference*. It is very easy to find the sum of an arithmetic series $u_1 + u_2 + u_3 + \ldots + u_n = a + (a+d) + (a+2d) + \ldots (a+(n-1)d) = na + d(1 + 2 + \ldots + (n-1)) = na + \frac{1}{2}n(n-1)d = \frac{1}{2}n(2a + (n-1)d)$, where we have used the result of the first worked example. As an example

$$17 + 21 + 25 + \ldots + 221 = 26(34 + 51 \times 4) = 6188,$$

since $a = 17, d = 4$ and $n = 52$.

Note that $u_n = \frac{1}{2}(u_{n-1} + u_{n+1})$, so that each term is the arithmetic mean of the terms on either side of it.

Exercises

5. Find the sum of the first 50 odd integers.

6. Locate all the terms in the following two arithmetic progressions that are equal:
   13, 18, 23, 28, ... and 7, 13, 19, 25, ...

7. Find the sum of all the natural numbers between 1 and 3000 inclusive that are not divisible by 2 or 3.

8. Characterize those positive integers that can be represented as the sum of two or more consecutive positive integers.

9. Find the least value of n such that $105 + 109 + 113 + \ldots + 101 + 4n > 1000000$.

4.1.3 Geometric progressions

A geometric progression is defined as a sequence (u_n) such that $u_1 = a, u_2 = ar, u_3 = ar^2, \ldots, u_n = ar^{n-1}$, where a and r are constants. The *first term* is a and since the quotient of any two consecutive terms is constant and equal to r it is called the *common ratio*. The sum of a geometric progression may be obtained as follows:

Recall from Week 2 the factorization

$$x^n - 1 = (x - 1)(x^{n-1} + x^{n-2} + \ldots + x + 1).$$

This may be recast in the form

$$1 + x + x^2 + \ldots + x^{n-1} = \frac{x^n - 1}{x - 1}, x \neq 1.$$

When $x < 1$, it is more convenient to rewrite the right-hand side as $(1 - x^n)/(1 - x)$. It follows that the sum of the first n terms of a geometric progression is

$$a + ar + ar^2 + \ldots + ar^{n-1} = a(1 + r + r^2 + \ldots + r^{n-1})$$

$$= a\frac{r^n - 1}{r - 1}, r \neq 1.$$

As an example

$$3 + 6 + 12 + 24 + \ldots + 3 \times 2^{49} = 3(2^{50} - 1)/(2 - 1) = 3(2^{50} - 1),$$

since $a = 3, r = 2$ and $n = 50$.
Note that if all terms of a geometric progression are positive then $u_n = \sqrt{(u_{n-1}u_{n+1})}$ so that each term is the geometric mean of the two terms on either side of it.

Exercises

10. Find the sum of $5 + 30 + 180 + 1080 + \ldots + 5 \times 6^{19}$.

11. Find the sum of $9 - 3 + 1 - (1/3) + (1/9) + \ldots$ to 13 terms. To what value does the sum approach as the number of terms increases?

12. Prove that the geometric mean of two positive numbers is less than or equal to their arithmetic mean.

13. What is the least value of n such that $1 + 5 + 25 + \cdots + 5^{n-1} > 1000000$?

Project

The divisors of 6 are 1,2,3,6. Their number is 4 and their sum is 12. We shall write $d(n)$ *for the number of divisors of* n and $\sigma(n)$ *for their sum.* Such functions defined on the positive integers are called *arithmetic functions.* It turns out to be possible to calculate the values of $d(n)$ and $\sigma(n)$ without listing the divisors. For example $d(200) = 12$ and $\sigma(200) = 465$. The project is to find out how to do it, with just a little bit of preliminary help. First a few results; you should check them and add a few of your own.

n	$d(n)$	$\sigma(n)$
5	2	6
6	4	12
7	2	8
8	4	15
9	3	13
49	3	57
63	6	104
72	12	195
100	9	217

Here are a few things to think about. If p is prime what are $d(p)$ and $\sigma(p)$? If $n = p^2$, where p is prime, then what are $d(n)$ and $\sigma(n)$? What can you say about n when $d(n)$ is odd? Make sure you prove your assertions and do not be satisfied with guesses that appear to fit the data. What happens if $n = p^3$, where p is prime? Suppose now both p and q are prime. What happens if $n = pq$? What happens if $n = pq^2$ or $n = p^2q^2$? What happens if $n = p^k q^m$? A hint is that you are not on the right track unless you are summing geometrical progressions when working out $\sigma(n)$. Now try the following:

(1) Find the smallest positive integer n for which $d(n) = 6$.

(2) Find a necessary and sufficient condition on n for $\sigma(n)$ to be odd.

(3) The integer m is said to be a *perfect number* if $\sigma(m) = 2m$. For example 6 is a perfect number since $\sigma(6) = 12$. There is another perfect number less than 30. Find it.

(4) Prove that if $2^n - 1 = p$ is prime then $2^{n-1}p$ is perfect.

4.2   Commentary: Week 4

1. $P(1)$ is true since $1^2 = (1 \times 2 \times 3)/6$. If $P(k)$ is true then $1^2 + 2^2 + \ldots + k^2 + (k+1)^2 = k(k+1)(2k+1)/6 + (k+1)^2 = (1/6)(k+1)(2k^2 + k + 6k + 6) = (1/6)(k+1)(2k^2 + 7k + 6) = (1/6)(k+1)(k+2)(2k+3)$ and hence $P(k+1)$ is true. And so $P(n)$ is true for all positive integers n by the principle of mathematical induction.

2. $P(1)$ is true since $1/(1 \times 2) = \frac{1}{2} = 1/(1+1)$. If $P(k)$ is true then $1/(1 \times 2) + 1/(2 \times 3) + \ldots + 1/\{k(k+1)\} + 1/\{k+1)(k+2)\} = k/(k+1) + 1/\{(k+1)(k+2)\} = 1/\{(k+1)(k+2)\} \times (k^2 + 2k + 1) = (k+1)/(k+2)$ and hence $P(k+1)$ is true. And so $P(n)$ is true for all positive integers n by the principle of mathematical induction.

3. $P(1)$ is true since $1^3 - 25 \times 1 = -24$ which is divisible by 6. If $P(k)$ is true then there exists an integer m such that $f(k) = k^3 - 25k = 6m$.
   Then $f(k+1) = (k+1)^3 - 25(k+1) = 6m + 3k^2 + 3k + 1 - 25 = 6m - 24 + 3k(k+1)$. But $k(k+1)$ is the product of two consecutive integers and is therefore even, and is equal to $2s$ say. Then $f(k+1) = 6(m + s - 4)$ and hence $P(k+1)$ is

true. And so $P(n)$ is true for all positive integers n by the principle of mathematical induction.

4. The correct conjecture is that $u_n = 2^n + 1$. $P(1)$ and $P(2)$ are true since $u_1 = 2 + 1 = 3$ and $u_2 = 2^2 + 1 = 4 + 1 = 5$. If $P(k-1)$ and $P(k)$ are true then $u_{k-1} = 2^{k-1} + 1$ and $u_k = 2^k + 1$. Then from the recurrence relation $u_{k+1} = 3(2^k + 1) - 2(2^{k-1} + 1) = 2^{k-1}(6-2) + (3-2) = 2^{k+1} + 1$ and hence $P(k+1)$ is true. And so $P(n)$ is true for all positive integers n by the principle of mathematical induction.

5. For this sum $a = 1, d = 2, n = 50$ and so the answer is $25(2 + 49 \times 2) = 2500$. It is probable that you knew beforehand that the sum of the first N odd numbers is N^2 for all positive integers N.

6. The terms in the first sequence are of the form $13 + 5n$ and those of the second sequence are of the form $7 + 6m$, where m and n are non-negative integers. We therefore require solutions of the equation $6m - 5n = 6$. From the theory of Week 1 the general solution of this equation is $m = 1 + 5t, n = 6t$ and so the common terms are of the form $13 + 30t$, for non-negative integers t.

7. The sum of all numbers between 1 and 3000 inclusive is $1500 \times 3001 = 4501500$. The sum of all even numbers between 2 and 3000 inclusive is $750 \times 3002 = 2251500$. The sum of all numbers divisible by 3 between 3 and 3000 inclusive is $500 \times 3003 = 1501500$. But in the last two categories we have counted numbers divisible by 6 twice so we must calculate their sum so that they are not subtracted out twice. Their sum is $250 \times 3006 = 751500$. It follows the sum of all integers between 1 and 3000 inclusive that are not divisible by 2 or 3

is

$$4501500 - 2251500 - 1501500 + 751500 = 1500000.$$

8. Since $1 + 2 + 3 + \ldots + k = \frac{1}{2}k(k+1)$ we have the sum of the consecutive integers $(m+1) + (m+2) + \ldots + (n-1) + n = \frac{1}{2}n(n+1) - \frac{1}{2}m(m+1) = \frac{1}{2}(n-m)(n+m+1)$. Now one of $n-m$ and $n+m+1$ is odd and the other is even, so this is an integer with an odd factor. It follows that all integers can be expressed as the sum of two or more consecutive positive integers except powers of 2. For example, if we wish to express 35 in this way then we require $(n-m)(n+m+1) = 70$ and one solution is $n-m = 2, n+m+1 = 35$ giving $n = 18, m = 16$ and $17 + 18 = 35$. Another solution is $n-m = 5, n+m+1 = 14$ giving $n = 9, m = 4$ and $5 + 6 + 7 + 8 + 9 = 35$. Yet another solution is $n-m = 7, n+m+1 = 10$ giving $n = 8, m = 1$ and $2 + 3 + 4 + 5 + 6 + 7 + 8 = 35$. (Note that $n-m = 1$ is not allowed since there have to be at least two terms in the sum.)

9. The sum to n terms is $2n^2 + 103n$. The smallest value of n for this to exceed 1000000 is $n = 682$ giving 1000494.

10. $a = 5$ and $r = 6$ so the sum is $5(6^{20} - 1)/(6 - 1) = 6^{20} - 1$.

11. $a = 9, r = -1/3$ so the sum is $9(1 - (-1/3)^{13})/(1 + 1/3) = 398581/59049$. As $r^n \to 0$ as n increases indefinitely, the sum tends to $9/(4/3) = 27/4$.

12. We want to prove that if a and b are positive then $2\sqrt{(ab)} \leq (a+b)$. this follows since $(a^2 + 2ab + b^2) \geq 4ab$, which in turn comes from $(a-b)^2 \geq 0$.

13. We require the least value of n such that $5^n > 4000001$, which is $n = 10$.

Project

If p is prime then its only divisors are 1 and p, so $d(p) = 2$ and $\sigma(p) = p+1$. Primes are characterized by either of these equations. If $n = p^2$, where p is prime, then the divisors are 1, p and p^2, so $d(n) = 3$ and $\sigma(n) = 1+p+p^2 = (p^3-1)/(p-1)$. The only examples in the Table in the text for when $d(n)$ is odd are 9, 49 and 100 and these are all when n is a perfect square. For an integer that is not a perfect square the divisors always pair off so that the product of the two in a pair equal n. For example, when $n = 6$ you get 1×6 and 2×3, and the number of divisors is 4. But when n is a perfect square, there is one and only one divisor, namely $\sqrt{n}$, that partners itself. In such cases the number of divisors must therefore be odd. For example, when $n = 100$ you get $1 \times 100, 2 \times 50, 4 \times 25, 5 \times 100$ and 10×10 , and the number of divisors is 9. If $n = p^3$ then $d(n) = 4$ and $\sigma(n) = (p^4 - 1)/(p - 1)$. If $n = pq$, where p and q are distinct primes, then $d(n) = 4$ and $\sigma(n) = (1 + p)(1 + q)$, since the 4 divisors are $1, p, q$ and pq. If $n = pq^2$, then $d(n) = 6$ and $\sigma(n) = (1 + p)(1 + q + q^2)$. If $n = p^2q^2$ then $d(n) = 9$ and $\sigma(n) = (1 + p + p^2)(1 + q + q^2)$. All of these are particular cases of the general result for $n = p^kq^m$, for which the divisors are of the form p^sq^t where $0 \le s \le k(k + 1$ values) and $0 \le t \le m(m + 1$ values), so their number is $d(n) = (k + 1)(m + 1)$. Their sum is equal to $(1 + p + p^2 + \ldots + p^k)(1 + q + q^2 + \ldots + q^m)$, since this product contains as its terms each one of the $(k+1)(m+1)$ divisors. Using the analysis for the sum of a geometric progression this can be simplified to

$$\sigma(n) = \{(p^{k+1} - 1)(q^{m+1} - 1)\}/\{(p - 1)(q - 1)\}$$

The above anaysis is easily extended to the case when n has more than 2 distinct prime factors. For example, when $n = 1008 = 2^4 \times 3^2 \times 7$ we have $d(1008) = 5 \times 3 \times 2 = 30$ and $\sigma(1008) = \{(2^5 - 1)(3^3-1)(7^2-1)\}/\{(2-1)(3-1)(7-1)\} = 31 \times 13 \times 8 = 3224$. The form of the general expressions for $d(n)$ and $\sigma(n)$ shows that they are both what are called multipicative functions. A *multiplicative function* $m(n)$ is one for which $m(n_1 n_2) = m(n_1)m(n_2)$, whenever n_1 and n_2 are co-prime. Now we give answers to the numbered questions.

(1) The smallest positive integer with $d(n) = 6$ is 12, which beats the other possible candidates, which are 18 and 32.

(2) $\sigma(n)$ is odd if and only if all its factors of the form $(1 + p + p^2 + \ldots + p^k)$ are odd. When $p = 2$ this provides no restriction on k. But when p is an odd prime k must be even. In other words all odd primes must occur to an even power. Thus a necessary and sufficient condition for $\sigma(n)$ to be odd is that n is either a perfect square or twice a perfect square.

(3) 28 is a perfect number. $28 = 2^2 \times 7$ so $\sigma(28) = (1+2+4)(1+7) = 7 \times 8 = 2 \times 28$.

(4) Consider now the integer $N = 2^{n-1}(2^n - 1)$, where $2^n - 1 = p$ is prime. We have $\sigma(N) = \sigma(2^{n-1}p) = (2^n - 1)(p + 1) = 2^n(2^n - 1) = 2^n p = 2N$. So when N is of this form it is perfect. For $n = 2, N = 6$ and for $n = 3, N = 28$. The next case is $n = 5$ and $N = 496$.

Primes of this form $2^n - 1$ are called *Mersenne primes* and it is thought that there are an infinite number of them. Of course $2^n - 1$ is composite if n is composite, so for a Mersenne prime n has to be prime. However, they are not frequent; for example there are only 12 primes $n < 257$ for which one gets a Mersenne prime. As this book goes to press there are 43 Mersenne primes known, the largest being $2^{30,402,457} - 1$, which is (in May 2006) the largest known prime and has $9,152,052$ digits. For every Mersenne prime there is an even perfect number. It is one of the unsolved problems of

Number Theory whether an odd perfect prime exists. Odd numbers up to about 10^{36} have been tested and none is perfect. Those who seek the record for finding the largest known prime number tend to search for Mersenne primes, because tests on them tend to be slightly easier to carry out than for other possible primes.

Chapter 5

Number Theory: Week 5

5.1 Rational approximations of irrational numbers, iteration, Pell's equation.

5.1.1 Rational numbers

The *rational numbers* consist of all the fractions, that is they are elements of the set $\mathbb{Q}$ consisting of all numbers of the form m/n, where m and n are integers and $n \neq 0$. When m and n are coprime the rational number is said to be in *reduced form*.

The Greeks were the first to realize that real numbers exist that are not expressible as fractions. Their early geometrical proofs relied upon the fact that a portion of a line segment was expressible as a fractional part of its length, and the discovery that this is not the case caused problems. Nowadays the fact that a right-angled isosceles triangle with shorter sides equal to 1 unit has a hypotenuse equal to $\sqrt{2}$ and that $\sqrt{2}$ cannot be expressed as a fraction is sometimes taken for granted but not proved at secondary school level. From a modern point of view, this fact about $\sqrt{2}$ may seem unremarkable, but for the Greeks it involved a reformulation of some of the basic ideas underlying geometry. It is of interest to see how the problem was overcome. Instead of saying that the ratio of two line segments $AB : CD = m : n$ for some integers m and n Eudoxus provided the following definition of ratio, whether the quantities involved can be expressed rationally in terms of each other or not.

5.1.2   Eudoxus' definition of ratio

$a : b = c : d$, where a, b, c, d are any real numbers (which may represent lengths, for example) if and only if for *all* integers m and n then $ma - nb$ is positive, zero or negative whenever $mc - nd$ is positive, zero or negative respectively. This definition contains implicitly the idea that given any ratio a/b, then there will be a host of fractions n/m such that $a/b > n/m$. There will also be a host of fractions n/m such that $a/b < n/m$. Possibly, just possibly, there will be some fraction n/m such that $a/b = n/m$. And furthermore, if the same fractions n/m are less than, equal to or greater than c/d, then a/b and c/d are the same real number. This way of defining real numbers is essentially one of the methods employed in modern analysis. It is as if Eudoxus had leaped 2000 years ahead of his time, just as it is now recognized that Archimedes was aware of the limiting processes involved in the rudiments of the integral calculus for calculating areas and volumes.

It is even possible to suggest that implicit in Eudoxus' definition is the idea that it is possible to find fractions n/m that get closer and closer to a number that cannot be expressed as a fraction. Numbers that cannot be expressed as a fraction are called *irrational numbers* and fractions n/m that are close to an irrational number are called *rational approximations* to that number.

Theorem 5.1 $\sqrt{2}$ is irrational.

Proof Suppose $\sqrt{2}$ is rational, then there exists integers m and n, which we may take to be coprime such that $\sqrt{2} = m/n$. then $m^2 = 2n^2$ and so m^2 and hence m is even. Putting $m = 2M$ we get $2M^2 = n^2$ and so n^2 and hence n is even. This means m and n have the common factor of 2. A contradiction establishes that no such m and n exist.

If integers m and n exist so that $m^2 = 2n^2$, then let us express each side in terms of its prime factors. Noting that a square has an even number of prime factors and $2n^2$ has an odd number of prime factors. Again a contradiction establishes that no such m and n exist.

The arithmetic mean of two distinct rational numbers is rational and lies between them, and so between any two rational numbers there lies another. It follows at once that between any two rational numbers there are an infinity of rational numbers. ■

Exercises

1. Prove that the sum of two rational numbers is rational.

2. Prove that the product of two rational numbers is rational.

3. Prove that $7/5 < \sqrt{2} < 17/12$.

4. Is it true that the sum of two irrational numbers is irrational?

5.1.3 Irrational numbers

The question of how to represent them naturally arises. We consider this question thoroughly in Week 6, and for now we give a statement of the answer. Rational numbers have decimal expansions that terminate, such as $1/40 = 0.025$ or that repeat like

$1/13 = 0.\overline{076923}$, where the line means that what is contained between them is repeated over and over again. On the other hand irrational numbers have non-terminating, non-repeating decimal expansions. For example $\sqrt{2} = 1.4142135623731\ldots$, just going on for ever without terminating or without repeats of any permanence.

Irrational numbers may be subdivided. Those that arise as the solutions of polynomial equations whose coefficients are rational numbers are called *algebraic numbers*. Those that do not are called *transcendental numbers*. For example $7^{1/3}$ is algebraic since it is a solution of the equation $x^3 = 7$. But π is transcendental. To prove that π is irrational is quite difficult, but to prove it is transcendental is very difficult indeed. There has been a lot of research over the last 100 years on transcendental numbers but there is still much that is not known.

Exercises

5. Prove that $\sqrt{2} + \sqrt{3}$ is algebraic.

6. Prove that between two integers there is an irrational number.

7. Prove that between two rational numbers there is an irrational number.

8. Prove that if r is rational and s is irrational then $r + s$ is irrational.

9. Prove that positive irrational numbers a and b exist such that a^b is rational.

5.1.4   Iterative procedures

An iterative procedure is one in which the terms of a sequence may be determined by the values of the terms preceding it.

As an example we give an iteration scheme for calculating $\sqrt{2}$ to any required degree of accuracy. This is

$$x_{n+1} = \frac{1}{2}(x_n + 2/x_n), n \geq 1 \quad \text{with} \quad x_1 = 3/2.$$

The starting value does not have to be $3/2$, but could be any sensibly chosen positive number (actually in this case any positive number will do, but often iteration is successful only if the starting point is reasonably close to the true answer). Let us see how it works, expressing each term to 10 decimal places.

n	$x(n)$
0	1.5
1	1.4166666667
2	1.4142156863
3	1.4142135624

After just three iterations we already have a number correct to 10 decimal places. As you can see convergence is very rapid.

If you want to try other examples, an iterative scheme for $\sqrt{N}$ is

$$x_{n+1} = \frac{1}{2}\left(x_n + \frac{N}{x_n}\right), n \geq 1 \text{ with } x_1 = \lfloor \sqrt{N} \rfloor,$$

the integer part of $\sqrt{N}$.

5.1.5 Rational Approximations

As mentioned above a rational approximation to an irrational number x is a fraction m/n that is close to x. It is well known that $22/7$ is a rational approximation to π good enough for most practical purposes. A better rational approximation is $355/113$, which agrees with π to 6 decimal places. There are in fact rational numbers arbitrarily close to any irrational number, but mathematicians like to put a measure on facts, so here is a theorem doing just that, but whose proof is not given in this book.

Theorem 5.2 [Dirichlet] If x is an irrational number, then there are infinitely many pairs of positive integers (a, b) such that $|a - bx| < 1/b$.

Implicit in this theorem is the idea that as b increases, as it is bound to so since there are an infinity of such pairs of integers, we can get an approximation as close to x as we please.

The iteration scheme outlined above enables one to find good rational approximations to $\sqrt{2}$. All you have to do is to start with $3/2$ and to keep the iteration going with fractions rather than decimals. You will find the sequence of approximations $17/12$, $577/408$, $665857/470832$. The last fraction differs from the true value of $\sqrt{2}$ by less that 1.6×10^{-12}.

Exercises

10. In the above iteration scheme for making rational approximations for $\sqrt{2}$ we start with $u_1 = 3$ and $v_1 = 2$ and then express $x_n = u_n/v_n$ as a fraction in the reduced form, with u_n and v_n integers. Express u_{n+1} and v_{n+1} in terms of u_n and v_n, and show $u_n^2 - 2v_n^2 = 1$ for all positive integers n. Hence show that $x_n \to \sqrt{2}$ as $n \to \infty$.

11. Starting with $x_1 = 7/4$ use the formula in the text with $N = 3$ to find a sequence of rational approximations to $\sqrt{3}$. Why do we suggest a starting value of $7/4$?

For a satisfactory rational approximation one needs the conjunction of the following conditions:

(i) An iterative scheme for which the formula is fairly straightforward, so that the denominator of the approximating fraction does not get magnified too greatly at each iteration;

(ii) A rapidly convergent scheme;

(iii) The existence of a good first approximation.

Condition (iii) can never be guaranteed, but conditions (i) and (ii) are feasible for the extraction of the pth root of an integer N. The best iteration scheme is a result of the following theorem:

Theorem 5.3 If $N > 0$ and u/v is a good rational approximation to $N^{1/p}$, where p is a positive integer, then

$$\frac{U}{V} = \frac{u\{(p-1)u^p + (p+1)v^pN\}}{v\{(p+1)u^p + (p-1)v^pN\}}$$

is a far better approximation, in the sense that if

$$(u/v)^p = N(1 + \varepsilon/N)$$

and $|\varepsilon/N| < 1$, then $(U/V)^p = N(1 + O(\varepsilon^3/N^3))$.

In the statement of the theorem the O notation means that after N the next term is of order ε^3/N^3. In other words a relative error of ε/N is converted after just one step of the iteration into a relative error of order ε^3/N^3. The proof of the theorem, which is omitted, is straightforward and depends only on the binomial theorem. The actual value of the cubic term is $(p^2 - 1)\varepsilon^3/(12p^2N^3)$. There are, of course smaller terms after the cubic term.

As an example, if we start with $u/v = 7/5$, one iteration to calculate $\sqrt{2}$ gives $U/V = 1393/985$, which is correct to better than 4×10^{-7}. As a second example, if we start with $u/v = 5/3$, one iteration to calculate $13^{1/5}$ gives $U/V = 78635/47079$, which is correct to better than 4×10^{-8}.

Exercises

12. Find a rational approximation to $5^{1/4}$ correct to 7 decimal places, using Theorem 5.1.5 with starting value $3/2$.

13. Find a rational approximation to $153^{1/9}$ correct to 8 decimal places, using Theorem 5.1.5 with starting value $7/4$.

Project

It is clear from the result of Exercise 10 that if we can find integers u and v such that

$$u^2 - 2v^2 = 1, \qquad (5.1)$$

then u/v is a rational approximation to $\sqrt{2}$. Obviously for large u and v, the 1 in Equation (5.1) is insignificant compared to the other terms and you should have a very good approximation. In fact we have $u^2/v^2 - 2 = 1/v^2$, giving an exact measure of how close u^2/v^2 is to 2.

The equation

$$u^2 - nv^2 = 1, \qquad (5.2)$$

when n is a positive integer that is not a perfect square is called Pell's equation, though the name is a misattribution. It was Lagrange who first proved that Equation (5.2) has infinitely many solutions for each integer n that is not a perfect square and that a method can be described to show how to obtain all the solutions by iteration.

We do not give proofs of general theorems, but make do with a description of how to obtain all solutions of Equation (5.1). It starts with the observation that $3 + 2\sqrt{2}$ is the smallest number of the form $u + v\sqrt{2}$, with u and v positive integers such that Equation (5.1) holds. Now form $(3 + 2\sqrt{2})(u + v\sqrt{2})$, where u, v is any solution of Equation (5.1). It equals $(3u + 4v) + (2u + 3v)\sqrt{2}$.

If we now put

$$\begin{aligned} U &= 3u + 4v, \\ V &= 2u + 3v, \end{aligned}$$

we find that $U^2 - 2V^2 = 9u^2 + 24uv + 16v^2 - 8u^2 - 24uv - 18v^2 = 1$. (See also (4) in the Commentary to Week 3.) In this way out of one solution u/v we have generated another U/V by iteration. The general theorem in this area is that if you start with the smallest solution then by repeating the iteration you get all the solutions.

Starting with $u = 3, v = 2$ one gets $U = 17, V = 12$. Successive rational approximations by this method are

$$3/2, 17/12, 99/70, 577/408, 3363/2378,$$

$$19601/13860, 114243/80782, 665857/470832.$$

It can be seen that some of these appeared in the iteration scheme referred to immediately after Theorem 5.25.1.5. But this iteration scheme is complete in the sense just described. The project is to answer the following questions.

(1) Find the first few rational approximations to the equation $u^2 - 5v^2 = 1$.

(2) There is a Pythagorean triple (56,33,65) with $z = 2y - 1$. One angle in this triangle is close to $60°$. Show that there exist integer-sided right-angled triangles in which one angle is arbitrarily close to $60°$.

5.2 Commentary Week 5

1. If a/b and c/d are two rational numbers then $a/b + c/d = (ad + bc)/bd$ and if a, b, c, d are integers then so are $ad + bc$ and bd. Also provided b and d are both non-zero, then bd is

non-zero. Note the importance of proving the denominator is non-zero when proving a number is rational.

2. The product of a/b and c/d is ac/bd, and bd is non-zero, as in 1.

3. Square and the results follow from $49 < 50$ and $288 < 289$.

4. No; for example $(1 + \sqrt{2}) + (1 - \sqrt{2}) = 2$. See the solution to Exercise (8) for why numbers like $(1 + \sqrt{2})$ are irrational.

5. It is a solution of the equation $x^4 - 10x^2 + 1 = 0$.

6. In fact between the integers n and $n + 1$ there lies the irrational number $\sqrt{\{n(n+1)\}}$. And the square root of any integer that is not a perfect square is irrational.

7. Suppose the two rational numbers are a/b and c/d. These may be rewritten as ad/bd and bc/bd. Now by the solution to Exercise 6 there is an irrational number lying between ad and bc. Dividing this irrational number by the rational number bd leaves the result irrational.

8. Suppose $r + s = t$ is rational, then $s = t - r$, being the difference of two rational numbers is rational. Contradiction establishes the result.

9. Either $s = \sqrt{2}^{\sqrt{2}}$ is rational. Or, if it is irrational $s^{\sqrt{2}} = 2$ is rational. Although it is not known whether s is rational or not we still have a solution to the problem.

10. Note that $u_1 = 3, v_1 = 2$ are odd and even respectively and are coprime. If we now assume u_n and v_n are odd and even respectively and are coprime, then the iteration scheme gives $u_{n+1} = u_n^2 + 2v_n^2$ and $v_{n+1} = 2u_n v_n$ which are odd and even

respectively and coprime. It follows that u_n and v_n are odd and even respectively and coprime for all positive integers n, by induction. Now $u_1^2 - 2v_1^2 = 9 - 8 = 1$. If we now assume $u_n^2 - 2v_n^2 = 1$, we have $u_{n+1}^2 - 2v_{n+1}^2 = u_n^4 + 4u_n^2 v_n^2 + 4v_n^4 - 8u_n^2 v_n^2 = (u_n^2 - 2v_n^2)^2 = 1$, and hence $u_n^2 - 2v_n^2 = 1$ for all positive integers n by induction. Since $u_n^2/v_n^2 - 2 = 1/v_n^2$ and since $v_{n+1} > 2v_n$ it follows that v_n increases without limit as $n \to \infty$ and hence $x_n = u_n/v_n \to \sqrt{2}$ as $n \to \infty$.

11. The sequence of rational numbers approximating $\sqrt{3}$ is 7/4, 97/56, 18817/10864, 708158977/408855776, this last fraction being correct to at least 11 decimal places. 7/4 is chosen since $7^2 - 3 \times 4^2 = 1$.

12. 643/430

13. 633420529/362200163

Project

(1) Starting with 9/4 the approximations to $\sqrt{5}$ are in turn 161/72, 2889/1292, 51841/23184, 930249/416020, this last fraction agreeing with $\sqrt{5}$ to 10 decimal places.

1. $z = 2y - 1$ gives $u^2 + v^2 = 2u^2 - 2v^2 - 1$ or $u^2 - 3v^2 = 1$. The triple (56,33,65) arises from $u = 7, v = 4$. Now if θ is the angle close to $60°$ we have $\cos\theta = y/z = \frac{1}{2} + 1/2z = \frac{1}{2} + 1/\{2(u^2 + v^2)\}$, so successive solutions of Pell's equation give right-angled triangles in which $\cos\theta$ becomes arbitrarily close to $\frac{1}{2}$.

Chapter 6

Number Theory: Week 6

6.1 Real numbers, decimal expansions, recurring decimals

6.1.1 Real numbers

These are the totality of all numbers, both rational and irrational. A convenient and familiar way of representing them is by decimal expansions. The idea given in Week 5 following Eudoxus' definition of ratio is one way of defining the real numbers. The construction due to Dedekind associates with each real number a so-called *Dedekind section*. Two subsets L and U are taken such that (1) $L \cap U = \emptyset$, the empty set; (2) $L \cup U = \mathbb{Q}$; (3) $L \neq \mathbb{Q}, U \neq \mathbb{Q}$; (4) If $x \in L$ and $y \in U$, then $x < y$, then such a cut defines a real number. Of course having made this definition you have to show that such entities behave like the real numbers we are familiar with. Two completeness properties that you must accept are as follows: (1) If you now perform a cut of the *real numbers* you get nothing extra and (2) that if a set S of real numbers is bounded above then there exists a least upper bound. That is, if $s \leq k$, for every $s \in S$, there exists a real number t such that $s \le t$, for every $s \in S$, and if $u < t$ there exists an $s \in S$ such that $s > u$. Also it is the case that if (x_n) is an increasing sequence, that is if $x_{n+1} > x_n$ for all positive integers n, and the sequence is bounded above then $\lim x_n$ exists as $n \to \infty$.

This resolves a problem that some students encounter with decimal expansions that go on for ever. Some students argue that $0.499999\ldots$, where the 9s go on for ever is the largest number less than 0.5. Students are told that 147.5 gets rounded up to 148 and that anything slightly less gets rounded down. This is, of course, correct. But it does not mean that $147.499999\ldots$ gets rounded down. 147.49999999999 with ten 9s gets rounded down, and so would 147.4 followed by a million 9s. Students argue because they are unfamiliar and sometimes even unwilling to accept the idea that there is no largest number less than 147.5. The resolution of the difficulty lies in the completeness of the real numbers. In this particular case we can define the sequence $x_n = 147.4999\ldots9$ with n 9s. This is an increasing sequence. It is bounded above by 147.5. By the last sentence of the previous paragraph x_n tends to a limit. Once we know that a limit exists we can call it x, and then we have $x = 147.499999\ldots$, so $10x = 1474.99999\ldots$ and subtracting $9x = 1327.5$ and so $x = 147.5$. In other words the only consistent interpretation is that $147.499999\ldots$ is actually equal to 147.5. It is perhaps annoying that there are two apparently different decimal expansions for the same real number, but it is better to have an annoyance than a misconception.

In case there should be any doubt about the calculation in the last paragraph, let us look a little more carefully at the recurring decimal $0.11111\ldots$, where the 1s go on for ever. If one stops after n 1s then the value of that number, by definition, is

$$1/10 + 1/100 + 1/1000 + \ldots + 1/(10^n),$$

and from the work in Week 4 on geometric progressions we can sum this to get $(1/9)(1 - (1/10)^n)$. Clearly as n gets larger what is subtracted from $1/9$ gets smaller and smaller. The limit we are interested in is that $(1/10)^n \to 0$ as $n \to \infty$. So the number $0.11111\ldots$ is equal to $1/9$, and similarly $0.99999\ldots$ is equal to 1.

In the remainder of this book, we adopt the notation that brackets around a part of a decimal expansion means that the bracketed sequence of numbers is repeated. Thus $0.4567(123)$ stands for $0.4567123123123123\ldots$, where the sequence 123 is repeated indefinitely. The length of the sequence, in this case 3, is called the *period* of the recurring decimal.

Exercises

1. Determine in fractional form the following recurring decimals:
   (a) $0.(4)$, (b) $0.(45)$, (c) $0.(459)$, (d) $0.6(459)$.

2. What is $0.(538461)$ as a fraction?

6.1.2 Terminating decimal expansions

A terminating decimal is one like 0.6 or 0.425. It is easily checked that these correspond in fractional form to $3/5$ and $17/40$.

Exercises

3. Which fractions correspond to (a) 0.35, (b) 0.86275 ?

4. What is the decimal expansion for (a) $19/20$, (b) $19/160$?

5. What is a necessary and sufficient condition for a fraction to be represented by a terminating decimal?

6.1.3   Recurring decimal expansions

We have seen above the method for converting a recurring decimal into a fraction. There is no doubt that the method always works, though it is a bit messy to write down a general case. Let us just see what happens with $0.54675(5742)$. First there is the part that does not repeat 0.54675. This is equal to $54675/100000$, which reduces to $2187/4000$. We then have to add on the recurring part which is $0.00001 \times 5742/9999 = 29/5050000$. We now complete the job by adding the non-recurring part $2187/4000$ to get a total of $5522233/10100000$.

Exercise

    6. Convert to fractions in reduced form:

        (a) $0.6(3)$

        (b) $0.5(037)$

        (c) $0.2375(432)$

I expect that you discovered that all fractions whose denominators are of the form $2^m \times 5^n$ convert into terminating decimals. What remains to be proved is that all fractions other than these lead to recurring decimals.

First let us convert $1/7$ into a recurring decimal. Using the usual long division process we obtain $0.142857\ldots$ I imagine you can see why $1/7$ repeats at this point; it is because a remainder of 1 has appeared in the long division process, which is the point where the division started. If we carried on the long division then the working for the next six decimal places would be identical to the working already done for the first six decimal places. The working of the division recurs, so the decimal recurs.

The period of a recurring decimal

The *period* of a recurring decimal is the number of decimal places in the block of digits that repeats, 6 in the case of $1/7$. The question to ask is why is the period 6 for $1/7$ and not some other number. The first observation is that when dividing by the integer 7 there can be at most 6 different remainders; since 7 cannot go exactly into 10, 20, 30, 40, 50, or 60 these six remainders are, of course, 1, 2, 3, 4, 5, 6. A repeat in the working must therefore occur after at most 6 divisions. However, do not think that the recurring expansion for $1/p$, where p is an odd prime, is always $(p-1)$. For example $1/37 = 0.(027)$ and has a period of only 3. Another clue about the period is that $1/7 = 142587/999999$.

Exercises

7. Find the recurring decimals for $1/13$ and $2/13$.

8. Find the remainders that get used in the long divisions to produce these expansions. What has the period of 6 got to do with the maximum possible period in this case ?

9. Work out $0.(3) \times 0.(5)$ as a recurring decimal.

10. Make a list of the recurring decimals for $k/37, k = 1$ to 36. Comment on your results.

You will observe that I have not proved that all fractions that do not terminate as decimals are recurring decimals. All that has been done is to look at some easy cases, but these cases should make you confident of the general result. Often in mathematics you simply

have to wait until more advanced work has been carried out before
you can see the way ahead, but you may discover by the end of
the project more than I have disclosed. You may surprise yourself
by the progress you make and you may also be interested to know
that we return to the topic of recurring decimals again in Weeks 8
and 9.

Project

There are several different strands to the project. It is not against
the spirit of the project to use your calculator.

(1) Write down the recurring decimals for $1/7$, $2/7$, $3/7$, $4/7$,
    $5/7$, $6/7$ and explain what is going on. Explain, do not just
    describe.

(2) An integer is such that when the last digit is transferred to
    the beginning the result is five times as large. What is the
    integer?

(3) Repeat (1) for the twelve fractions with denominators equal
    to 13.

(4) What is the period of the recurring decimal for $1/239$?

(5) Find the prime factors of 111, 1111, 11111 (one of them is
    41), 111111 and 1111111(one of them is 4649). Find out what
    this has to do with periods of $1/37$, $1/101$, $1/41$, $1/7$, $1/13$,
    $1/239$. Observe, describe and explain.

6.2   Commentary   Week 6

1. (a) If $x = 0.(4)$ then $10x = 4.(4)$ and $9x = 4$, so $x = 4/9$.
   (b) If $x = 0.(45)$ then $100x = 45.(45)$ and $99x = 45$, so

$x = 5/11$.

(c) If $x = 0.(459)$ then $1000x = 459.(459)$ and $999x = 459$, so $x = 17/37$.

(d) If $x = 0.6(459)$ then $x = 6/10 + 17/370 = 239/370$.

2. $538461/999999 = 7/13$.

3. (a) $0.35 = 35/100 = 7/20$.
   (b) $0.86275 = 86275/100000 = 3451/4000$.

4. (a) $19/20 = 95/100 = 0.95$.
   (b) $19/160 = 11875/100000 = 0.11875$.

5. The denominator has to divide exactly into 10^n for some integer $n \geq 1$. In other words the denominator must only have 2s and 5s as factors. Then and only then can the fraction be converted into an equivalent one with a power of 10 in the denominator, and hence written down as a decimal that terminates. For example, the multiplier for $19/160$ is $5^4 = 625$.

6. (a) $0.6(3) = 6/10 + 3/90 = 19/30$.
   (b) $0.5(037) = 5/10 + 37/9990 = 68/135$.
   (c) $0.2375(432) = 2375/10000 + 432/9990000 = 87891/370000$.

7. $1/13 = 0.(076923)$ and $2/13 = 0.(153846)$.

8. For $1/13$ the successive remainders are 10, 9, 12, 3, 4, 1 and for $2/13$ they are 7, 5, 11, 6, 8, 2. Note that between the two of them all the 12 remainders of 13 get used. It is shown later in the book that the period of a recurring decimal for $1/p$, where p is an odd prime, must be a divisor of $(p-1)$.

9. $0.(3) \times 0.(5) = 1/3 \times 5/9 = 5/27 = 185/999 = 0.(185)$. There is obviously scope here for an interesting investigation as to whether one can learn to do arithmetic (addition,

subtraction, multiplication, and division) with recurring decimals without changing into fractions and changing back afterwards. Can one predict the period in terms of the periods of the data?

It is not actually all that difficult to show that all fractions which do not have only powers of 2 or 5 in the denominator recur. First I will give the example of $1/84 = 1/(4 \times 3 \times 7)$. Take 84. Multiply by 25 to convert any powers of 2 or 5 to powers of 10. Then $1/84 = 25/2100$. Take 21 and multiply by the smallest number to make the denominator a string of 9s. This number is 47619. Hence $1/84 = 25/2100 = 1190475/99999900$. Hence $100/84 = 1190475/999999 = 1 + 190476/999999 = 1.(190476)$ and $16/84 = 0.(190476)$ and so finally $1/84 = 0.01(190476)$. The crucial step is the one that converts 21 to 999999, by finding the multiple 47619. So what you have to be able to prove is that any integer whose prime factors exclude any powers of 2 or 5 can be multiplied by some integer to get a string of 9s. Although more advanced theory enables this to be proved easily enough, there is an elementary method, which establishes the result. To be precise it shows that all integers m, which contain factors other than 2s and 5s, can be multiplied by an integer that yields an integer consisting of a string of 9s followed by a string of 0s, where it is possible that the string of 0s is void. It involves a technique we have not yet encountered, called the *pigeonhole principle*. It is very simple and asserts that if there are n pigeonholes and $(n + 1)$ objects to be placed in them, then one of the pigeonholes must have two or more objects in it. Call this assertion $P(n)$. This principle is proved by induction on n. Clearly if there is 1 pigeonhole and 2 objects then there are 2 objects in that pigeonhole. So $P(1)$ is true. If $P(k)$ is true, then suppose there are $(k+1)$ pigeonholes and $(k+2)$ objects. Take one of the pigeonholes at random. If it has two objects the induction is complete. If it has less than two objects, we are left with k remaining pigeonholes and at least $(k + 1)$ objects, so, from the truth of $P(k)$, one of these remaining pigeonholes has at least two objects and again the induction is complete. Hence $P(n)$ is true for all positive integers n. The application here is to construct the remainders when $0, 9, 99, 999, 9999\ldots$ etc. are divided by m. The possible remainders form the pigeonholes and they are m in number, namely $0, 1, 2, 3, \ldots, (m - 1)$. The actual remainders found during this process are the objects and hence by the $(m + 1)^{\text{th}}$ remainder there must have been a repeat. If the first occurrence of the repeated number is from the integer with k 9s and the second occurrence with repeated remainder is from the number with t 9s, then the number $999\ldots900\ldots0$ with $(t - k)$ nines and k zeros is exactly divisible by m. It follows that $1/m$ recurs. Take again the case of $m = 84$. The remainders are $0, 9, 15, 75, 3, 39, 63, 51, 15$. So $t = 8$ and $k = 2$ and 99999900 is an exact multiple of 84, the multiplier being 1190475. It follows that $100/84 = 1190475/999999 = 1 + 190476/999999$ and hence $16/84 = 0.(190476)$ and $1/84 = 0.01(190476)$.

10.

$$1/37 = 0.(027), \quad 10/37 = 0.(270), \quad 26/37 = 0.(702).$$
$$2/37 = 0.(054), \quad 20/37 = 0.(540), \quad 15/37 = 0.(405).$$
$$3/37 = 0.(081), \quad 30/37 = 0.(810), \quad 4/37 = 0.(108).$$
$$5/37 = 0.(135), \quad 13/37 = 0.(351), \quad 19/37 = 0.(513).$$
$$6/37 = 0.(162), \quad 23/37 = 0.(621), \quad 8/37 = 0.(216).$$
$$7/37 = 0.(189), \quad 33/37 = 0.(891), \quad 34/37 = 0.(918).$$
$$9/37 = 0.(243), \quad 16/37 = 0.(432), \quad 12/37 = 0.(324).$$
$$11/37 = 0.(297), \quad 36/37 = 0.(972), \quad 27/37 = 0.(729).$$
$$14/37 = 0.(378), \quad 29/37 = 0.(783), \quad 31/37 = 0.(837).$$
$$17/37 = 0.(459), \quad 22/37 = 0.(594), \quad 35/37 = 0.(945).$$
$$18/37 = 0.(486), \quad 32/37 = 0.(864), \quad 24/37 = 0.(648).$$
$$21/37 = 0.(567), \quad 25/37 = 0.(675), \quad 28/37 = 0.(756).$$

The period is always 3. They fall into 12 sets of 3 in which the digits cycle. For example $3/37 = 0.(081)$ so $30/37 = 10 \times 0.(081) = 0.(810)$ and $300/37 = 10 \times 0.(810) = 8.(108)$ and subtracting 8 gives $4/37 = 0.(108)$. This sort of behaviour always happens.

Project

(1) $1/7 = 0.(142857)$ so $10/7 = 1.(428571)$ and $3/7 = 0.(428571)$. Then $30/7 = 4.(285714)$ and $2/7 = 0.(285714)$. Now $20/7 = 2.(857142)$ so that $6/7 = 0.(857142)$. Finally $60/7 = 8.(571428)$ and $4/7 = 0.(571428)$.

(2) Look at the recurring decimals for $1/7$ and $5/7$. You will then agree that the integer is 142857. Can you see why this answer is not unique?

(3) One cycle of 6 is $1/13 = 0.(076923)$, $10/13 = 0.(769230)$, $9/13 = 0.(692307)$, $12/13 = 0.(923076)$, $3/13 = 0.(230769)$. The other cycle of 6 is $2/13 = 0.(153846)$, $7/13 = 0.(538461)$, $5/13 = 0.(384615)$, $11/13 = 0.(846153)$, $6/13 = 0.(461538)$.

(4) Following the procedure in the text above the remainders of $0, 9, 99, 999, \ldots,$ on division by 239 are 0, 9, 99, 43, 200, 97, 23, 0 and so 9999999 is divisible by 239, the quotient being 41841 and so $1/239 = 0.(0041841)$.

(5) $111 = 37 \times 3$, so $999 = 37 \times 27$. It follows that $1/37$ has a period of 3. See Exercise 10 above. Also $1/27$ has a period of 3.
$1111 = 11 \times 101$, so $9999 = 99 \times 101$. It follows that $1/101$ has a period of 4.
$11111 = 41 \times 271$, so both $1/41$ and $1/271$ have a period of 5.
$111111 = 3 \times 37 \times 13 \times 11 \times 7$, so as 7 and 13 have not

appeared before both $1/7$ and $1/13$ have a period of 6. $1/37$ has a period of 3, $1/11$ has a period of 2, $1/3$ has a period of 1. Since 1, 2, 3 are divisors of 6 it follows that $1/37$, $1/11$, $1/3$ repeat every 6 places, though 6 is not the minimum period. This is why 37, 11 and 3 also divide 111111.

$1111111 = 4649 \times 239$, so both $1/239$ and $1/4649$ have periods of 7. As we have seen in (4) $1/239 = 0.(0041841)$ and since $9999999 = 4649 \times 2151$ it follows that $1/4649 = 0.(0002151)$. A little amusement is that $999999999 = 81 \times 37 \times 333667 = 81 \times 12345679$ and hence $1/81 = 0.(012345679)$. Now $1/3$ has a period of 1, $1/3^2$ has a period of 1, $1/3^3$ has a period of 3 and $1/3^4$ has a period of 9.

Chapter 7

Number Theory: Week 7

7.1 More on squares and integers represented as the sum of squares

We have already covered enough theory for you to be able to manage the first set of Exercises, and it is suggested that you try these problems before we embark on some new ideas and techniques.

1. The four-digit integer $aabb$ is a square. Find a and b.

2. Prove that the sum of the squares of five successive positive integers is never a square.

3. The triangular number $T_n = \frac{1}{2}n(n+1)$ for $n = 0, 1, 2, 3, \ldots$. Show how to find all values for which T_n is a perfect square and find the first four such triangular numbers.

Consider the following:

$$3^2 + 4^2 = 25 \qquad 7^2 + 1^2 = 50,$$
$$4^2 + 6^2 = 52 \qquad 10^2 + 2^2 = 104,$$
$$5^2 + 9^2 = 106 \qquad 14^2 + 4^2 = 212.$$

You can probably generalize this.

4. Prove that if the integer n is the sum of two squares then $2n$ is also.

There is a very useful algebraic identity:

$$(ax + by)^2 + (ay - bx)^2 = (a^2 + b^2)(x^2 + y^2).$$

For example, putting $a = 3, b = 2, x = 5, y = 9$ it gives $33^2 + 17^2 = (3^2 + 2^2)(5^2 + 9^2)$.

Exercises

5. Factorize $(ax - by)^2 + (ay + bx)^2$.

6. Express 1378 as the sum of two squares in two different ways.

7. What is the smallest integer that can be expressed as the sum of two squares in two different ways?[1]

8. Now put $a = 5, b = 6, x = 12, y = 10$ and construct similar numerical results to those for $a = 3, b = 2, x = 5, y = 9$.

Theorem 7.1 Let $S(2)$ be the set of all integers that can be expressed as the sum of two squares (including the case when one of those squares is 0). Prove that if $g \in S(2)$ and $h \in S(2)$, then $gh \in S(2)$.

---

[1]We do not deem $p^2 + q^2$ and $q^2 + p^2$ to be different expressions in this context.

Exercise

9. Theorem 7.1 is in mathematics what is called *closure property*. Use the material in the text prior to the statement of the theorem to prove that $S(2)$ is closed under multiplication.

The positive integers are closed under multiplication and they have the property that they are all expressible as multiples of 1 and the positive primes. As we see shortly the same sort of things happen with the set $S(2)$.

Exercises

10. Express all the primes between 5 and 97 inclusive as the sum of two perfect squares in as many ways as you can.

11. Prove that no prime of the form 3 (mod 4) is expressible as the sum of two perfect squares.

From the results so far the following theorem holds:

Theorem 7.2 The following and only the following integers belong to $S(2)$, and can be expressed as the sum of two perfect squares (one of which may be zero):

$$2^k pq \ldots su^2v^2 \ldots x^2,$$

where k is a non-negative integer, $p, q, \ldots, s$ are primes of the form 1 (mod 4) and $u, v, \ldots, x$ are primes of the form 3 (mod 4). In this expression some primes may be repeated, and such elements include those in which there is no prime of either one form or the other.

In view of the closure property the only part of this theorem unproved is that odd primes of the form 1 (mod 4) are all uniquely expressible as the sum of two positive integer squares. This result is not proved in this book, but you should accept the result and be prepared to use it.

Exercise

12. If p_1, p_2, p_3 are distinct primes of the form $1 \pmod 4$, in how many different ways can p_1, p_2, p_3 be expressed as the sum of two positive integer squares?

7.1.1   The triangular numbers

These are $0, 1, 3, 6, 10, 15, \ldots$.. The nth triangular number is $T_n = \frac{1}{2}n(n+1)$. They are closely related to the squares in view of the fact that $8T_n + 1 = (2n+1)^2$.

Exercises

13. Prove that $4(T_m + T_n) + 1 = (m+n+1)^2 + (m-n)^2$.

14. What positive integers can be expressed as the sum of two triangular numbers (including 0)?

15. Form a hypothesis as to which positive integers can be expressed as the sum of at most three triangular numbers.

Although in general it is difficult to say how mathematicians of previous ages compare with the best of those today, it is safe to say that Gauss was one of the greatest mathematicians who ever lived. Like Archimedes he used the word *Eureka* (in large letters on a manuscript) when he proved his result about three triangular numbers, so I shall call the result Gauss's Eureka. It seems almost certain that you will have framed the correct hypothesis in Exercise

15. Unfortunately it is another result that we do not prove in this book.

Exercises

16. Use Gauss's Eureka to prove that all positive integers of the form 3 (mod 8) are expressible as the sum of three perfect squares.

17. Prove that all integers of the form 7 (mod 8) are expressible as the sum of four squares.

18. Express the results about Pythagorean triples in terms of triangular numbers.

Project

The *quaternions* are the set of entities of the form $aE + uI + vJ + wK$, where a, u, v, w are real numbers and E, I, J, K are the quaternion units satisfying $E^2 = E, I^2 = J^2 = K^2 = -E, IJ = -JI = K, JK = -KJ = I, KI = -IK = J$ and $EI = I, EJ = J, EK = K$.

(1) Prove that if the above quaternion is denoted by Q and Q^* has the same a but has u, v, w replaced by $-u, -v, -w$ respectively, then $QQ^* = a^2 + u^2 + v^2 + w^2$.

(2) Now let P and Q be two quaternions with integer a, u, v, w. By proving that

$$(PQ)(PQ)^* = (PP^*)(QQ^*)$$

show that an integer represented by the sum of four integer squares multiplied by another such integer is equal to an integer that is itself represented by the sum of four integer squares.

7.2   Commentary   Week 7

1. Suppose $n^2 = 1100a + 11b = 11(100a + b) = 11(99a + a + b)$. Since n^2 is divisible by 11, it must be divisible by 11^2, which in turn means $11 \mid (a+b)$. But $0 < a+b < 19$, so $a+b = 11$. Now since n^2 is a square, b cannot be 2,3,7 or 8. Since $0 < a < 10$, b cannot be 0 or 1. Nor can $b = 5$, since then the square would end in 25, not 55. Now 5566 is not a square, and so $7744 = 88^2$ is the only possibility.

2. The sum of the squares from $(n-2)$ to $(n+2)$ inclusive is equal to $5(n^2 + 2)$. If this is a perfect square then $5 \mid (n^2 + 2)$; that is $n^2 = 5m - 2$. But integers equal to $3 \pmod 5$ are never perfect squares. The contradiction establishes the result.

3. If $T_n = x^2$ for non-negative integers n and x we have $(2n + 1)^2 - 8x^2 = 1$. We now refer to the project in Week 5, where Pell's equation $u^2 - 2v^2 = 1$ is analysed. The solutions of this equation, by considering it $\pmod 4$, must be such that u is odd and v is even, so they are all suitable in this case. The first four are $(u, v) = (1, 0), (3, 2), (17, 12), (99, 70)$. These correspond to $(n, x) = (0, 0), (1, 1), (8, 6), (49, 35)$.

4. If $n = a^2 + b^2$, then $(a + b)^2 + (a - b)^2 = 2n$.

5. It is also true that $(ax - by)^2 + (ay + bx)^2 = (a^2 + b^2)(x^2 + y^2)$.

6. We already have $1378 = 33^2 + 17^2$. Using the second factorization we also have $1378 = 37^2 + 3^2$.

7. $(1^2 + 2^2)(1^2 + 3^2) = 1^2 + 7^2 = 5^2 + 5^2 = 50$.
The next lowest come from $(1^2 + 2^2)(2^2 + 3^2) = 1^2 + 8^2 = 4^2 + 7^2 = 65$.

8. It gives $120^2 + 22^2 = 122^2 + 0^2$. Whenever $ax = by$ or $ay = bx$ the result degenerates and produces a Pythagorean triple.

9. This follows immediately from Exercise 5.

10. $5 = 1^2 + 2^2, 13 = 2^2 + 3^2, 17 = 1^2 + 4^2, 29 = 2^2 + 5^2, 37 = 1^2 + 6^2, 41 = 4^2 + 5^2, 53 = 2^2 + 7^2, 61 = 5^2 + 6^2, 73 = 3^2 + 8^2, 89 = 5^2 + 8^2, 97 = 4^2 + 9^2$, and that is all. Two points to note are (i) that no prime of the form 3 (mod 4) is amongst them and (ii) all expressions for primes of the form 1(mod 4) are unique.

11. A perfect square is either 0 (mod 4) or 1(mod 4), so that the sum of two perfect squares cannot be 3 (mod 4).

12. 4 ways. For example $5 \times 13 \times 17 = (1^2 + 4^2) \times 65 = (1^2 + 4^2)(1^2 + 8^2)$ or $(1^2 + 4^2)(4^2 + 7^2) = 4^2 + 33^2 = 12^2 + 31^2 = 23^2 + 24^2 = 9^2 + 32^2$.
    It is not difficult to generalize the result to cover the question of how many essentially different ways there are of expressing any integer as the sum of two squares.

13. $4(T_m + T_n) + 1 = 2m(m+1) + 2n(n+1) + 1 = (m+n+1)^2 + (m-n)^2$.

14. From the solution to Exercise 13 we see that if we take an even square and an odd square, add them up and subtract 1, and finally divide by 4, then such a number is always expressible as the sum of two triangular numbers.
    For example $\frac{1}{4}(48^2 + 59^2 - 1) = T(53) + T(5)$.

15. The result that we call Gauss's Eureka is that all positive integers are expressible as the sum of no more than three triangular numbers.

16. Suppose the integer $N = T_k + T_m + T_n$, then

$$8N + 3 = (2k + 1)^2 + (2m + 1)^2 + (2n + 1)^2.$$

17. From Exercise 16 we have

$$8N + 7 = (2k + 1)^2 + (2m + 1)^2 + (2n + 1)^2 + 2^2.$$

18. The equation $(L + M + 1)^2 + (L - M)^2 = N^2$ may be written as $T_L + T_M = 2T_{2k}$ provided $L = l^2 - m^2 + 2ml + 2l$, $M = m^2 - l^2 + 2ml + 2m$ and $k = T_l + T_m$. For example, with $l = 10, m = 13$ we have $L = 211, M = 355, N = 585, k = 146$ and $567^2 + 144^2 = 585^2$ is equivalent to $T_{211} + T_{355} = 2T_{292}$. It can be shown that every primitive Pythagorean triple has an equivalent form in which one triangular number is the average of two others.

Project

We have

$$(aE + uI + vJ + wK)(bE + xI + yJ + zK)$$

$$(ab - ux - vy - wz)E + (ax + ub + vz - wy)I$$

$$+(ay + vb + wx - uz)J + (az + wb + uy - vx)K.$$

One can now verify that

$$(a^2 + u^2 + v^2 + w^2)(b^2 + x^2 + y^2 + z^2)$$

$$= (ab - ux - vy - wz)^2 + (ax + ub + vz - wy)^2$$

$$+(ay + vb + wx - uz)^2 + (az + wb + uy - vx)^2$$

that is $(PP^*)(QQ^*) = (PQ)(PQ)^*$.

This is a closure rule that says that the product of two expressions that are the sums of four integer squares is also the sum of four integer squares.

We know that primes of the form 1 (mod 4) are expressible as the sum of two integer squares, we know from Exercises 16 and 17 that primes of the form 3 (mod 8) and 7 (mod 8) are expressible as the sums of three and four integer squares respectively. It follows by the closure relationship that all integers are expressible as the sum of no more than four integer squares. This theorem is attributed to Lagrange.

So although squares and triangular numbers are closely linked, there is the subtle difference in the representation of positive integers, in that only three triangular numbers are needed, whereas four squares are needed. It turns out that this means there is a slightly stronger result about the representation of integers as the sum of squares. This is that an odd integer is always expressible as the sum of four integer squares, where the integers involved may themselves be chosen to have a sum of 1. For example $27 = 4^2 + (-3)^2 + 1^2 + (-1)^2$ and $29 = (-4)^2 + 3^2 + 2^2 + 0^2$.

Chapter 8

Number Theory: Week 8

8.1   Arithmetic modulo a prime number, Fermat's little theorem and Carmichael numbers

Exercises

1. Copy and complete the following multiplication tables:

$x \pmod 5$	1	2	3	4
1	1	2	3	4
2	2	4	1	3
3				
4				

$x \pmod 7$	1	2	3	4	5	6
1	1	2				
2	2	4	6	1	3	
3						
4						
5						
6						

$x \pmod{11}$	1	2	3	4	5	6	7	8	9	10
1										
2										
3										
4										
5										
6										
7	7	3	10	6	2	9	5	1	8	4
8										
9										
10										

2. What do you notice in each case about the array of answers?

3. For each value of $m, m = 1$ to 4, work out the smallest positive value of n such that $m^n = 1 \pmod 5$.

4. For each value of $m, m = 1$ to 6, work out the smallest positive value of n such that $m^n = 1 \pmod 7$.

5. For each value of $m, m = 1$ to 10, work out the smallest positive value of n such that $m^n = 1 \pmod{11}$.

Theorem 8.1 If p is an odd prime and $(a, p) = 1$, then

$$a, 2a, 3a, \ldots, (p - 1)a$$

(mod p) is a rearrangement of the integers

$$1, 2, 3, \ldots, (p-1).$$

Proof Since $(a, p) = 1$ none is 0 (mod p), so the theorem is true provided no two are equal (mod p). Suppose, in fact, that $ma = na$(mod p), then $(m-n)a = 0$ (mod p). Since $(a, p) = 1$ it follows that $m = n$(mod p). But $0 < m, n < p$ and hence $m = n$ It follows that the integers are all different and are therefore a rearrangement of $1, 2, 3, \ldots, (p-1)$. ∎

Corollary It follows that for every $a \in \{1, 2, 3, \ldots, (p-1)\}$ there exists a unique partner b such that $ab = ba = 1$ (mod p). The partner is called the inverse of a and is sometimes written as a^{-1}.

The set $\mathbb{Z}_p = \{0, 1, 2, 3 \ldots, (p-1)\}$ under the operations $+$(mod p) and $\times$(mod p) is what is known algebraically as a *finite field*, which basically means that the ordinary rules of arithmetic are valid, and in particular you can divide by any non-zero number, with the convention that $m/a = a^{-1}m$ (mod p). For those familiar with the terminology, $\mathbb{Z}_p$ is a cyclic group of order p under $+$ (mod p) and $\mathbb{Z}_p \backslash \{0\}$ is an abelian group of order $(p-1)$ under $\times$ (mod p).

Theorem 8.2 [Fermat's little theorem] Let p be an odd prime.

$$\text{If } (a, p) = 1 \text{ then } a^{p-1} = 1(\text{mod } p). \tag{8.1}$$

$$\text{and for every integer } m, m^p = m(\text{mod } p). \tag{8.2}$$

Proof 1 We know from Theorem 8.1 that if $(a, p) = 1$, then

$$(1a)(2a)(3a) \ldots ((p-1)a) = (1)(2)(3) \ldots (p-1)(\text{mod } p),$$

and since $(p-1)!$ is coprime to p we may cancel it from both sides leaving Equation (8.1). Equation (8.2) is immediate once (8.1) is proved.   ∎

For those familiar with finite group theory we give another argument.

Proof 2 For any element $a \in \mathbb{Z}_p \backslash \{0\}$ let n be the smallest positive integer such that $a^n = 1 \pmod{p}$. Then $\{1, a, a^2, \ldots, a^{n-1}\}$ forms a cyclic subgroup with n elements in the entire group, which is $(p-1)$, so $(p-1) = kn$ and so $a^{p-1} = a^{kn} = (a^n)^k = 1^k = 1 \pmod{p}$.   ∎

Finally we give a third way to demonstrate this important result.

Proof 3 In this proof you need to know what is meant by a cyclic permutation. It is very simple: for example, the cyclic permutations of $abcde$ are $abcde, bcdea, cdeab, deabc, eabcd$ and are five in number.

Suppose we have a lot of beads of m different colours. Out of these we are going to make necklaces with exactly p beads. First we make a string of beads with p beads. Since there are m colours the first bead can be any of m colours and likewise the second and so on. There are therefore m^p different strings of beads. From these we remove the m strings in which all the beads are of the same colour. This leaves $m^p - m$ strings. We now join up the ends of the strings to form necklaces. Two strings that differ only by having a different cyclic permutation of the same set of beads form indistinguishable necklaces. Since there are p cyclic permutations of p beads on a string, the number of distinct necklaces is $(m^p - m)/p$. Because of its meaning this must be an integer. Equation (8.2) follows.   ∎

This type of proof is called a *combinatorial proof*, because it relies on an argument involving counting. Alternatively it can be called a *bijective proof*, because it involves setting up a $1 - 1$ correspondence with a set which can be counted. Such proofs need considerable care, for as they can be rather verbal in character they can be misleading, as the next Exercise shows.

Exercise

6. Where does Proof 3 go wrong when p is not prime?

Those unfamiliar with group theory should still be made familiar with what is meant by the order of an element (mod p). It was the aim of Exercises 3, 4, 5 to give numerical evidence of what the order of an element is and what is its main property. If $(a, p) = 1$ and p is an odd prime, then the *order* of a (mod p) is the smallest positive integer n such that $a^n = 1$ (mod p).

Theorem 8.3 The order of a (mod p) divides $(p - 1)$.

Proof Let n be the order of a and suppose n does not divide $(p - 1)$, then $(p - 1) = qn + r$, where, by the Euclidean algorithm studied in Week 1, $0 < r < n$. Then, by Theorem 8.2 we have $1 = a^{p-1} = a^{qn+r} = (a^n)^q a^r = a^r$, since $a^n = 1$, by definition. But this contradicts the definition that n is the *smallest* positive integer such that $a^n = 1$. It follows that $n \mid (p - 1)$. ∎

An immediate application of Theorems 8.2 and 8.3 is in the theory of recurring decimals studied in Week 6. If we suppose that p is an odd prime other than 5, then let n be the order of 10 so that $10^n = 1$ (mod p). This means that $(10^n - 1)$ is divisible by p and n is the smallest positive integer for which this is so. It follows that $1/p$ recurs with period n and furthermore $n \mid (p - 1)$. Numerical evidence was gathered in Week 6 to illustrate this.

Fermat's little theorem can be used to show that an integer is not prime. For example $2^{64} = 16 \neq 1 \pmod{65}$ and hence 65 is not prime. Of course, there are easier ways of showing that 65 is not prime, but when dealing with very large numbers it is possible by such means to show that an integer is composite without knowing any of its prime factors. Fermat's little theorem deals with large numbers as efficiently as it deals with small numbers, as the following examples show.

Examples

(1) We work out $7^{44} \pmod{13}$. From Theorem 8.2 $7^{12} = 1 \pmod{13}$. Hence $7^{36} = 1 \pmod{13}$. So $7^{44} = 7^8 \pmod{13}$. Now $7^2 = 10 \pmod{13}$, so $7^4 = 100 = 9 \pmod{13}$ and $7^8 = 81 = 3 \pmod{13}$.

(2) We solve the congruence $x^{15} = 48 \pmod{59}$. We have $x^{30} = 48^2 = 3 \pmod{59}$ so $x^{60} = 9 \pmod{59}$. But by Theorem 8.2 $x^{58} = 1 \pmod{59}$, so we have $x^2 = 9 \pmod{59}$ leading to $x = 3$ or $56 \pmod{59}$.

(3) We investigate whether there are any solutions of the congruence $x^3 = 5 \pmod{13}$. If there were then $x^6 = 25 = -1 \pmod{13}$ and $x^{12} = 1 \pmod{13}$, which is compatible with Theorem 8.2. It is now worth seeking the solutions.
The cubes of 1, 2, 3, ..., 12 (mod 13) are 1, 8, 1, 12, 8, 8, 5, 5, 1, 12, 5, 12. So the solutions are $x = 7, 8, 11 \pmod{13}$.

Exercises

7. Use Fermat's little theorem to show that 16637 is not prime.

8. Solve $x^{97} = 5 \pmod{11}$.

9. Solve $x^{15} = 27 \pmod{73}$.

10. Find an integer $0 < x < 59$ such that $x = 9^{50} \pmod{59}$.

The converse of Fermat's little theorem is not true. The counterexample with the least exponent is 340, since $2^{340} = 1 \pmod{341}$. In fact $2^5 = 1 \pmod{31}$ and $2^{10} = 1 \pmod{11}$. Hence $2^{340} = 1 \pmod{31}$ and $2^{340} = 1 \pmod{11}$ and so $2^{340} = 1 \pmod{341}$. We say that 341 is a *pseudoprime to the base* 2. There are an infinite number of pseudoprimes to the base 2, or indeed to any base. So Fermat's little theorem cannot definitely establish that an integer is prime, but it may suggest that a number is prime.

In Theorem 8.3 it is proved that the order of an element (mod p), where p is an odd prime, divides $(p-1)$. It has not been shown here that an element exists which actually has order $(p-1)$. If such an element exists it is called a *primitive root modulo p*. In fact such elements do exist, which means that the group $\mathbb{Z}_p \backslash \{0\}$ is cyclic. The number of distinct primitive roots is also known. We do not establish these results in this book.

Exercises

11. Work out 4! (mod 5), 6! (mod 7) and 10! (mod 11), decide on a probable theorem and prove it.

12. For p an odd prime factorize $x^{p-1} - 1 \pmod{p}$.

A composite integer m such that $a^m = a \pmod{m}$ for every integer such that $1 \le a \le m$ is called a Carmichael number. The first four Carmichael numbers are 561, 1105, 1729, and 2465. It was only proved in 1984 that there are an infinite number of Carmichael numbers, a conjecture originally made by Carmichael himself in 1910.

Exercise

13. Prove that 561 is a Carmichael number.

The numbers $1, 2, 3, \ldots, p-1$, where p is prime are called a *complete set of residues* (mod p). Any set of $p-1$ integers congruent to them also forms a complete set.

The numbers $1^2, 2^2, 3^2, \ldots, (p-1)^2 \bmod p$ are called *quadratic residues* (mod p). In the project that follows you may assume the existence of primitive roots modulo p where p is an odd prime.

Project

(1) Prove that 1,2,4 are the distinct quadratic residues (mod 7).

(2) Work out the distinct quadratic residues (mod 7).

(3) How many quadratic residues are there (mod p), where p is an odd prime? Justify your answer.

(4) For which primes p is -1 a quadratic residue? Prove your assertion.

(5) Find the solutions of the congruence $x^2 + 8x + 14 = 0$ (mod 23).

(6) For which primes p is 2 a quadratic residue? Prove your assertion.

8.2   Commentary   Week 8

1. The tables are as follows.

x (mod 5)	1	2	3	4
1	1	2	3	4
2	2	4	1	3
3	3	1	4	2
4	4	3	2	1

x (mod 7)	1	2	3	4	5	6
1	1	2	3	4	5	6
2	2	4	6	1	3	5
3	3	6	2	5	1	4
4	4	1	5	2	6	3
5	5	3	1	6	4	2
6	6	5	4	3	2	1

x (mod 11)	1	2	3	4	5	6	7	8	9	10
1	1	2	3	4	5	6	7	8	9	10
2	2	4	6	8	10	1	3	5	7	9
3	3	6	9	1	4	7	10	2	5	8
4	4	8	1	5	9	2	6	10	3	7
5	5	10	4	9	3	8	2	7	1	6
6	6	1	7	2	8	3	9	4	10	5
7	7	3	10	6	2	9	5	1	8	4
8	8	5	2	10	7	4	1	9	6	3
9	9	7	5	3	1	10	8	6	4	2
10	10	9	8	7	6	5	4	3	2	1

2. In all cases with multiplication (mod p) with p prime, each residue in the answer table appears once and once only in each row and in each column. This is proved in Theorem 8.1. Because the multiplication process is commutative ($ab = ba$) the table is symmetrical about the main diagonal. Numbers whose product is 1 are called *inverse* numbers. For example 7 and 8 are inverse (mod 11).

3. For the table (mod 5) we have for the smallest integer n for each m for which $m^n = 1, 1^1 = 1, 2^4 = 1, 3^4 = 1, 4^2 = 1$. As explained in the text after Exercise 6 this smallest integer n is called the order of m, and it is proved in Theorem 8.3 that $n \mid (p-1)$.

4. The orders of 1, 2, 3, 4, 5, 6 (mod 7) are 1, 3, 6, 3, 6, 2 respectively. Note these are all divisors of 6.

5. The orders of the residues (mod 11) for 1, 2, 3, 4, 5, 6, 7, 8, 9, 10 are 1, 10, 5, 5, 5, 10, 10, 10, 5, 2 respectively, once more illustrating the remarks concerning divisibility.

6. In Proof 3 of Fermat's little theorem the fact that p is prime is used in stating that the p cyclic permutations of a string are distinguishable from one another. If p is not prime this is not necessarily the case. For example if $p = 6$ and $m = 2$ the 6 cyclic permutations of $ababab$ are $ababab, bababa, ababab,$ $bababa, ababab, bababa,$ which fall into two lots of identical strings.

7. We prove 16637 is composite by showing that $2^{16636} \neq 1$ (mod 16637). We have $2^{14} = 16384 = -253$ (mod 16637),so $2^{28} = 14098$ (mod 16637). Hence $2^{56} = 8002$ (mod 16637) and $2^{112} = 12828$ (mod 16637).
Then $2^{224} = 1017$ (mod 16637) and $2^{448} = 2795$ (mod 16637). Carrying on this way by squaring we get $2^{896} = 9272$ (mod 16637) and $2^{1792} = 6605$ (mod 16637) and $2^{3584} = 3811$ (mod 16637) and $2^{7168} = -380$ (mod 16637) and $2^{14336} = 11304$ (mod 16637) and $2^{16128} = 2^{14336} \times 2^{1792} = 12701$ (mod 16637) and $2^{16576} = 2^{16128} \times 2^{448} = 12574$ (mod 16637). $2^{16632} = 2^{16576} \times 2^{56} = 13209$ (mod 16637) and $2^{16636} = 13209 \times 16 = 11700$ (mod 16637). Note that $2^{16380} = 1 \pmod{16637}$, a result that we refer to later. This sort of calculation is fairly

easy provided you use a calculator to do the squaring and you obtain $x \pmod{16637}$ from the simple algorithm $16637 \times \{(x/16637) - \lfloor x/16637 \rfloor\}$, where the symbol $\lfloor y \rfloor$ denotes the integer part of y. The larger the integer the more efficient the method is compared with dividing the integer by all primes less than its square root.

8. Since $x^{10} = 1 \pmod{11}$, we need only solve $x^7 = 5 \pmod{11}$ or $5x^3 = 1 \pmod{11}$. Multiplying by 2 we get $x^3 = -1 = 10 \pmod{11}$. The cubes of the numbers $1, 2, 3, \ldots 10 \pmod{11}$ are 1,8,5,9,4,7,2,6,3,10 respectively. The solution is therefore $x = 10 \pmod{11}$.

9. If $x^{15} = 27 \pmod{11}$, we need only solve $x^{75} = 27^5 = 27 \pmod{73}$, but $x^{72} = 1 \pmod{73}$ by Fermat's little theorem, so $x^3 = 27 \pmod{73}$, so one solution is $x = 3 \pmod{73}$. The question arises as to whether there are any other solutions. So if $y^3 = 27 \pmod{73}$, we have $(yx^{-1})^3 = 1 \pmod{73}$ and so it is necessary to find solutions of the equation $z^3 = 1$ other than $z = 1$ and then $y = zx$ is also a solution for any such z. Since $3 \mid 72$ there are solutions other than $z = 1 \pmod{73}$. Now you need to look up in a table of primitive roots what is the smallest integer that is a primitive root of 73, and the answer is 5. It follows that $5^{24}, 5^{48} \pmod{73}$ are the two possible values of z that give new solutions. Now $5^{24} = 8 \pmod{73}$ so the other solutions are 24 and 46 $\pmod{73}$.

10. $9^2 = 22 \pmod{59}$, so $9^4 = 484 = 12 \pmod{59}$ and $9^8 = 144 = 26 \pmod{59}$. Hence $9^{16} = 676 = 27 \pmod{59}$ and $9^{32} = 729 = 21 \pmod{59}$.
It follows that $9^{50} = 21 \times 27 \times 22 \pmod{59} = 25 \pmod{59}$.

11. $4! = 24 = -1 \pmod{5}$. Also $6! = 720 = -1 \pmod{7}$ and $10! = 3628800$, which on division by 11 gives 329890 and

remainder 10, so $10! = -1 \pmod{11}$. Wilson's theorem states that for all primes p it is the case that $(p-1)! = -1 \pmod{p}$. The case $p = 2$ is trivial, so we may suppose that p is an odd prime. First we ask the question when an element $x, 0 < x < p$, is its own inverse? For this to be true we must have $x = x^{-1} \pmod{p}$, that is $x^2 = 1 \pmod{p}$. This implies $(x+1)(x-1) = 0 \pmod{p}$. Since $0 < x < p$ this means $x = 1$ or $x = (p-1)$. This means that of the elements from 2 to $(p-2)$ inclusive they fall into $(p-3)/2$ pairs of *distinct* elements (a, b) such that $ab = 1 \pmod{p}$. This means that the product of all these $(p-3)$ elements is $+1 \pmod{p}$. Multiplying by 1 and $(p-1) = -1 \pmod{p}$ we get $(p-1)! = -1 \pmod{p}$.

12. For each residue $a \pmod{p}$ we have $a^{p-1} = 1 \pmod{p}$. This means that each of $1, 2, 3, \ldots, (p-1)$ is a solution of the equation $x^{p-1} = 1 \pmod{p}$. But this equation is of a degree $(p-1)$ so $1, 2, 3, \ldots, (p-1)$ exhaust the solutions of this equation. It follows by the remainder theorem that

$$x^{p-1} - 1 = (x-1)(x-2)(x-3)\ldots(x-p+1) \pmod{p}. \quad (8.3)$$

For example putting $p = 5$ we have

$$(x-1)(x-2)(x-3)(x-4)$$

$$= x^4 - 10x^3 + 35x^2 - 50x + 24 = x^4 - 1 \pmod{5}.$$

Note that putting $x = 0$ in (8.3) provides another proof of Wilson's theorem. In fact it gives much more, telling us that

$$1^k + 2^k + 3^k + \cdots + (p-1)^k = 0 \pmod{p}$$

for $1 \le k \le (p-2)$.

13. We want to prove $a^{561} = a$ (mod 561) for all integers a such that $1 \leq a < 561$. It is sufficient to prove that $a^{561} = a$ (mod 3), $a^{561} = a$ (mod 11) and $a^{561} = a$(mod 17), since $561 = 3 \times 11 \times 17$ as a product of primes. For the first of these if $3 \mid a$, then both sides are 0 (mod 3) and if 3 does not divide a we can use Fermat's little theorem to get $a^{561} = (a^{280})^2 a = a$ (mod 3). For the second congruence if $11 \mid a$ then both sides are 0 (mod 11) and if 11 does not divide a we can use Fermat's little theorem to get $a^{561} = (a^{56})^{10} a = a$ (mod 11). For the third congruence if $17 \mid a$ then both sides are 0 (mod 17) and if 17 does not divide a we can use Fermat's little theorem to get $a^{561} = (a^{35})^{16} a = a$ (mod 17). A Carmichael number is therefore one which gives the appearance of being a prime, when tested by Fermat's little theorem. The method of proof provides a sufficient criterion for a positive integer m to be a Carmichael number. It must be odd, no prime p appearing in its prime factorization must appear to a power greater than 1, and for each prime p appearing it must be the case that $(p - 1) \mid (m - 1)$. It can be proved that the criterion is also necessary and that there are an infinite number of Carmichael numbers. Despite this, testing for possible primality by using Fermat's little theorem is a very powerful tool and with minor modifications to overcome the problem of Carmichael numbers can be made into a foolproof test.

Project

(1) $1^2 = 1, 2^2 = 4, 3^2 = 2, 4^2 = 2, 5^2 = 4, 6^2 = 1$ (mod 7). It follows that 1, 2, 4 are the three quadratic residues (mod 7).

(2) 1, 4, 9, 5, 3 are the five quadratic residues (mod 11). 1, 4, 9,

16, 8, 2, 15, 13 are the eight quadratic residues (mod 17). 1, 4. 9, 16, 6, 17, 11, 7, 5 are the nine quadratic residues (mod 19).

(3) It appears from the evidence in (2) that there are precisely $\frac{1}{2}(p-1)$ quadratic residues for a given odd prime p. This is in fact the case, as $x^2 = y^2 \pmod{p}$ if and only if $x = y$ or $x = (p-y) \pmod{p}$.

(4) -1 is a quadratic residue $\pmod{p}$ if, and only if $p = 1 \pmod 4$. We are looking for elements x such that $x^2 = -1 \pmod{p}$. Such an element must satisfy $x^4 = 1 \pmod{p}$, so the order of x is 4. (It cannot be 3 since $x^6 = -1 \pmod{p}$.) Now by Theorem 8.3 it follows that $4 \mid (p-1)$, so for such an element to exist it is necessary that $p = 1 \pmod 4$. It is sufficient because a primitive root g exists such that $(p-1)$ is the order of g and when $p-1$ is a multiple of 4, we have $x = g^{(p-1)/4}$ satisfies $x^2 = g^{(p-1)/2}$ and since this squares to 1 $\pmod{p}$ it must be 1 or $-1 \pmod{p}$. But it cannot be 1, since the order of g is not $(p-1)/2$ and hence we have identified an element x such that $x^2 = -1 \pmod{p}$. This is the first step in proving that every prime of this form is expressible as the sum of two integer squares.

(5) We have $(x+4)^2 = 2 \pmod{23}$. Hence $x+4 = 5$ or 18 $\pmod{23}$. This means that $x = 1$ or 17 $\pmod{23}$.

(6) This is a generalization of (4). Let g be a primitive root modulo p then a is a quadratic residue $\pmod{p}$ if it is an even power of g. So suppose $a = g^{2m}$ then $a^{(p-1)/2} = (g^{(p-1)})^m = 1^m = 1 \pmod{p}$. On the other hand if a is an odd power of g, say $a = g^{2m+1}$, then $a^{(p-1)/2} = (g^{(p-1)})^m g^{(p-1)/2} = 1^m g^{(p-1)/2} = g^{(p-1)/2}$. Since the square of this is equal to 1 $\pmod{p}$ and g is primitive, then $g^{(p-1)/2} = -1 \pmod{p}$. In

other words a is a quadratic residue (mod p), where p is an odd prime, if and only if $a^{(p-1)/2} = 1 \pmod{p}$. This verifies the result of (4) again, since $(-1)^{(p-1)/2} = 1$ if and only if $(p-1)/2$ is even. This is for primes p that are of the form $1 \pmod{4}$. This criterion for elements a that are quadratic residues is called Euler's criterion. When $a = 2$ we require those primes p such that $2^{(p-1)/2} = 1 \pmod{p}$. We give the result and leave it to you to discover the reason. Look it up in a textbook, if necessary. The result is that 2 is a quadratic residue if and only if p is a prime of the form $1 \pmod{8}$ or $7 \pmod{8}$.

Chapter 9

Number Theory: Week 9

Euler's totient function, the Chinese remainder theorem

We now generalize the work of Week 8 to include congruences modulo m, where m is not necessarily prime. We observe that the congruence $a^k = 1 \pmod{m}$ can only hold if a and m are coprime. For if this equation is true, then there exists an integer n such that $a^k - nm = 1$. Hence, if $(a, m) = h$ we have $h \mid a^k - nm$, that is $h \mid 1$ and so $h = 1$. It is natural therefore, for a positive integer m, to consider the set $\{a : 1 \leq a \leq m, (a, m) = 1\}$.

It is the standard notation to denote the number of elements in this set by $\phi(m)$, the number of positive integers less than m that are coprime to m. It is called *Euler's totient function* (or sometimes *Euler's ϕ-function*. Thus $\phi(6) = 2$, since out of 1, 2, 3, 4, 5 only 1 and 5 are coprime to 6.

Exercises

1. Show that $\phi(8) = 4$ and evaluate $\phi(m)$ for $m = 1$ to 12.

2. Work out $\phi(p)$, where p is prime.

3. Prove that $\phi(p^2) = p(p-1)$, where p is prime.

4. Make a list of the positive integers less than 18 that are co-prime to 18, and hence show that $\phi(18) = 6$. For each of these positive integers a work out $a^6 \pmod{18}$.

Fermat's little theorem and results such as those in Exercise 4 suggest the following theorem.

Theorem 9.1 If a is any positive integer coprime to m, then $a^{\phi(m)} = 1 \pmod{m}$.

Proof Suppose the distinct residues $\pmod{m}$ that are coprime to m are denoted by $c_1, c_2, c_3, \ldots, c_{\phi(m)}$ and a is any element of this set. Then we claim that $ac_1, ac_2, ac_3, \ldots, ac_\phi(m) \pmod{m}$ are distinct, for if not, suppose $ac_j = ac_k \pmod{m}$, with $j \neq k$, then $a(c_j - c_k) = 0 \pmod{m}$. But $(a, m) = 1$, so $c_j = c_k \pmod{m}$. But each c_k lies between 1 and $(m-1)$ inclusive, and hence $c_j = c_k$. Contradiction establishes the result. This means that this set is simply a rearrangement of the residues, so their products are equal. Cancelling out the common expression $c_1 c_2 c_3 \ldots c_{\phi(m)}$ which is allowable, since each of the terms in the product is coprime to m, we are left with the required result $a^{\phi(m)} = 1 \pmod{m}$. ∎

The proof follows exactly the same steps as in the proof of Fermat's little theorem. The *order* of a is defined, as before as the least positive integer n, such that $a^n = 1 \pmod{m}$. And it follows exactly as in Theorem 8.3 that $n \mid \phi(m)$. From Theorem 9.1 it follows that every element a coprime to m has an inverse b also coprime to m such that $ab = ba = 1 \pmod{m}$. If we denote the set $\{c_1, c_2, c_3 \ldots, c_{\phi(m)}\}$ by G_m, then G_m is an Abelian group under $x \pmod{m}$. We stated in Week 8 that $G_p = \mathbb{Z}_p \backslash \{0\}$, when

p is prime, is a cyclic group, so that there exists a primitive root. It can be proved, but we do not give the proof in this book, that a residue coprime to m exists with order $\phi(m)$ if and only if m takes on any of the values $1, 2, 4, p^k, 2p^k$, where p is any odd prime and k is any positive integer. Such a residue is called a *primitive root modulo m*.

Exercises

5. Find the value of $\phi(25)$ and find a primitive root modulo 25.

6. What is the analogue of Wilson's theorem concerning the value of the product $M = c_1 c_2 c_3 \ldots c_{\phi(m)}$?

If you are set an exercise such as the following: 'Find a positive integer that has a remainder 1 when divided by 2, a remainder of 2 when divided by 3 and a remainder of 3 when divided by 5', then it is easy to solve mentally. First you note that the integer is odd, then you might say that to be of the form $3t + 2$, it is possibly 5, 11, 17, 23, ... Finally you might observe that 23 satisfies the conditions of the problem. If you were then asked to find some more integers with the same property, you would guess that as odd numbers repeat with a period of 2, multiples of three with a period of 3 and multiples of five with a period of 5 then you would have to jump ahead by multiples of $2 \times 3 \times 5 = 30$, and hence that the general solution is probably 23 (mod 30).

Exercise

7. Solve in the above fashion the problem of finding positive integers that have a remainder 5 when divided by 7 and a remainder of 6 when divided by 9.

Whilst such exercises are straightforward when the numbers involved are small and the number of conditions imposed are few, they are less so for large numbers or when more conditions are involved. Also there is the question of how sure we are of getting all the solutions by a method that is not dependent on some general theory, and how do we know whether the conditions imposed are self-contradictory.

Theorem 9.2 [The Chinese Remainder Theorem] Suppose that m and n are two coprime integers, then the equations

$$x = a \ (\bmod \ m) \ \text{ and } x = b \ (\bmod \ n)$$

have common solution $x = x_0$ and the full set of solutions consists of those x of the form $x = x_0 \pmod{mn}$.

Clearly if two simultaneous congruences with respect to coprime moduli have a solution, then any finite number of simultaneous congruences with respect to mutually coprime moduli have a solution. This is because one can solve the first two, then from their solution and the third congruence one may obtain a solution by the same process and so on. The proof of the theorem provides a constructive method of solution, though in applications it is usually the mere existence of a solution that is required.

Proof Since m and n are coprime there exist integers c and d such that $cn = 1 \pmod{m}$ and $dm = 1 \pmod{n}$. Furthermore $cn = 0 \pmod{n}$ and $dm = 0 \pmod{m}$. We now form the integer $x_0 = acn + bdm$, and observe it provides one solution to the problem. Now any two solutions must have a difference that is $0 \pmod{m}$ and $0 \pmod{n}$ and, since m and n are coprime, it follows that the second solution differs from the first by some multiple of mn. ■

As an example let us see how it works for the pair $x = 7 \pmod{8}$ and $x = 3 \pmod{5}$. We have $a = 7, b = 3, m = 8, n = 5$. We have $5 \times 5 = 1$ (mod 8) so $c = 5$ and $2 \times 8 = 1$ (mod 5) so $d = 2$. We then form $x_0 = 7 \times 5 \times 5 + 3 \times 2 \times 8 = 175 + 48 = 223$ (mod 40). More simply $x = 23$ (mod 40) is the general solution.

Exercises

8. Find the smallest positive integer that gives remainders 1, 2, 3, 4 when divided by 3, 5, 7, 11 respectively.

9. Solve the equations $6x = 9$ (mod 15) and $3x = 17$ (mod 44) first as separate equations, and then as a simultaneous pair.

That m, n should be mutually coprime is a sufficient condition for solutions to exist, but it is not necessary. For example $x = 3$ (mod 5) and $x = 8$ (mod 10) obviously have solutions. But $x = 3$ (mod 5) and $x = 1$ (mod 10) obviously do not. They are said to be *inconsistent*.

Exercises

10. Work out $\phi(15)$ and show it is equal to $\phi(5)\phi(3)$.

11. Find the common solutions to the equations $x = j$ (mod 3), $x = k$ (mod 5) for the 8 cases $j = 1, 2$ and $k = 1, 2, 3, 4$.

The idea of an arithmetic function was introduced in the project for Week 4. These are functions defined on the positive integers. We now introduce a very important concept in the theory of numbers, that of a multiplicative function. A *multiplicative function* is an arithmetic function f with the property that $f(mn) = f(m)f(n)$, whenever m and n are coprime.

Exercise

12. In Week 4 we introduced two functions $d(n)$ and $\sigma(n)$, the number of divisors of n and their sum respectively. Prove that they are multiplicative.

Theorem 9.3 Euler's totient function is multiplicative.

Proof   Let m and n be coprime, and let $a_j, j = 1$ to $\phi(m)$ be the elements of G_m and b_k, $k = 1$ to $\phi(n)$ be the elements of G_n. We show that every element of G_{mn} arises from one and only one pair (a_j, b_k) and hence that their number $\phi(mn) = \phi(m)\phi(n)$.

First of all given a pair (a_j, b_k) we can create a solution e_{jk} of the simultaneous congruences $x = a_j \pmod{m}$ and $x = b_k \pmod{n}$, by Theorem 9.2. The expression for $e_{jk} = a_j c_j n + b_k d_k m$ contains two terms. In the first term a_j, c_j, n are all coprime to m and in the second term b_k, d_k, m are all coprime to n. It follows that e_{jk} is coprime to mn. We can now reduce $e_{jk} \pmod{mn}$ so that it lies in the range 1 to $(mn - 1)$ so that it belongs to G_{mn}. It is also clear that if j or k is altered we must get an altered e_{jk}.

Secondly, given an element e_l belonging to G_{mn} we can reduce it $\pmod{n}$ to give an element a_j, and since e_l is coprime to mn it follows that a_j is coprime to m and so belongs to G_m. Similarly we can reduce $e_l \pmod{n}$ to give an element b_k which belongs to G_n.

Furthermore if two elements e_s, e_t give rise to the same pair (a_j, b_k), then $e_s = e_t \pmod{m}$ and $e_s = e_t \pmod{n}$, and since m and n are coprime this means $e_s = e_t \pmod{mn}$. In this way we have established a bijection between $G_m \times G_n$ and G_{mn}, thus establishing the theorem. ■

This theorem enables us to work out $\phi(m)$ for all positive integers m provided $\phi(p^k)$ is known for all primes p and all positive integers k . This is, in fact, quite easy. To determine $\phi(p^k)$ we go back to its definition as the number of positive integers

a such that $1 \leq a \leq p^k$ that are coprime to p^k. But as p is prime these are just the integers that are not multiples p. So we must subtract their number from p^k to get the required amount. The multiples of p are just $1p, 2p, 3p, \ldots, (p^{k-1})p$ and are p^{k-1} in number. Hence $\phi(p^k) = p^k - p^{k-1}$. For example $\phi(81) = 3^4 - 3^3 = 81 - 27 = 54$. In general, if we have a complicated number such as 1000, we express it in terms of its prime factors and obtain $1000 = 2^3 \times 5^3$ and then, since ϕ is multiplicative $\phi(1000) = \phi(2^3)\phi(5^3) = (2^3 - 2^2) \times (5^3 - 5^2) = 4 \times 100 = 400$. This enables us to do some wonderful arithmetic.

For example if asked to work out the last three digits of 277^{416} we can work (mod 1000) to get $277^{416} = 277^{400} \times 277^{16} = 277^{16}$ (mod 1000), since 277 is coprime to 1000. Now $277^2 = 729$ (mod 1000), so $277^4 = 729^2 = 441$ (mod 1000), $277^8 = 441^2 = 481$ (mod 1000) and $277^{16} = 481^2 = 361$ (mod 1000).

Exercises

13. Work out $\phi(37), \phi(464)$ and $\phi(2560)$.

14. Suppose $m = p^a q^b \ldots w^k$ is the decomposition of m into its prime factors, where $p, q, \ldots w$ are distinct primes and $a, b, \ldots k$ are positive integers. Prove that $\phi(m) = m(1 - 1/p)(1 - 1/q) \ldots (1 - 1/w)$. Check this formula for $m = 1000$.

15. Show there is a power of 3 that ends with the digits 000003.

16. For what values of m is $\phi(m) = 10$?

17. For what values of m is $\phi(m) = \frac{1}{2}m$?

18. Evaluate 221^{333} (mod 9).

Project

(1) What is $\phi(24)$?

(2) List all the elements of G_{24} consisting of all the integers between 1 and 24 inclusive that are coprime with 24.

(3) Produce a square multiplication table (mod 24) for the products of all the elements of G_{24}.

(4) What is the smallest integer n such that $11^n = 1$ (mod 24)? Are there any elements of order 4?

(5) Solve the simultaneous congruence $5x = 7$ (mod 8), $2x = 1$ (mod 3).

9.1   Commentary Week 9

1. The elements of G_8 are 1,3,5,7 so $\phi(8) = 4$.
   $\phi(1) = 1, \phi(2) = 1, \phi(3) = 2, \phi(4) = 2, \phi(5) = 4, \phi(6) = 2, \phi(7) = 6, \phi(8) = 4, \phi(9) = 6, \phi(10) = 4, \phi(11) = 10, \phi(12) = 4$.

2. Obviously, since only 1 and p divide p, it follows that $\phi(p) = p - 1$.

3. The integers $a, 1 \leq a \leq p^2$ that are not coprime with p^2 are $p, 2p, 3p, 4p \ldots, p^2$ and are p in number. It follows that $\phi(p^2) = p^2 - p = p(p - 1)$.

4. The positive integers less than 18 that are coprime to 18 are 1, 5, 7, 11, 13, 17, so that $\phi(18) = 6$. The orders of 5 and 11 are 6, the orders of 7 and 13 are 3 and the order of 17 is 2, so $a^6 = 1$ (mod 18) in all cases.

5. From Exercise 3, $\phi(25) = 20$. The powers of 2 (mod 25) are 2, 4, 8, 16, 7, 14, 3, 6, 12, 24, so $2^{10} = -1$ (mod 25). This means that 2 has order 20 (mod 25) and is therefore a primitive root. Other primitive roots are 8, 3, 12, 23, 17, 22 and 13. I wonder if you can see why there are $\phi(\phi(25))$ primitive roots.

6. If there is a primitive root the argument used in proving Wilson's theorem holds good and the product $M = -1$. Otherwise there may be elements of order 2 other than 1 and -1 as well as those that pair off with their inverses. In such cases it is clear that $M^2 = 1$, so that in all cases $M = 1$ or $M - 1$. Examples of $M = 1$ are when $m = 8, 12, 15$.

7. Those that are 5 (mod 7) are 5, 12, 19, 26, 33, ... and those that are 6 (mod 9) are 6, 15, 24, 33, ... so the solution appears to be 33 (mod 63).

8. 367.

9. $6x = 9$ (mod 15) means that $6x = 9 + 15k$ for integers k, so we can divide by 3 to get $2x = 3$ (mod 5), which in turn means $x = 4$ (mod 5). $3x = 17$ (mod 44) means $3x = 17$ (mod 4) and $3x = 17$ (mod 11). This in turn means that $x = 3$ (mod 4) and $x = 2$ (mod 11). We now apply the Chinese Remainder theorem with $a = 3, b = 2, m = 4, n = 11$. Now $cn = 1$ (mod m) gives $c = 3$ and $dm = 1$ (mod n) gives $d = 3$. Then $x = acn + bdm = 99 + 24 = 123$ (mod 44) or 35 (mod 44). If we now want to solve the congruences simultaneously we need to use the Chinese Remainder theorem on the two congruences $x = 4$ (mod 5) and $x = 35$ (mod 44), the solution of which is $x = 79$ (mod 220).

10. $\phi(15) = 8 = 2 \times 4 = \phi(3)\phi(5)$

11. The eight solutions are $t \pmod{15}$ according to the table below

j	1	1	1	1	2	2	2	2
k	1	2	3	4	1	2	3	4
t	1	7	13	4	11	2	8	14

The eight values of t are the eight positive integers less than 15 that are coprime to 15.

12. $d(p^k) = k+1$ for a prime p and $d(p^k q^l) = (k+1)(l+1) = d(p^k)d(q^l)$ for two distinct primes p and q etc. The multiplicative property of the function d now follows by expressing m and n in terms of their prime factors. Similar considerations hold for the function σ.

13. $\phi(37) = 36$, since 37 is prime. But $\phi(464) = 224$, since $464 = 2^4 \times 29$, so that $\phi(464) = 8 \times 28$. $\phi(2560) = 1024$, since $2560 = 2^9 \times 5$, so that $\phi(2560) = 2^8 \times 4$.

14. From the multiplicative property of ϕ we have
$$\begin{aligned} \phi(m) &= (p^a - p^{a-1})(q^b - q^{b-1})\ldots(w^k - w^{k-1}) \\ &= p^a q^b \ldots w^k (1 - 1/p)(1 - 1/q)\ldots(1 - 1/w) \\ &= m(1 - 1/p)(1 - 1/q)\ldots(1 - 1/w). \end{aligned}$$
For $m = 1000$ this gives $\phi(m) = 1000 \times \frac{1}{2} \times \frac{4}{5} = 400$.

15. $\phi(1000000) = 1000000 \times \frac{1}{2} \times \frac{4}{5} = 400000$. Hence $3^{400001} = 3 \pmod{1000000}$.

16. $\phi(m) = 10$ when $m = 11$ and $m = 22$.

17. $\phi(m) = \frac{1}{2}m \Rightarrow (1 - 1/p)(1 - 1/q)\ldots(1 - 1/w) = \frac{1}{2}$, which occurs only when $m = 2^a$, for some positive integer a.

18. $\phi(9) = 6$ so $221^{333} \pmod 9 = 221^3 \pmod 9 = 5^3 \pmod 9 = 8 \pmod 9$.

Project

(1) $\phi(24) = 24 \times \frac{1}{2} \times \frac{2}{3} = 8$.

(2) The elements of G_{24} are 1,5,7,11,13,17,19,23.

(3) The table is as follows.

$x \pmod{24}$	1	5	7	11	13	17	19	23
1	1	5	7	11	13	17	19	23
5	5	1	11	7	17	13	23	19
7	7	11	1	5	19	23	13	17
11	11	7	5	1	23	19	17	13
13	13	17	19	23	1	5	7	11
17	17	13	23	19	5	1	11	7
19	19	23	13	17	7	11	1	5
23	23	19	17	13	11	7	5	1

(4) No since all the elements are of order 2.

(5) $5x = 7 \pmod 8$ implies $x = 3 \pmod 8$ and $2x = 1 \pmod 3$ implies $x = 2 \pmod 3$. Using the notation of the text we have $a = 3, b = 2, m = 8, n = 3$. Now $cn = 1 \pmod m$ gives $c = 3$ and $dm = 1 \pmod n$ gives $d = 2$. One solution is therefore $x_0 = anc + bdm = 27 + 32 = 59$, so the general solution is $x = 11 \pmod{24}$.

Chapter 10

Number Theory: Week 10

10.1 Sequences, generating functions, modulo-periodic sequences

A *sequence* (a_n) is a set of numbers a_n indexed by the non-negative integers $n = 1, 2, \ldots$, so that they are countable in number. In Week 10 we are concerned with numbers that are integers, though analysis of such sequences often involves irrational numbers and even complex numbers. We suppose there is some rule or set of rules that enables us to calculate each a_n from the previous terms $a_0, a_1, a_2, \ldots, a_{n-1}$.

If we form the related sequence (b_n) with $b_n = a_n \pmod{m}, 0 \leq b_n \leq m - 1$ we call such a sequence a *sequence modulo* m. If there exist integers N and T such that $b_{n+T} = b_n$ for all $n \geq N$ then we say that the sequence is a *periodic sequence modulo* m or a *modulo-periodic sequence*. If $N = 1$, so that the sequence starts being periodic from the outset, then we say that the sequence is a *pure periodic sequence*. If T is as small as possible then it is called the *period*. We have already met some periodic sequences in Weeks 8 and 9, for example the powers of 3 (mod 7) are 3, 2, 6, 4, 5, 1, 3, 2,

6, 4, 5, 1, 2, 3, ... and form a pure periodic sequence modulo 7 with period 6. Fermat's little theorem and its generalization inevitably produce pure periodic sequences modulo m, with period a factor of $\phi(m)$.

By a *generating function* we mean a function f with formula $f(x)$ in closed form, which, when expanded gives the terms of the sequence, so that for sufficiently small values of x we have

$$f(x) = a_0 + a_1 x + a_2 x^2 + a_3 x^3 + \ldots + a_n x^n + \ldots$$

By determining such functions we can not only obtain the terms of the sequence, but by giving x suitable values we can deduce the sums of some interesting *series*. As a first example consider $f(x) = 5/(1 - 2x) = 5(1 + 2x + 2^2 x^2 + \ldots + 2^n x^n + \ldots)$, so that $a_n = 5 \times 2^n$ which is a geometric sequence first introduced in Week 4. The series expansion for $f(x)$ is valid for $|x| < \frac{1}{2}$ and putting $x = 1/3$ we get $5(1 + 2/3 + 4/9 + 8/27 \ldots) = 15$.

Exercises

1. Find in closed form (that is, not as a series) the generating function for the geometric series with $a_n = ar^n, n = 0, 1, 2, \ldots$, where a and r are constants.

2. Find in closed form the generating function for the arithmetic sequence with $a_n = a + nd, n = 0, 1, 2 \ldots$, where a and d are constants.
   (Provided $|x| < 1, 1 + 2x + 3x^2 + \ldots + (n + 1)x^n + \ldots = (1 - x)^{-2}$.)

Both the geometric and arithmetic sequences can be generated by linear recurrence relations. A $(k + 1)^{\text{th}}$ order homogeneous linear recurrence relation is one in which $a_0, a_1, \ldots, a_k$ are given and then

$a_{n+k+1} = c_0 a_{n+k} + c_1 a_{n+k-1} + \ldots + c_k a_n, n = 0, 1, 2, \ldots$, where $c_0, c_1, \ldots c_k$ are constants. In this Week, unless otherwise told, all the a_i and c_j are integers. That is to say there are $(k + 1)$ starting values and then each term in succession is obtained from the previous $(k + 1)$ terms by a linear relationship independent of n. For example the Fibonacci sequence 1, 1, 2, 3, 5, 8, 13, 21, ... is obtained by the 2nd order homogeneous linear recurrence relation $a_0 = 1, a_1 = 1$ and $a_{n+2} = a_{n+1} + a_n, n = 0, 1, 2, \ldots$, with $c_0 = 1$ and $c_1 = 1$. A linear recurrence relation is made *inhomogeneous* if to the right hand side of the recurrence relation is added a function $g(n)$.

A geometric sequence arises from a 1st order homogeneous linear recurrence relation with $a_0 = a$ and $a_{n+1} = r a_n, n = 0, 1, 2, \ldots$ However, it is possible to produce the same sequence by the non-linear 2nd order recurrence relation $a_0 = a, a_1 = ar, a_{n+2} a_n = a_{n+1}^2, n = 0, 1, 2, \ldots$. When solving a problem about a non-linear recurrence relation it is always worthwhile investigating if it is equivalent to a linear one.

Exercises

3. Find a 2nd order homogeneous linear recurrence relation for the arithmetic sequence given by $a_n = 3 + 5n, n = 0, 1, 2, \ldots$.

4. Find the generating function for the arithmetic sequence given by $a_n = 3 + 5n$ in the form $f(x) = (cx + d)/(px^2 + qx + r)$, where the constants c, d, p, q, r are to be determined. Can you see the connection between p, q, r and the coefficients of the 2nd order linear recurrence relation?

10.1.1   Partial Fractions

In what follows knowledge of partial fractions is required. It is assumed that the reader is familiar with adding algebraic fractions. For example

$$\frac{3}{(x+2)} - \frac{5}{(2x+3)} = \frac{3(2x+3) - 5(x+2)}{(x+2)(2x+3)} = \frac{(x-1)}{(x+2)(2x+3)}.$$

All you need to know is how to work from right to left, rather than from left to right.

Thus given $(x-1)/\{(x+2)(2x+3)\}$ you suppose it is equal to $A/(x+2) + B/(2x+3)$, where A and B are found by appreciating that $A(2x+3) + B(x+2) = (x-1)$ for all x. This is achieved if we can arrange $2A + B = 1$ and $3A + 2B = -1$, giving $A = 3$ and $B = -5$.

Exercises

5. Put into partial fractions the expression

$$\frac{12x - 13}{(2x-3)(3x-2)}.$$

6. Put into partial fractions in the form

$$k + \frac{a}{x+2} + \frac{b}{x-2}$$

the expression

$$\frac{2x^2}{x^2 - 4},$$

where k, a, b are constants to be determined.

From Exercise 6 you should observe that if the degree of the numerator is greater than or equal to that of the denominator you must first divide out before following the given procedure for what remains. Since any real polynomial can be factored into linear and quadratic factors over the real numbers, it follows that we have to cope with cases in which the denominator contains quadratic factors. Also we need to know how to handle repeated linear factors. The following example should make this clear.

If we add the algebraic fractions

$$\frac{5}{x-3} + \frac{2}{(x-3)^2} - \frac{2x+1}{x^2+x+1}$$

we get

$$\frac{3x^3 + 3x^2 - 20x - 22}{(x-3)^2(x^2+x+1)}.$$

The question then is how to work backwards. Well, for the repeated factor $(x-3)^2$ you put

$$\frac{A}{x-3} + \frac{B}{(x-3)^2}$$

or you could put

$$\frac{Ex+F}{(x-3)^2},$$

(but it is more useful in applications to adopt the first expression). For the quadratic factor x^2+x+1 you put

$$\frac{Cx+D}{(x^2+x+1)}.$$

So you try to find A, B, C, D so that

$$3x^3 + 3x^2 - 20x - 22$$

$$= A(x - 3)(x^2 + x + 1) + B(x^2 + x + 1) + (Cx + D)(x - 3)^2$$

for all x. Putting $x = 3$ gives $13B = 26$ so $B = 2$. Equating the coefficients of x^3 you get $A + C = 3$. Equating the absolute coefficients you get $-3A + B + 9D = -22$. Putting $x = 2$ you get $-7A + 7B + 2C + D = -26$. These equations lead to $A = 5, B = 2, C = -2, D = -1$.

Exercises

7. Put into partial fractions
$$\frac{x^2 - 2x - 1}{(x + 1)^2(2x^2 + 2x + 1)}.$$

8. Put into partial fractions
$$\frac{x}{x^3 - 12x + 16}.$$

Theorem 10.1 Let the sequence (a_n) be defined by $a_0 = a, a_1 = b, a_{n+2} = ca_{n+1} + da_n, n = 0, 1, 2 \ldots$, where a, b, c, d are constants, then the generating function for the sequence (a_n) is given by
$$f(x) = \frac{a + (b - ca)x}{1 - cx - dx^2}.$$

Proof Nothing more is required than to verify
$$(1 - cx - dx^2)(a + bx + a_2x^2 + a_3x^3 + \ldots) = a + (b - ca)x.$$

That the absolute coefficients and the coefficients of x are equal follows by inspection, and that all other coefficients vanish follows from the recurrence relation. Of course the series expansion is only valid for values of x satisfying $|cx + dx^2| < 1$, but that only matters if we want to make a deduction by giving x a certain value. ∎

Exercise

9. Formulate and prove a theorem analogous to Theorem 10.1 for homogeneous linear recurrence relations of the 3rd order.

We give some examples of the use of Theorem 10.1.

Examples

(1) Find the nth term of the sequence defined by $a_0 = 1, a_1 = 11, a_{n+2} = 5a_{n+1} - 6a_n, n = 0, 1, 2, \ldots$.
Here $a = 1, b = 11, c = 5, d = -6$, so the generating function

$$f(x) = \frac{1 + 6x}{1 - 5x + 6x^2} = \frac{1 + 6x}{(1 - 2x)(1 - 3x)} = \frac{9}{1 - 3x} - \frac{8}{1 - 2x},$$

in partial fraction form.

It follows that

$$f(x) = 9(1 + 3x + \ldots + 3^n x^n + \ldots) - 8(1 + 2x + \ldots + 2^n x^n + \ldots)$$

and hence that $a_n = 9 \cdot 3^{n+2} - 8 \cdot 2^{n+3}$.

(2) Find the nth term of the Fibonacci sequence defined by $a_0 = 1, a_1 = 1$, and $a_{n+2} = a_{n+1} + a_n, n = 0, 1, 2 \ldots$.

Here $a = 1, b = 1, c = 1, d = 1$, so the generating function $f(x) = 1/(1 - x - x^2)$. Now let $\alpha = \frac{1}{2}(1 + \sqrt{5})$ and $\beta = \frac{1}{2}(1 - \sqrt{5})$, so that $f(x) = 1/\{(1 - \alpha x)(1 - \beta x)\}$, since $\alpha + \beta = 1$ and $\alpha\beta = -1$. In partial fractions this becomes $f(x) = (\alpha/\sqrt{5})(1 - \alpha x)^{-1} - (\beta/\sqrt{5})(1 - \beta x)^{-1}$ from which we get Binet's famous formula $a_n = (\alpha^{n+1} - \beta^{n+1})/\sqrt{5}$. Of course it does not look at first sight that this expression for a_n is an integer, but this may be checked to be true. Since $|\beta| < 1$, it follows that $a_n \approx (1/\sqrt{5})\alpha^{n+1}$, the approximation being increasingly good for large n. For instance $a_{10} = 89$ and $(1/\sqrt{5})\alpha^{11} = 88.99775$ to 5 decimal places. Its exact value is $199\sqrt{5}/10 + 89/2$ and as an approximation to 89 it provides $199/89$ as a rational approximation to $\sqrt{5}$, which is correct to 3 decimal places. Another interesting fact is that the ratio of consecutive terms $a_{n+1}/a_n \to \alpha$ as $n \to \infty$. The number $\alpha = \frac{1}{2}(1 + \sqrt{5})$ is the *golden ratio*, a number that occurs frequently in geometrical and numerical problems. And architecturally, if the length to the height of a room is in the ratio $\alpha : 1$ it is supposed to be particularly pleasing to the eye.

(3) Find the nth term of the sequence defined by $a_0 = 0, a_1 = 3$ and $a_{n+2} = 8a_{n+1} - 25a_n, n = 0, 1, 2, \ldots$.
This is an example of an oscillating sequence with increasing amplitude, and the method of solution by means of a generating function involves the use of complex numbers. So, if you have not used complex numbers before, you can omit the working below, and instead prove by induction that the answer is $a_n = 5^n \sin n\phi$, where $\phi = \arctan(3/4)$. In this example we have $a = 0, b = 3, c = 8, d = -25$ so the generating function is $f(x) = 3x/(1 - 8x + 25x^2) = 3x/\{(1 - (4 + 3i)x)(1 - (4 - 3i)x)\} = (i/2)(1 - 5e^{-i\phi}x)^{-1} - (i/2)(1 - 5e^{i\phi}x)^{-1}$. The coefficient of x^n in the expansion of $f(x)$ is $(i/2)5^n e^{-in\phi} - (i/2)5^n e^{in\phi} = 5^n \sin n\phi$.

Exercises

10. The sequence (a_n) is defined by $a_0 = 0, a_1 = 2, a_{n+2} = 4(a_{n+1} - a_n)$. For which values of n is a_n a power of 2?

11. Find a second order homogeneous linear recurrence relation for the sequence whose n^{th} term is $(1/\sqrt{3})(\alpha^{n+1} - \beta^{n+1})$, where $\alpha = (1 + \sqrt{3})$ and $\beta = (1 - \sqrt{3})$.

12. Find the generating function for the sequence whose n^{th} term is n^2, and hence find a third order homogeneous linear recurrence relation for this sequence. Hence find the sum of the infinite series whose n^{th} term is $n^2/2^n$.

13. The sequence (a_n) is defined by $a_0 = 1, a_1 = 3, a_{n+2} = 2a_{n+1} - 2a_n, n = 0, 1, 2 \ldots$. Find a closed form expression for a_n.

It turns out that a sequence of integers derived by a set of rules is very often a periodic sequence modulo m. We first give a number of examples to illustrate the idea.

Examples

(4) The sequence (n^2) (mod 10) is

$$0, 1, 4, 9, 6, 5, 6, 9, 4, 1, 0, 1, \ldots$$

with a period of 10.

(5) The sequence (n^2) (mod 4) is 0, 1, 0, 1, $\ldots$ with a period of 2.

(6) The Fibonacci sequence 1, 1, 2, 3, 5, 8, 13, 21, 34, 55, 89, 144, $\ldots$ (mod 7) becomes 1, 1, 2, 3, 5, 1, 6, 0, 6, 6, 5, 4, 2, 6, 1, 0, 1, 1, $\ldots$ with a period of 16.

(7) The sequence (3^n) (mod 11) is 1, 3, 9, 5, 4, 1, 3, $\ldots$ with a period of 5.

You will recognize that Example (4) is a consequence of Fermat's little theorem. In fact we know from the theory of Week 8 that a period must exist and must be a factor of 10. It is useful to have some general theorems to cover other integer sequences, so that one is not confronted with having to create *ad hoc* proofs of their periodicity. Of course the proofs of the periodicity in Examples (4) and (5) are very easy, and the periodicity in Example (6) is not too difficult, but it is no proof at all just to write down the first 18 terms. In addition one needs an inductive proof based on the first 18 terms, together with an argument based on the linear recurrence relation.

We use the notation $(b_n) = (a_n (\text{mod } m))$. First we prove a very general theorem.

Theorem 10.2 Suppose that (a_n) is a sequence of integers in which $a_{n+r} = F(a_{n+r-1}, a_{n+r-2}, \ldots, a_n)$, where F is a polynomial in r variables with integer coefficients, then (b_n) is a periodic sequence.

Proof Consider the ordered r-tuples

$$(b_0, b_1 \ldots, b_{r-1}), (b_1, b_2, \ldots, b_r), \ldots, (b_k, b_{k+1}, \ldots, b_{k+r-1}), \ldots$$

where two r-tuples are equal if and only if all r entries are equal. Since each entry can take on only m values the number of distinct r-tuples is m^r. It follows that eventually there must be a repeat. Since the function F depends only on the values (mod m) of the elements of the r-tuple, once the repeat has occurred all succeeding values reoccur with the same period. (The reason F is taken to be a polynomial with integer coefficients is to ensure that all a_n in the sequence are integers.)   ∎

If $T(m)$ is the least integer such that $b_{N+T} = b_N$ for all $N \geq n$ then $T(m)$ is called the *period* modulo m.

Theorem 10.3 If $S(m)$ is any integer such that $b_{N+S} = b_N$ for all $N \geq n$ then $T(m) \mid S(m)$.

Proof Suppose not, then by the Euclidean algorithm $S = Tq + r$, where $0 < r < T$ and $b_N = b_{N+S} = b_{N+Tq+r} = b_{N+r}$ for all $N \geq n$, contradicting the hypothesis that T is the least integer with this property. ∎

It is clear that for a sequence generated as above it will not only be a periodic sequence modulo m, but also a periodic sequence modulo m^* for any other integer $m^* > 1$. In general the periods $T(m)$ and $T(m^*)$ are unrelated. However it is clear that if $m^* \mid m$, then $T(m^*) \mid T(m)$. This is because if $a_{N+T(m)} = a_N \pmod{m}$ for all $N \geq n$, then $a_{N+T(m)} = a_N \pmod{m^*}$ for all $N \geq n$ and so by Theorem 10.3 $T(m^*) \mid T(m)$.

Theorem 10.4 Suppose the least common multiple of m and $m^* = [m, m^*] = M$.
Then $T(M) = [T(m), T(m^*)]$

Proof Since $m \mid M$ and $m^* \mid M$ it follows from the text prior to the theorem that $T(m) \mid T(M)$ and $T(m^*) \mid T(M)$ and hence $[T(m), T(m^*)] \mid T(M)$.

Furthermore, we have $a_{N+[T(m),T(m^*)]} = a_N$ both $\pmod{m}$ and $\pmod{m^*}$, for all $N \geq n$, so that $a_{N+[T(m),T(m^*)]} = a_N \pmod{[m, m^*]}$ for all $N \geq n$, and hence by Theorem 10.3 we have $T(M) \mid [T(m), T(m^*)]$. ∎

Exercises

14. Prove that if (c_n) and (d_n) are two periodic modulo m sequences with periods T_c and T_d respectively then $(c_n \pm d_n)$ and $(c_n d_n)$ are periodic modulo m with period a factor of $[T_c, T_d]$.

15. Prove that the sequence $(a_n \pmod{m})$, where $a_n = n^3$ is a

pure periodic sequence with period a factor of m.

16. Prove that the sequence $(a_n \pmod 6)$, where $a_n = n^3 + 8n$ is periodic, and find its period.

17. In the Fibonacci sequence defined in Example (2) are there any terms whose last digit is 0?

18. In the sequence defined by $a_0 = 1, a_1 = 2, a_{n+2} = 2a_{n+1} - a_n, n \geq 0$, find the period of $a_n \pmod 7$.

Theorem 10.5 Suppose that (a_n) is a sequence defined by the homogeneous linear recurrence relation $a_{n+2} = k_1 a_{n+1} + k_2 a_n, n \geq 0$, where a_0, a_1, k_1, k_2 are integers, then $(a_n \pmod m)$ is a pure periodic sequence $\pmod m$ provided $(k_2, m) = 1$. In particular it is pure periodic if $k_2 = \pm 1$.

Note that the theorem generalizes to homogeneous linear recurrence relations of higher order than 2.

Proof From Theorem 10.2 we know that $(a_n \pmod m)$ is a periodic sequence modulo m. That is there exist natural numbers n and T such that $a_{N+T} = a_N \pmod m$ for all $N \geq n$. From the recurrence we have $k_2 a_{n+T-1} = a_{n+T+1} - k_1 a_{n+T} = a_{n+1} - k_1 a_n \pmod m = k_2 a_{n-1} \pmod m$, and since $(k_2, m) = 1$ it follows that $a_{n+T-1} = a_{n-1} \pmod m$. Continuing this process backwards a total of n times we see that $(a_n \pmod m)$ is pure periodic. ∎

An immediate corollary is that $(a_n \pmod p)$ is pure periodic if p is prime and provided k_2 is not a multiple of p.

Theorem 10.6 If $(a, m) = 1$, then $(a^n \pmod m)$ is pure periodic with a period a factor of Euler's function $\phi(m)$.

Proof Since $a_{n+1} = aa_n$ and $(a, m) = 1$ the result follows immediately from Theorem 10.5 and its corollaries. ∎

Exercises

19. Find the period of $(a^n \pmod{10})$ for all positive integers a.

20. Prove that $(n^n \pmod{10})$ is a pure periodic sequence of period 20.

21. Find all integers n such that $11 \mid (2^n + 1)$.

22. Given $a_0 = 0, a_1 = 1, a_{n+2} = 3a_{n+1} - a_n, n \geq 0$, show that a_{2n+1} is never divisible by 2001 for any positive integer n.

Project

(1) For the Fibonacci sequence find the periodicity (mod m) for all integers $m = 2$ to 10.

(2) Let S_n be the sum of the first n terms of the Fibonacci sequence. Investigate the periodicity of the sequence $(S_n \pmod{m})$ for $m = 2$ to 10.

Commentary

10.2   Commentary Week 10

Commentary

1. $a(1 + rx + r^2x^2 + \ldots) = a/(1 - rx), |x| < 1/r$.

2. $a + (a + d)x + (a + 2d)x^2 + \ldots = a/(1 - x) + dx/(1 - x)^2 = \{a + (d - a)x\}/(1 - x)^2, |x| < 1.$

3. $a_0 = 3, a_1 = 8, a_{n+2} = 2a_{n+1} - a_n, n \geq 0.$

4. $a = 3, d = 5$, so from Exercise 2 $f(x) = (3 + 2x)/(1 - 2x + x^2)$. The recurrence relation is $a_{n+2} - 2a_{n+1} + a_n = 0$ and the same coefficients $1, -2, 1$ appear in the denominator of the generating function.

5. $2/(2x - 3) + 3/(3x - 2).$

6. $2 + 8/(x^2 - 4) = 2 + 2/(x - 2) - 2/(x + 2).$

7. $2/(x + 1)^2 - 3/(2x^2 + 2x + 1).$

8. $1/\{9(x - 2)\} + 1/\{3(x - 2)^2\} - 1/\{9(x + 4)\}.$

9. Let $a_0 = a, a_1 = b, a_2 = c$ and $a_{n+3} = da_{n+2} + ea_{n+1} + fa_n, n \geq 0$, where a, b, c, d, e, f are constants, then the generating function for the sequence (a_n) is $f(x) = \{a + (b - da)x + (c - db - ea)x^2\}/(1 - dx - ex^2 - fx^3).$

10. $f(x) = 2x(1 - 2x)^2 = 2x + 8x^2 + 24x^3 + 64x^4 + \ldots + (n2^n)x^n + \ldots$ so a_n is a power of 2 when n is a power of 2.

11. $\alpha + \beta = 2, \alpha\beta = -2$ and $(1 - \alpha x)(1 - \beta x) = 1 - 2x - 2x^2$ It follows that the recurrence relation is $a_{n+2} = 2(a_{n+1} + a_n).$

12. $x(1 + x)/(1 - x)^3.$
    The third order linear recurrence relation is $a_{n+3} = 3a_{n+2} - 3a_{n+1} + a_n, n \geq 0, a_0 = 0, a_1 = 1, a_2 = 4, a_3 = 9.$
    Putting $x = \frac{1}{2}$ in the generating function, the sum of the series is 6.

13. $a = 1, b = 3, c = 2, d = -2$ so the generating function is
$f(x) = (1 + x)/(1 - 2x + 2x^2)$.
Putting this into partial fractions you get

$$f(x) = \frac{1}{2}(1 - 2i)/(1 - \sqrt{2}xe^{i\pi/4}) + \frac{1}{2}(1 + 2i)/(1 - \sqrt{2}xe^{i\pi/4})$$

and hence $a_n = 2^{n/2}(\cos n\pi/4 + 2\sin n\pi/4)$.

14. We have $c_{N+Tc} = c_N$ (mod m) for all $N \geq n$ and $d_{p+Td} = d_p$
(mod m) for all $P \geq p$. Hence for all $Q \geq q \geq \max(n, p)$ we
have $c_{Q+[Tc,Td]} = c_Q$ (mod m) for all $Q \geq q$ and $d_{Q+[Tc,Td]} = d_Q$ (mod m). It follows from Theorem 10.3 that the period of
the three sequences $(c_n \pm d_n)$ and $(c_n d_n)$ is a factor of $[T_c, T_d]$.

15. We have $(n + m)^3 = n^3 + 3mn^2 + 3m^2n + m^3 = n^3$ (mod m)
and hence by Theorem 10.3 the period is a factor of m. Very
often it is equal to m, but not always. For example when
$m = 9$, the period is 3.

16. By Exercises 14 and 15 a_n is periodic with period a factor of
6. Working mod 6 we have $a_0 = 0, a_1 = 3, a_2 = 0, a_3 = 3 \ldots$,
so the period is 2.

17. Working mod 10 we have for the successive terms of the Fibonacci sequence 1, 1, 2, 3, 5, 8, 3, 1, 4, 5, 9, 4, 3, 7, 0, 7, 7,
4, 1, 5, 6, 1, 7, 8, 5, 3, 8, 1, 9, 0, 9, 9, 8, 7, 5, 2, 7, 9, 6, 5, 1,
6, 7, 3, 0, 3, 3, 6, 9, 5, 4, 9, 3, 2, 5, 7, 2, 9, 1, 0, 1, 1, ... with
a period of 60 (see Theorem 10.5) and the following terms in
the sequence end in a zero $a_{14(\text{mod}15)}$.

18. Working mod 7 the successive terms of the sequence are 1,
2, 3, 4, 5, 6, 0, 1, ... The linear recurrence relation in fact
defines the natural numbers and so the period is 7.

19. For $a = 0, 1, 2, 3, 4, 5, 6, 7, 8, 9 \pmod{10}$ the periods (mod 10) of a_n are 1, 1, 4, 4, 2, 1, 1, 4, 4, 2 respectively.

20. Since the maximum period of $n^k \pmod{10}$ for constant k is 10, and the maximum period of $a^n \pmod{10}$ for constant a is 4 the period of n^n is $[4, 10] = 20$.

21. Working $\pmod{11}$ successive terms of the sequence $2^n + 1$ are 2, 3, 5, 9, 6, 0, 10, 8, 4, 7, 2, 3, ... with period 10, so the values of n for which $2^n + 1$ is divisible by 11 are 5 $\pmod{10}$.

22. Working mod 3 the successive terms of the sequence a_n are 0, 1, 0, 2, 0, 1, ... with period 4 and a_{2n+1} is not divisible by 3 for any n, so is certainly not divisible by 2001.

Project

(1) The periods $\pmod{m}$ $m = 2, 3, 4, 5, 6, 7, 8, 9, 10$ of the Fibonacci sequence are 3, 8, 6, 20, 24, 16, 12, 24, 60. Notice that for $n \geq 3$ the period is even, and that if m_1 and m_2 are coprime, then $T(m_1 m_2) = T(m_1)T(m_2)$. Try to prove these facts. For the next question it is useful to have a period. These are :

$$m = 2 : 1, 1, 0$$

$$m = 3 : 1, 1, 2, 0, 2, 2, 1, 0$$

$$m = 4 : 1, 1, 2, 3, 1, 0$$

$$m = 5 : 1, 1, 2, 3, 0, 3, 3, 1, 4, 0, 4, 4, 3, 2, 0, 2, 2, 4, 1, 0$$

$$m = 6 : 1, 1, 2, 3, 5, 2, 1, 3, 4, 1, 5, 0, 5, 5, 4, 3, 1, 4, 5, 3, 2, 5, 1, 0$$

$$m = 7 : 1, 1, 2, 3, 5, 1, 6, 0, 6, 6, 5, 4, 2, 6, 1, 0$$

$$m = 8 : 1, 1, 2, 3, 5, 0, 5, 5, 2, 7, 1, 0$$

$$m = 9 : 1, 1, 2, 3, 5, 8, 4, 3, 7, 1, 8, 0, 8, 8, 7, 6, 4, 1, 5, 6, 2, 8, 1, 0$$

$$m = 10 : 1, 1, 2, 3, 5, 8, 3, 1, 4, 5, 9, 4, 3, 7, 0, 7, 7, 4, 1, 5, 6, 1, 7,$$
$$8, 5, 3, 8, 1, 9, 0, 9, 9, 8, 7, 5, 2, 7, 9, 6, 5, 1, 6, 7, 3, 0, 3, 3, 6,$$
$$9, 5, 4, 9, 3, 2, 5, 7, 2, 9, 1, 0.$$

(2) There is a theorem that covers this part, which you might have guessed. We define $S_0 = a_0, S_1 = a_0 + a_1, \ldots, S_n = a_0 + a_1 + \ldots + a_n$. Let $(a_n \pmod m)$ be a pure periodic sequence of period $T(m)$. Let $a_0 + a_1 + \ldots + a_{T(m)-1} = S \pmod m$. Then $(S_n \pmod m)$ is a pure periodic sequence of period $cT(m)$, where c is the least positive constant such that $cS = 0 \pmod m$. In particular if $S = 0 \pmod m$ the period is $T(m)$ and if $(S, m) = 1$ then the period is $mT(m)$. In general $c = m/(S, m)$. All the theorem is saying is that it takes c blocks of the period of (a_n) to form a block that is the period of (S_n).

$m = 2$: $S = 0 \pmod 2$, so the period is 3.
$m = 3$: $S = 0 \pmod 3$, so the period is 8.
$m = 4$: $S = 0 \pmod 4$, so the period is 6.
$m = 5$: $S = 0 \pmod 5$, so the period is 20.
$m = 6$: $S = 0 \pmod 6$, so the period is 24.
$m = 7$: $S = 0 \pmod 7$, so the period is 16.
$m = 8$: $S = 0 \pmod 8$, so the period is 12.
$m = 9$: $S = 0 \pmod 9$, so the period is 24.
$m = 10$: $S = 0 \pmod{10}$, so the period is 60.

An Introduction to Inequalities

Introduction

The subject of inequalities provides a rich source of material for mathematics competitions, and from that point of view is usually classed as algebra. However, many inequalities are more honestly thought of as part of *mathematical analysis*, and yet more are so-called *geometric inequalities*. Geometrical inequalities often have the following flavour. One has a geometrical configuration and two particular points of interest. If these points are sufficiently natural it should be possible to calculate their distance apart, or its square, in terms of geometric data. The method of doing this might be trigonometry, areal co-ordinates, statics or whatever. The point is that the resulting quantity must be at least 0, and this gives rise to an inequality. Perhaps the most celebrated example of this technique is Euler's calculation that given that O and I are the circumcentre and incentre of a triangle with circumradius R and inradius r, then $OI^2 = R^2 - 2Rr$. Not only is this a beautiful formula in its own right, it follows that $R^2 - 2Rr = R(R - 2r) \geq 0$ so $2r \leq R$.

The result known as *Jensen's Theorem* or *Jensen's inequality* is a general and wide ranging result which allows one to prove a large number of particular inequalities, and should be in every problem solver's tool kit.

We have appended a summary of the results known as *Schur's inequality* and *Muirhead's inequality*. These techniques are particularly pertinent when dealing with the symmetric polynomials inequalities which have ofter surfaced in mathematics competitions. We refer the serious student of inequalities to the notes of Hojoo Lee which are currently available in the Internet. Readers will also find the statement of the celebrated Erdös-Mordell inequality in the Addendum.

Mr Jack Shotton of Portsmouth Grammar School, and a member of the United Kingdom International Mathematical Olympiad teams of 2005 and 2006, kindly supplied the material on Schur's theorem and Muirhead's theorem which may be found in the Addendum. Mr Bill Richardson generously redrew and greatly improved the diagrams.

Christopher J Bradley, Bristol, June 2006.

Chapter 11

Inequalities: Week 1

11.1   Definitions, basic properties, solution of numerical inequalities, some simple ideas

11.1.1   The ordering of the real numbers

This states what you have always taken for granted, namely that given any pair of real numbers a and b, then one of the following three relationships must hold:

$$\text{Either } a > b, \text{ or } a = b \text{ or } a < b.$$

A symbol is used to combine either the first two or the last two of these; thus $a \geq b$ means that a is greater than or equal to b and $a \leq b$ means that a is less than or equal to b. It is permissible to write $a < x < b$ if **both** $a < x$ **and** $x < b$ and then x lies in the *open interval* (a, b). Likewise it is permissible to write $a \leq x \leq b$ when x lies in the *closed interval* $[a, b]$.

On the other hand if $x < -5$ **or** $x > 3$ it is not permissible to write $3 < x < -5$.

Subsets of the real numbers, such as the rational numbers and integers are ordered and inherit their ordering from that of the real numbers. The positive integers are said to be *well-ordered* because in addition to the ordering, it is the case that every subset of positive integers has a least member.

11.1.2   How to manipulate inequalities

The ordering of real numbers obeys the following rules:

(1) If $a > b$ and c is any other real number then $a + c > b + c$ and $a - c > b - c$.

(2) If $a > b$ and $c > 0$ then $ac > bc$ and $a/c > b/c$, but if $c < 0$ then $ac < bc$ and $a/c < b/c$.

(3) If $a > b$ and $b > c$ then $a > c$.

Rule (2) says in words that if you multiply an inequality by a negative number then you have to reverse the direction of the inequality. Thus $5 > 3$, but $-10 < -6$.

Analogous rules apply when $>$ is exchanged with $<$; and when $>$ and $<$ are replaced by $\geq$ and $\leq$ respectively.

Examples 11.1

1. If $a > b$ and $c > d$ is it true that $a + c > b + d$?
   Yes. We have from rule (1) that $a + c > b + c$ and also from rule (1) that $b + c > b + d$. Then from rule (3) $a + c > b + d$.

2. If $a > b$ and $c > d$ is it true that $a - c > b - d$?
   No. Take $a = 5, b = 4, c = 3, d = 1$ as a counter example.

3. If $a > b$ and $c > d$ is it true that $ac > bd$?
   No. Take $a = -7, b = -10, c = 3, d = -5$ as a counter

example. However, if all of a, b, c are positive then it is true that $ac > bd$. For then by rule (2) $ac > bc$ and by rule (2) $bc > bd$ and then by rule (3) $ac > bd$.

4. If $x^2 \leq 16$, what can you say about x?

We have $16 - x^2 \geq 0$, so $(4 - x)(4 + x) \geq 0$ and since the terms in brackets cannot both be negative they must be non-negative and hence $-4 \leq x \leq 4$. It is a common fallacy, but not amongst good mathematicians, that the solution to this inequality is $x \leq 4$.

Exercises 11.1

1. If $a > b$, is it true that $1/a < 1/b$? If $1/a < 1/b$ is it true that $a > b$?

2. Solve the inequality $x^3 > 8$.

3. Solve the inequality $x^4 \geq 16$.

11.1.3   Some numerical problems

We now give a few examples of the sort of numerical problems that are part of the syllabus in the final years at school in many countries, followed by a set of exercises. Of course school syllabuses vary widely around the world. Readers are advised to check that they are familiar with the ideas involved before proceeding to study new work.

Examples 11.2

1. Find the values of x satisfied by the inequality

$$3(x - 1) - 2(4x + 5) > x + 5.$$

Tidying up we have $-5x - 13 > x + 5$ or $6x < -18$, so that $x < -3$.

2. Solve the quadratic inequality

$$x^2 - 5x - 6 \leq .0$$

Factorizing we get $(x - 6)(x + 1) \leq 0$. Since $x + 1 > x - 6$ it follows that $x + 1 \geq 0$ and $x - 6 \leq 0$ and hence the solution is $-1 \leq x \leq 6$.

The diagram illustrates the interval involved.

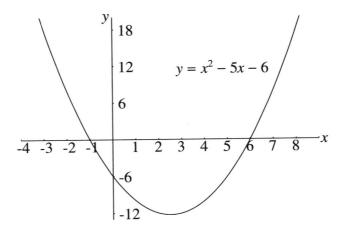

3. Solve the quadratic inequality

$$x^2 - 5x + 6 > 0$$

Factorizing we get $(x - 3)(x - 2) > 0$. Both bracketed expressions must be negative or positive, and hence $x < 2$ or $x > 3$.

4. For what values of x is

$$\frac{1}{x - 1} > \frac{1}{2x + 5}?$$

You cannot cross multiply as you would with an equation, because with unknown values in the denominators you do not know whether you are multiplying by a positive or negative quantity. So you take both terms on to the left-hand side and deal with the two terms as an algebraic fraction to get

$$\frac{x + 6}{(x - 1)(2x + 5)} > 0$$

You can now see that the inequality holds when $-6 < x < -2.5$ or $x > 1$. The next diagram shows the result.

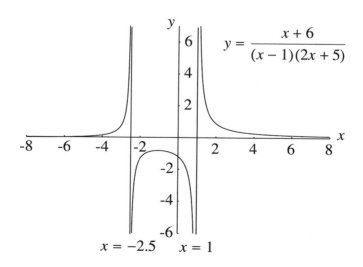

5. If $x \geq 0, y \geq 0, x + 2y \leq 20, 3x + y \leq 30$ find the maximum value of $x + y$.

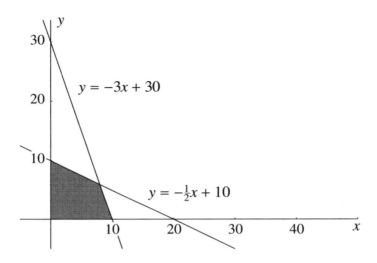

This is an example of what is called *linear programming*, in which the maximum or minimum of a linear function of several variables is required, subject to a number of linear inequalities in those variables. There is a vast literature on this topic, and in this book we only show how to deal with a simple 2 variable problem by graphical means. In such problems the linear function obtains its maximum or minimum at a vertex or on the boundary of the given region (or on or close to the boundary if there is a requirement that x and y have to be integers). The region defined by the inequalities is shaded and the maximum value of $x + y$ is 14 at the vertex $(8,6)$. However, the maximum of $4x + y$ is 40 at the vertex $(10, 0)$, which shows that the vertex required depends on the function to be maximized or minimized.

6. Given
$$y = \frac{x - 1}{(x - 2)(x - 3)},$$
show that $y \leq -2\sqrt{2} - 3$ or $y \geq 2\sqrt{2} - 3$.
A problem such as this can be solved by calculus methods to

find the points where $dy/dx = 0$, but an algebraic method exists. On multiplying up we have

$$x^2 y - x(5y + 1) + (6y + 1) = 0.$$

For real values of x the discriminant must be non-negative, and hence

$$(5y + 1)^2 \geq 4y(6y + 1).$$

This quadratic inequality reduces to $(y + 3)^2 \geq 8$, which is what is required to be proved.

Exercises 11.2

1. Find all values of x for which $x^2 + 7x + 10 < 0$.

2. Find all values of x for which $4/(x - 2) < 3/(x + 2)$.

3. Find all values of x for which $3x/(x - 7) > 1/(x - 3)$.

4. Prove that, for all real x, $(x - 3)/(x - 2)^2 \leq 1/4$.

5. Find the maximum value of

$$\frac{a + x}{\sqrt{(b^2 + x^2)}}$$

for real values of x.

6. If $x \geq 0, y \geq 0, 2x + 5y \leq 34$ and $3x + 4y \leq 37$ find the maximum value of $x + 2y$.

7. Show that if $p > m > 0$, then for all real values of x,

$$\frac{p - m}{p + m} \leq \frac{x^2 - 2mx + p^2}{x^2 + 2mx + p^2} \leq \frac{p + m}{p - m}.$$

8. Find the maximum and minimum values of

$$\frac{x+4}{x^2+4x+9}$$

   as x varies over all real values.

9. If $0 \le x \le 1$ prove that

$$\frac{x^2(1-x)}{(1+x)} \le \left\{ \frac{\sqrt{5}-1}{2} \right\}^5.$$

10. If

$$y = \frac{x-k+1}{(x-k)(x-k-1)},$$

   where k is constant, prove that $y^2 + 6y + 1 \ge 0$ and hence find bounds on y.

11.1.4   Some simple ideas

Most inequalities arise from the very simple idea that all squares are non-negative. This leads naturally to the idea that an expression that is the sum of squares is non-negative. The most obvious applications of these ideas are as follows:

(1) $(x-y)^2 \ge 0 \Rightarrow x^2 + y^2 \ge 2xy$, with equality if, and only if, $x = y$.

(2) $(x-y)^2 + (y-z)^2 + (z-x)^2 \ge 0 \Rightarrow x^2 + y^2 + z^2 \ge yz + zx + xy$, with equality if, and only if, $x = y = z$.

Setting $a = x^2$ and $b = y^2$ (1) may be rewritten as

$$\sqrt{ab} \le \frac{a+b}{2}$$

which in words states that the arithmetic[1] mean of two positive quantities is greater than or equal to their geometric mean. Equality occurs when the numbers are equal. In other words if you fix the sum of two numbers their product is maximized when the numbers are equal, or if the product of two numbers is fixed their sum is minimized when the two numbers are equal. Applications of this inequality and its generalization to several variables are so frequent that we shall in future refer to it as the AM/GM inequality.

Applied to the positive numbers $1/a$ and $1/b$ it gives

$$\frac{\frac{1}{a} + \frac{1}{b}}{2} \geq \sqrt{\frac{1}{ab}}$$

which simplifies to $\sqrt{(ab)} \geq h$, where

$$\frac{2}{h} = \frac{1}{a} + \frac{1}{b}.$$

The quantity h is called *harmonic mean* of a and b, and this inequality tells us that the harmonic mean is less than or equal to the geometric mean.

The result (1) may also be rewritten as $\frac{1}{2}(x^2 + y^2) \geq \{(x + y)/2\}^2$, showing that the arithmetic mean of the squares of two numbers is greater than the square of their mean. Taken together we have therefore shown that for two positive numbers

Harmonic Mean $\leq$ Geometric Mean
$\leq$ Arithmetic Mean $\leq$ Root Mean Square.

We show in a later section that this is true for several positive numbers.

---

[1]when used adjectivally, the word arithmetic is stressed on the penultimate syllable, so it rhymes with *alphabetic*

The diagram below illustrates HM < GM < AM < RMS for two unequal positive numbers.

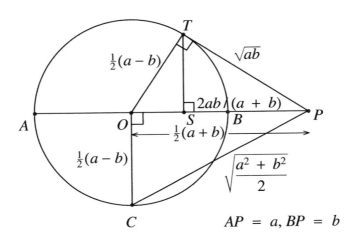

$$HM = SP, GM = TP, AM = OP, RMS = CP$$

In attempting to prove that an expression is the sum of squares it is often necessary to have recourse to 'completing the square'. For example if you are given the expression $x^2 + x + 1$, it can be rewritten as $(x + \frac{1}{2})^2 + \frac{3}{4}$, showing it to be strictly positive for all real x. This is a particular case of the following general theorem:

Theorem 1 Given that a, b, c are real constants and $a \neq 0, Q(x) \equiv (ax^2 + bx + c)$. It follows that $Q(x) \geq 0$ for all real x if, and only if, $a > 0$ and $b^2 \leq 4ac$.

Proof We have
$$Q(x) = \frac{(2ax + b)^2 + 4ac - b^2}{4a}.$$

Clearly if $a > 0$ and $4ac \geq b^2, Q(x) \geq 0$ for all real x, and equality holds when $x = -b/(2a)$ if $4ac = b^2$. Conversely if $Q(x) \geq 0$ for all real x it must be non-negative for very large values of x, and hence $a > 0$, and secondly it must be non-negative for $x = -b/(2a)$ and hence $4ac \geq b^2$. It is immediate that $Q(x) \leq 0$ for all real x if, and only if, $a < 0$ and $4ac \geq b^2$. ∎

We now give some examples of the above results followed by a set of exercises.

Examples 11.3

1. Prove that if $a, b, c > 0$ then $a^3 + b^3 + c^3 \geq 3abc$.
   We have

   $$a^3 + b^3 + c^3 - 3abc = (a + b + c)(a^2 + b^2 + c^2 - bc - ca - ab),$$

   and, since $a + b + c > 0$, this by (2) above is non-negative.

2. Prove that if $a, b, c, d > 0$ then

   $$(a + b + c + d)(a^3 + b^3 + c^3 + d^3) \geq (a^2 + b^2 + c^2 + d^2)^2.$$

   We have $a^2 + b^2 \geq 2ab$, so $ba^3 + ab^3 \geq 2a^2b^2$. There are six such relations involving all possible pairs of letters. Adding them together provides the result.

3. Show that if $a, b, c > 0$ and $(1 + a)(1 + b)(1 + c) = 8$ then $abc \leq 1$.

   We have $(1 + a) \geq 2\sqrt{a}$. Multiply three such inequalities together and the result follows immediately.

4. If a, b, c are the sides of a triangle prove that $(b + c - a)(c + a - b)(a + b - c) \leq abc$. We have $(b + c - a)(c + a - b) = c^2 - (a - b)^2 \leq c^2$. Multiplying the three inequalities like this together and taking positive square roots provides the answer.

5. Prove that if $0 < x, y, z < 1$ and $xyz = (1-x)(1-y)(1-z)$ then $xyz \leq 1/8$.

We have $x^2y^2z^2 = x(1-x)y(1-y)z(1-z)$. Now $(2x-1)^2 \geq 0$, so $x(1-x) \leq \frac{1}{4}$.

Multiplying three such inequalities together and taking positive square roots yields the required result.

6. Given $xy + yz + zx = -1$ prove that $x^2 + 5y^2 + 8z^2 \geq 4$. When does equality hold? Does the expression have a greatest value subject to the same condition? We have $x^2 + 5y^2 + 8z^2 = (x+2y+2z)^2 + (y-2z)^2 - 4(xy+yz+zx) \geq 4$. Equality holds when $x + 2y + 2z = 0$ and $y = 2z$, that is when $x = -6k, y = 2k, z = k$ for some constant k. But $xy + yz + zx = -1$ so $k = \pm\frac{1}{4}$. Then $(x, y, z) = \pm(-\frac{3}{2}, \frac{1}{2}, \frac{1}{4})$. Now

$$x = \frac{-1 - yz}{y + z}.$$

When $y = N+1, z = -N, x = N^2+N+1$ then $x^2 + 5y^2 + 8z^2 > N^4$, so there is no greatest value.

7. If $x, y > 0$ and $x^2 + y^2 = 1$ prove that $x^3 + y^3 \geq \sqrt{2}xy$.

We have $0 \leq (x-y)^2(x^4 + 2x^3y + x^2y^2 + 2xy^3 + y^4)$. On multiplying out this gives $x^6 + 2x^3y^3 + y^6 \geq 2x^2y^2(x^2 + y^2) = 2x^2y^2$. The result follows by taking positive square roots.

8. Prove that if $a, b, c > 0$ then

$$a^3 + b^3 + c^3 + 3abc \geq b^2c + bc^2 + c^2a + ca^2 + a^2b + ab^2.$$

The left-hand side minus the right-hand side is equal to

$$a(a^2 + 3bc - ab - b^2 - ca - c^2) + b^3 + c^3 - b^2c - bc^2$$
$$= a\{(a - \tfrac{1}{2}b - \tfrac{1}{2}c)^2 - (5/4)(b - c)^2\} + (b + c)(b - c)^2.$$

Now this would evidently be non-negative if $b + c \geq 5a/4$ But this is not always the case. However there are two other expressions obtained by singling out b and c rather than a and it is impossible for all of $b+c < 5a/4, c+a < 5b/4, a+b < 5c/4$ to hold simultaneously, since $a + b + c > 0$. The inequality is thus seen to be true.

9. (i) Find the maximum value of $x^2y - y^2x$ when $0 \leq x \leq 1$ and $0 \leq y \leq 1$.

   (ii) Find the maximum value of $x^2y - y^2x + y^2z - z^2y + z^2x - x^2z$ when $0 \leq x \leq 1, 0 \leq y \leq 1, 0 \leq z \leq 1$. (BMO)

In part (i) $xy(x - y)$ is maximized for any y when $x = 1$ and $y(1 - y) \leq \frac{1}{4}$.
In part (ii) the expression factorizes as $(x - y)(y - z)(x - z)$ which is maximized for any y when $x = 1$ and $z = 0$ and again $y(1 - y) \leq \frac{1}{4}$. In both cases the maximum is achieved when $y = \frac{1}{2}$.

10. Maximize $f(x, y, z) \equiv x^4 + y^4 - 2z^4 - 3\sqrt{2}xyz$ subject to the side condition $x^2 + y^2 + z^2 = 1$.
From the side condition $x^4 + y^4 + 2x^2y^2 = 1 - 2z^2 + z^4$. Hence $f(x, y, z) = 1 - 2z^2 - z^4 - 2u^2 - 3\sqrt{2}uz$, where $u = xy$. We first minimize $g(u, z) = 2u^2 + 3\sqrt{2}uz$ for fixed z. In fact $g(u, z) = 2\{(u + 3\sqrt{2}z/4)^2 - 9z^2/8\} \geq -9z^2/4$, with equality if, and only if, $u = -3\sqrt{2}z/4$.
Then $f(x, y, z) \leq 1 + \frac{1}{4}z^2 - z^4 = 65/64 - (z^2 - 1/8)^2 \leq 65/64$ with equality if, and only if, $z^2 = 1/8$. Equality is possible, since the simultaneous equations $x^2 + y^2 = 7/8$ and $xy = \pm3/8$ permit solutions.

Exercises 11.3

1. Prove that

(i) $x^4 + x^2 - 2x + 3 > 0$;

(ii) $x^4 - 4x^3 + 5x^2 - 2x + 1 > 0$.

2. Prove that if $a, b, c > 0$ then $(a + b)(b + c)(c + a) \geq 8abc$.

3. If $x, y > 0$ show that $1/x + 1/y \geq 4/(x + y)$.

4. If $x, y, z > 0$ show that $1/x + 1/y + 1/z \geq 9/(x + y + z)$.

5. Prove that if $a, b > 0$ then $(a+b)(a^2+b^2)(a^3+b^3) \leq 4(a^6+b^6)$.

6. Prove that for all real x, y, z, w

$$x^2 + y^2 + z^2 + w^2 + 1 \geq x + y + z + w.$$

7. Prove that for all real values of a, b, c

(i) $a^4 + b^4 + c^4 \geq b^2c^2 + c^2a^2 + a^2b^2 \geq abc(a + b + c)$;

(ii) $b^8c^8 + c^8a^8 + a^8b^8 \geq a^4b^4c^4(a^4+b^4+c^4) \geq a^5b^5c^5(a+b+c)$.

8. Minimize $(x+y)(y+z)$ subject to $xyz(x+y+z) = 1$.(BMO)

9. If a, b, c are the sides of a non-degenerate triangle and $x + y + z = 0$ prove

$$x^2(b^2 + c^2 - a^2) + y^2(c^2 + a^2 - b^2) + z^2(a^2 + b^2 - c^2) \geq 0.$$

10. Let $0 < a < \sqrt{2}$. Prove that

$$\{(a+2)/(a+1)\}^2 + a^2 < 4 \quad \text{and} \quad (a+2)/(a+1) + a < 2\sqrt{2}.$$

Deduce that if a is rational then there exists a rational number b satisfying $a < b < \sqrt{2}$.

11. Prove that $(p^2 + q^2)(u^2 + v^2) \geq 8qv(pu - qv)$. When does equality hold? (DM)

12. Prove that if $a, b, c > 0$ then $a^5 + b^5 + c^5 \geq 5abc(b^2 - ac)$. When does equality hold? (DM)

13. Prove that if $x > 1$ then $x + 3/(x - 1) - 2\sqrt{(x + 2)} \geq 0$. When does equality hold?

14. If $ad - bc = 1$ prove that $a^2 + b^2 + c^2 + d^2 + ac + bd \geq \sqrt{3}$.

15. Prove that if a, b, c are the sides of a triangle then

$$2(b^2c + bc^2 + c^2a + ca^2 + a^2b + ab^2) \geq a^3 + b^3 + c^3 + 9abc.$$

(Hint: Put $a = m + n, b = n + l, c = l + m$ and use Example 11.3.8)

16. Use Examples 11.3.1 and 11.3.8 to show that if $a, b, c > 0$ then

$$5(a^3 + b^3 + c^3) + 3abc \geq 3(b^2c + bc^2 + c^2a + ca^2 + a^2b + ab^2).$$

Generalize.

17. If $a, b, c > 0$ prove that

$$a^4 + b^4 + c^4 + 2abc(a + b + c) \geq (ab + bc + ca)(a^2 + b^2 + c^2).$$

18. If a, b, c are the sides of a triangle prove that for all real l, m, n

$$a^2l^2 + b^2m^2 + c^2n^2 - (b^2 + c^2 - a^2)mn$$

$$-(c^2 + a^2 - b^2)nl - (a^2 + b^2 - c^2)lm \geq 0$$

with equality if, and only if, $l = m = n$.

19. Prove that if $z > 0$, then $(3 - z)/(1 + z) \leq 1/z$. Hence deduce that if $a, b, c > 0$ then $a(3a - b)/(ca + bc) + b(3b - c)/(ab + ca) + c(3c - a)/(bc + ab) \leq (a^3 + b^3 + c^3)/(abc)$.

20. If x, y, z are positive real numbers prove that

$$(x^2 + y^2 + z^2)(yz + zx + xy) \geq 3(x + y + z)xyz.$$

21. If $0 \leq x_j \leq 1, j = 1$ to n, find the maximum value of $S = \frac{1}{2} \sum_j \sum_k (x_j - x_k)^2$.

22. Given $3(x^2 + y^2) + 4xy = 10$ find the maximum and minimum values of
$$f(x, y) \equiv (x^2 - 3)^2 + (y^2 - 3)^2.$$

23. Find all real values of t for which $abc + 3t \geq (ab + bc + ca)t + 1$ whenever a, b, c are non-negative real numbers satisfying $a + b + c = 3$.

24. Find the maximum and minimum values of $x^4 + y^4 - 2xy$ given $x^2 + y^2 = 1$.

Before concluding this section we describe briefly a few standard methods that are sometimes useful, and which may be thought of as providing additional techniques rather than additional theory.

The first of these is induction, which may sometimes be useful when the inequality to be established contains an arbitrary positive integer n or sometimes the induction is on the number n of variables appearing in the inequality. A warning, however, is that often induction does not work or may lead to something too complicated, despite the inequality being true. The second of these involves fractions. For example, if you have a fraction between 0 and 1 and add the same integer to numerator or denominator then you increase the fraction. The reverse occurs if you have an improper fraction greater than 1.

Theorem 2 If a, b, c are positive integers such that $a < b$, then $\frac{a}{b} < \frac{a+c}{b+c}$. Also if $a > b$ then $a/b > (a + c)/(b + c)$.

The proof is trivial and left to the reader.

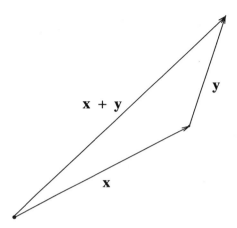

Theorem 3 Suppose $a_j, b_j, j = 1$ to n are positive integers such that $a_1/b_1 < a_2/b_2 < \ldots < a_n/b_n$, then

$$\frac{a_1}{b_1} < \frac{a_1 + a_2 + \ldots + a_n}{b_1 + b_2 + \ldots + b_n} < \frac{a_n}{b_n}.$$

Proof The proof is by induction on n. For the case $n = 2$ we are required to prove

$$\frac{a_1}{b_1} < \frac{a_1 + a_2}{b_1 + b_2} < \frac{a_2}{b_2}.$$

For the left-hand inequality we need to prove $a_1(b_1 + b_2) < b_1(a_1 + a_2)$, which is true since $a_1 b_2 < b_1 a_2$. The right-hand inequality is proved in the same way.

Now put $(a_1 + a_2)/(b_1 + b_2) = c_1/d_1$ then by the same argument repeated several times we have $a_1/b_1 < c_1/d_1 < (c_1 + a_3)/(d_1 + b_3) < a_3/b_3$, since $c_1/d_1 < a_2/b_2 < a_3/b_3$. Though the inductive step has only been argued from $n = 2$ to $n = 3$, it is easy to see that it may be repeated. ∎

Perhaps the most common technique of all is 'to give something away' of which the theorems on fractions above are examples. Another context in which this may take place is to replace a series that cannot be summed by an easier one that can. For example $1+1/4+1/9+\ldots+1/n^2 > 1/2+1/6+\ldots+1/\{n(n+1)\} = n/(n+1)$. In the limit as $n \to \infty$ this gives $\pi^2 > 6$, which is true, but not very interesting. Too much has been given away to provide a nice inequality.

Examples 11.4

1. If $x, y, z > 0$ prove that $x/(x+y) + y/(y+z) + z/(z+x) < 2$.
    By Theorem 2 the left-hand side is less than

    $$(x+z)/(x+y+z) + (y+x)/(x+y+z) + (z+y)/(x+y+z) < 2.$$

2. Prove that for positive integers n we have

    $$\frac{(2n)!}{2^{2n}(n!)^2} < \frac{1}{\sqrt{(2n)}}.$$

    The square of the left-hand side

    $$= \{(1/2) \times (3/4) \times \ldots \times (2n-1)/(2n)\}^2$$

    $$< (1/2) \times (2/3) \times (3/4) \times (4/5) \times \ldots$$

    $$\times (2n-1)/(2n) \times (2n)/(2n+1)$$

    $$= \frac{1}{2n+1} < \frac{1}{2n}.$$

    Now take positive square roots.

3. Prove that for $n \geq 1$ we have $(n/e)^n < n! < e(n/2)^n$. For the left-hand inequality the case $n = 1$ is true since $1/e < 1$.

Suppose the inequality is true for $n = k$, that is $k! > k^k e^{-k}$. Then

$$(k+1)! > (k+1)k^k e^{-k} > (k+1)^{k+1} e^{-(k+1)}$$

since $e > (1 + 1/k)^k$. The result now follows by induction. For the right-hand inequality the case $n = 1$ is true because $1 < e/2$. Likewise the case $n = 2$ is true since $2 < e$. Suppose the inequality is true for $n = k$, that $k! < e(k/2)^k$. Then $(k+1)! < e(k+1)(k/2)^k < e\{(k+1)/2\}^{k+1}$ because $2k^k < (k+1)^k$ for $k \geq 2$. The result now follows by induction.

Exercises 11.4

1. Prove that if $p/m < q/n$ then $p/(p+m) < (p+q)/(p+q+m+n) < q/(q+n)$.

2. Prove that if $a_j > 1, j = 1$ to n, then $2^{n-1}(a_1 a_2 \ldots a_n + 1) \geq (a_1 + 1)(a_2 + 1) \ldots (a_n + 1)$.

3. Prove that for all positive integers $n \geq 2$

$$\frac{1}{\sqrt{(4n+1)}} < (1/2)(3/4)(5/6) \ldots (2n-1)/(2n) < \frac{1}{\sqrt{(3n+1)}}.$$

4. Prove that $\sqrt{(4n+2)} > \sqrt{n} + \sqrt{(n+1)}$ for all positive integers n. Can there exist an integer N such that $\sqrt{n} + \sqrt{(n+1)} < N < \sqrt{(4n+2)}$?

5. If a, b, c are the sides of a triangle prove that $a/(b+c)+b/(c+a) + c/(a+b) < 2$.

6. Given a, b, c, d are positive real numbers, find all the possible values of the sum

$$\frac{a}{a+b+d} + \frac{b}{a+b+c} + \frac{c}{b+c+d} + \frac{d}{a+c+d}. \quad \text{(IMO 1974)}$$

7. Prove that $1/31 + 1/81 + 1/151 + \ldots + 1/(10N^2 + 20N + 1) + \ldots < 3/40$.

8. Prove that for all positive integers n

$$1/\sqrt{(2n+1)} < (2/3) \times (4/5) \times (6/7) \times \ldots \times (2n)/(2n+1)$$

$$< 1/\sqrt{(n+1)}.$$

9. Prove by induction that for all positive integers n we have

$$\frac{(2n)!}{2^{2n}(n!)^2} \leq \frac{1}{\sqrt{(3n+1)}}.$$

10. Let F_n be the nth term of the Fibonacci sequence

$$1, 1, 2, 3, 5, 8, \ldots$$

Prove that

$$1/3 + 1/3^2 + 2/3^3 + 3/3^4 + 5/3^5 + \ldots + F_n/3^n < 3/5.$$

11. A square is given with a unit side. A quadrilateral is inscribed with one vertex on each of the four sides of the square. If the vertices are constrained to lie on the middle third part of each of the sides find the maximum and minimum values of its area. (BG)

12. By considering the area between the curve $y = 1/x$, the x-axis and the lines $x = 1$ and $x = n$ prove that

$$\log(1 + 1/n) < (1 + 1/2 + 1/3 + 1/4 + \ldots + 1/n) - \log n < 1.$$

11.2   Hints and Answers   Week 1

Exercises 11.1

1. Try some positive and negative values.

2. $x > 2$.

3. $x \leq -2$ or $x \geq 2$.

Exercises 11.2

1. $-5 < x < -2$.

2. $x < -14$ or $-2 < x < 2$.

3. $x < 1$ or $7/3 < x < 3$ or $x > 7$.

4. Use the method of Example 11.2.6 The maximum is attained at $x = 4$.

5. Use the method of Example 11.2.6 or the substitution $x = b \tan u$. The maximum is $\{\sqrt{(a^2 + b^2)}\}/b$.

6. 15.

7. Use the method of Example 11.2.6.

8. The maximum is 0.5 when $x = -1$ and the minimum is -0.1 when $x = -7$.

9. If all else fails use calculus.

10. Curiously enough the answer really is independent of k. So the bounds are the same as in Example 11.2.6.

Exercises 11.3

1.   (i) Write as $x^4 + (x+?)^2 + ?$.

(ii) Write $5x^2 = 4x^2 + x^2$.

2. $a + b \geq 2\sqrt{(ab)}$ etc.

3. Put $1/x = u, 1/y = v$.

4. Put $1/x = u, 1/y = v, 1/z = w$ and use Example 11.3.1 twice.

5. $ba^2 + ab^2 \leq a^3 + b^3$ (why?) and $a^6 + b^6 \geq 2a^3b^3$

6. $x^2 - x + \frac{1}{4} = (x - \frac{1}{2})^2$.

7.   (i) You will need to use $a^2(b^2 + c^2) \geq 2a^2bc$ etc.

(ii) Part (i) needs to be used twice.

8. Put $x + y + z = s, xyz = 1/s$ and show $(x + y)(y + z) = sy + 1/(sy)$.

9. Put $z = -x - y$ and either use the sine and cosine rules to show the inequality is equivalent to $(x \sin B + y \sin A \cos C)^2 + y^2 \sin^2 A \cos^2 C \geq 0$ or a version of Theorem 1 and the fact that in a triangle $(a+b+c)(b+c-a)(c+a-b)(a+b-c) > 0$.

10. For the first inequality use $(2-a^2)(a+2) > 0$ expand, multiply by a and do some completing the square. For the second inequality note that since $0 < a < \sqrt{2}$ then $1 - \sqrt{2} < a + 1 - \sqrt{2} < 1$ and hence$(a + 1 - \sqrt{2})^2 < 1$. The rational number between a and $\sqrt{2}$ is $\frac{1}{2}\{a + (a + 2)/(a + 1)\}$.

11. $p^2v^2 + q^2u^2 \geq 2pquv$, so the given expression is $\geq (pu - 3qv)^2 + ?$. Equality is when $u = \sqrt{3}v$ and $p = \sqrt{3}q$.

12. The inequality is obviously true if $b^2 \leq ac$, so suppose $b^2 = kac$, where $k > 1$. You will have to show that $k^{\frac{4}{5}} - 5k^{\frac{1}{2}}(k-1)$ has a minimum of -2 when $k = \frac{1}{2}(3 + \sqrt{5})$, the square of the golden mean.

13. The given expression is equal to $\{(x-1) + \sqrt{(x+2)}\}^2/(x-1)$. Equality holds when $x = \frac{1}{2}(3 + \sqrt{13})$.

14. $a^2 + b^2 + c^2 + d^2 + ac + bd - \sqrt{3}(ad - bc)$ is the sum of two perfect squares.

15. Put $a = m+n, b = n+l, c = l+m$ and then the inequality reduces to that of Example 11.3.8.

16. Use a convex combination of the inequalities in Examples 11.3.1 and 1.3.8 so that if $l \geq 0$ and $m \geq 0$ then

$$(l + m)(a^3 + b^3 + c^3) + 3(m - l)abc$$
$$\geq m(a^2b + b^2c + c^2a + b^2a + c^2b + a^2c).$$

17. This is similar to Example 11.3.8, but harder. The left-hand side minus the right-hand side comes to

$$\{a^2 - \frac{1}{2}(b + c)a - (1/8)(b - c)^2\}^2 - \frac{9a}{8}(b - c)^2(b + c) +$$
$$(3/64)(b - c)^2(21b^2 + 22bc + 21c^2)$$

and also to similar expressions by cyclic change of a, b, c. Then not all of $(21b^2 + 22bc + 21c^2) < 24a(b+c)$ and the other two such inequalities obtained by cyclic change of a, b, c can all hold simultaneously.

18. Use the cosine rule and $\cos A = -\cos(B + C)$. The given expression comes to

$$(al - bm \cos C - cn \cos B)^2 + (bm \sin C - cn \sin B)^2.$$

Equality is when $l = m = n$.

19. If $y > 0$ we have $y(3 - z)/(1 + z) \geq y/z$ and two similar inequalities by cyclic change of x, y, z Now add them and put $x = c/b, y = a/c, z = b/a$.

20. $x^2/y \geq 2x - y$ and two similar inequalities obtained by cyclic change of x, y, z can be added together to get $x^2/y + y^2/z + z^2/x \geq x + y + z$. Similarly $x^2/z + y^2/x + z^2/y \geq x + y + z$. Now add these together and multiply by xyz.

21. It is helpful to shift the variables to lie between $-\frac{1}{2}$ and $\frac{1}{2}$. When n is even the maximum value is $n^2/4$ and when n is odd the maximum value is $\frac{1}{4}(n^2 - 1)$.

22. Using the square of the side condition to eliminate $x^4 + y^4$ we obtain $f(x, y) = 10 - (2/9)(xy + 2)^2$ showing $f(x, y) \leq 10$ with equality when $xy = -2$ and $x^2 + y^2 = 6$, that is when $x^2 = 3 + \sqrt{5}$ and $y^2 = 3 - \sqrt{5}$ (or *vice versa*). Now use the side condition to show that the minimum value of $xy = -5$, showing that $f(x, y) \geq 8$ with equality when $x = \sqrt{5}$ and $y = -\sqrt{5}$ (or *vice versa*).

23. Put $a = 3/2, b = 3/2, c = 0$ to give $t \geq 4/3$. The inequality does hold when $t = 4/3$ by Example 11.3.8. and it is easy to see it holds for all $t \geq 4/3$.

24. Using the side condition we obtain $x^4 + y^4 - 2xy = \frac{3}{2} - \frac{1}{2}(2xy + 1)^2$, and again using the side condition we find $-\frac{1}{2} \leq xy \leq \frac{1}{2}$. It follows that the maximum and minimum are $\frac{3}{2}$ and $-\frac{1}{2}$ respectively.

Exercises 11.4

1. This is similar to Theorem 2.

2. The case $n = 1$ is trivial. The case $n = 2$ is true since, if $a, b > 1$ then $ab + 1 \geq a + b$ so that $2(ab + 1) \geq (a + 1)(b + 1)$. Then if $c > 1$ we have $4(abc + 1) \geq 2(ab + 1)(c + 1)$ by the same argument and this is $\geq (a + 1)(b + 1)(c + 1)$. You now have enough to set up an induction argument for the general case.

3. Induction works for both inequalities.

4. Take positive square roots of $4n^2 + 4n + 1 > 4n(n + 1)$ to give $2n + 1 > 2\sqrt{n}\sqrt{(n + 1)}$. Now add $2n + 1$ to both sides and take positive square roots again. There is no such integer since $\sqrt{n} + \sqrt{(n + 1)} > \sqrt{(4n + 1)}$.

5. See Example 11.4.1.

6. $1 < \text{Sum} < 2$. Use arguments similar to Theorems 2 and 3.

7. The sum $= 1/31 + 1/81 + 1/151 + \ldots < (1/10)(1/3 + 1/8 + 1/15 + \ldots) = 3/40$.

8. If N is the given fraction then $N > (1/2) \times (3/4) \times (5/6) \ldots \times (2n - 1)/(2n)$ and $N < (3/4) \times (5/6) \times (7/8) \times \ldots \times (2n + 1)/(2n + 2)$. Now form inequalities for N^2 in two different ways.

9. No hints are necessary.

10. Use $x/(1 - x - x^2) = F_1 x + F_2 x^2 + F_3 x^3 + \ldots + F_n x^n + \ldots$ with $x = \frac{1}{3}$.

11. $2/3 \leq \text{Area} \leq 4/3$.

12. The sum of the upper rectangles $= 1 + 1/2 + 1/3 + 1/4 + \ldots + 1/(n - 1) >$ the integral of $1/x$ from 1 to $n = \log n >$ the sum of the lower rectangles $= 1/2 + 1/3 + 1/4 + \ldots + 1/n$.

Chapter 12

Inequalities: Week 2

12.1 The AM/GM inequality, several proofs, applications and related inequalities

12.1.1 The AM/GM Inequality

There are several proofs of this inequality, and in this book we give six of them, four in this Section, one in Week 4 and one in Week 6. The first proof is a curious form of induction, the second and third proofs are more direct and give more insight into the meaning of the inequality and the fourth arises from the study of polynomial equations having a full complement of strictly positive roots. The latter proof has the advantage that it reveals a whole string of related inequalities. The theme of the fourth proof is taken up again in Week 5. The statement of the theorem is as follows:

Theorem 4 Let $x_1, x_2, \ldots, x_n$ be positive numbers. Then their arithmetic mean is not less than their geometric mean. That is

$$\frac{x_1 + x_2 + \ldots + x_n}{n} \geq (x_1 x_2 \ldots x_n)^{1/n}.$$

Proof 1 (Using induction) The case $n = 1$ is trivial. The case $n = 2$ has been given in Week 1 and derives from $(\sqrt{x_1} - \sqrt{x_2})^2 \geq 0$. We now make the induction hypothesis that the result is true for $n = 2^k$. Then take $y_1 = (1/n)(x_1 + x_2 + \ldots + x_n)$ and $y_2 = (1/n)(x_{n+1} + x_{n+2} + \ldots + x_{2n})$ and from the case $n = 2$ we have $\{1/(2n)\}(x_1 + x_2 + \ldots + x_{2n}) = \frac{1}{2}(y_1 + y_2) \geq \sqrt{(y_1 y_2)}$. But, by the induction hypothesis, $y_1 \geq (x_1 x_2 \ldots x_n)^{1/n}$ and $y_2 \geq (x_{n+1} x_{n+2} \ldots x_{2n})^{1/n}$ and so $\sqrt{(y_1 y_2)} \geq (x_1 x_2 \ldots x_{2n})^{1/(2n)}$ and the result is therefore true for $2n = 2^{k+1}$. It follows by induction that the result is true for n equal to any integer power of 2. It is now very easy to fill the gaps. For example, if we want to prove that $(1/6)(x_1 + x_2 + \ldots + x_6) \geq (x_1 x_2 \ldots x_6)^{1/6}$ we start from $(1/8)(x_1 + x_2 + \ldots + x_8) \geq (x_1 x_2 \ldots x_8)^{1/8}$, which we know to be true, and we set $x_7 = x_8 = m = (1/6)(x_1 + x_2 + \ldots + x_6)$. Then $(1/8)(x_1 + x_2 + \ldots + x_8) = (1/8)(6m + m + m) = m \geq (x_1 x_2 \ldots x_6 mm)^{1/8} \Rightarrow m^{3/4} \geq (x_1 x_2 \ldots x_6)^{1/8} \Rightarrow m \geq (x_1 x_2 \ldots x_6)^{1/6}$, as required. All other cases of filling the gaps follow similarly by taking redundant variables equal to the arithmetic mean of the given variables. ∎

Proof 2 (Working with fixed geometric mean g) Either all the variables are equal to g, in which case AM= GM= g, or, since $x_1 x_2 \ldots x_n = g^n$, there must be two variables, say x_j and x_k such that $x_j < g < x_k$. If we now replace these variables by $y_j = g$ and $y_k = x_j x_k / g$, then the geometric mean of the new variables remains equal to g, but the arithmetic mean is changed from k to $k + (g + x_j x_k / g - x_j - x_k)/n$, where k is some constant. This is a decrease of $(1/gn)(x_k - g)(g - x_j)$. Now, either all the variables are equal to g or we can repeat the process. At each turn the geometric mean remains the same, but the arithmetic mean is decreased.

Furthermore, at each turn a new variable is introduced which is equal to g. The process therefore terminates after at most $(n-1)$ turns. At this point we know that AM = GM, so at the start AM $\geq$ GM. The attraction of this particular proof is the clear demonstration that if a number of positive variables have a fixed product then their arithmetic mean is minimized when the variables are equal. ∎

Proof (Working with fixed arithmetic mean m) Either all the variables are equal to m, or, since, $x_1 + x_2 + \ldots + x_n = nm$, there must be two variables, say x_j and x_k, such that $x_j < m < x_k$. If we now replace these variables by $y_j = m$ and $y_k = x_j + x_k - m$, then the arithmetic mean of the new variables remains the same, but the nth power of the geometric mean is increased by a factor $m(x_j + x_k - m)/x_j x_k$. This factor is indeed greater that 1 indicating an increase, since

$$m(x_j + x_k - m) - x_j x_k = (m - x_j)(x_k - m) > 0.$$

Now, either all the variables are equal to m or we can repeat the process. At each turn the arithmetic mean remains the same and the geometric mean increases. Furthermore, at each turn a new variable is introduced, which is equal to m. The process therefore terminates after at most $(n-1)$ turns. At this point we know that AM = GM, so that at the start GM $\leq$ AM. The attraction of this particular proof is the clear demonstration that if a number of positive variables have a fixed sum their geometric mean is maximized when they are equal. ∎

Proof 4 (Using the theory of equations)
Suppose $x_1, x_2, \ldots, x_n$ are the roots of the equation in x/y

$$f(x, y) \equiv$$
$${}^nC_0 x^n - {}^nC_1 p_1 x^{n-1} y + {}^nC_2 p_2^2 x^{n-2} y^2 - \ldots + (-1)^{nn} C_n p_n^n y^n$$

$$= 0.$$

The signs of the terms alternate signifying that all the roots are positive. Here p_1 is the arithmetic mean of the $^nC_1$ variables $x_1, x_2, \ldots, x_n$. Note that p_2^2 is the arithmetic mean of the $^nC_2$ variables

$$x_1x_2, x_1x_3, \ldots, x_2x_3, \ldots, x_{n-1}x_n,$$

and p_3^3 is the arithmetic mean of the $^nC_3$ variables

$$x_1x_2x_3, x_1x_2x_4, \ldots, x_{n-2}x_{n-1}x_n$$

and so on until $p_n^n = x_1x_2 \ldots x_n$.

Now the roots of $f = 0$ are all positive and so the roots of $\partial f/\partial x = 0$ and $\partial f/\partial y = 0$, which separate those of $f = 0$, must all be positive. Proceeding in this way, it follows that so are the roots of the equation $\partial^{j+k} f/\partial x^j \partial y^k = 0$ for $j + k = n - 2$. On giving j the values $0, 1, \ldots, (n - 2)$ in succession we obtain the $(n - 1)$ equations

$$p_l^l x^2 - 2p_{l+1}^{l+1}xy + p_{l+2}^{l+2}y^2 = 0, (l = 0, 1, 2, \ldots, n - 2), \qquad (12.1)$$

where $p_0 = 1$. Since the roots are real we have $p_{l+1}^{2(l+1)} \leq p_l^l p_{l+2}^{l+2}$. Furthermore, unless the roots of $f = 0$ are all equal, these quadratic equations have distinct roots and $\geq$ is replaced by $>$. Now $p_0 = 1$, so the first quadratic equation gives $p_1 \geq p_2$. A simple induction using $(*)$ now shows that $p_1 \geq p_2 \geq p_3 \geq \ldots \geq p_n$ with equality if, and only if, $x_1 = x_2 = \ldots = x_n$. Note that these relations are not sufficient for the equation $f = 0$ to have n positive real roots, they are necessary but not sufficient. ∎

To make this clearer we write out these inequalities in full in the case of four positive variables a, b, c, d.
We have

$$
\begin{aligned}
(a + b + c + d)/4 &\geq \{(ab + ac + ad + bc + bd + cd)/6\}^{\frac{1}{2}} \\
&\geq \{(abc + abd + acd + bcd)/4\}^{\frac{1}{3}} \\
&\geq (abcd)^{\frac{1}{4}}.
\end{aligned}
$$

Observe that $p_1 \geq p_4$ is the AM/GM inequality on 4 variables.

12.1.2 Root Mean Square

When multiplied out and simplified $p_1 \geq p_2$ gives

$$3(a^2 + b^2 + c^2 + d^2) \geq 2(ab + ac + ad + bc + bd + cd).$$

This may in turn be written in the form $\{(a^2 + b^2 + c^2 + d^2)/4\}^{\frac{1}{2}} \geq \{(a + b + c + d)/4\}$. This is the inequality Root Mean Square $\geq$ Arithmetic Mean in 4 variables. In general the inequality $p_1 \geq p_2$ gives RMS $\geq$ AM in n variables. This is because the inequalities

$$\frac{x_1^2 + x_2^2 + \ldots + x_n^2}{n} \geq \left(\frac{x_1 + x_2 + \ldots + x_n}{n} \right)^2$$

and

$$\left(\frac{x_1 + x_2 + \ldots x_n}{n} \right)^2 \geq \frac{2}{n(n-1)} (x_1 x_2 + x_1 x_3 + \ldots + x_{n-1} x_n)$$

transform into one another. This is left as an exercise for the reader. Those familiar with school statistics will recognise RMS $\geq$ AM as the same as $E(X^2) - \{E(X)\}^2 = Var X \geq 0$.

12.1.3 The Harmonic Mean

The *harmonic mean* h of n positive variables is defined by the equation

$$\frac{n}{h} = \frac{1}{x_1} + \frac{1}{x_2} + \frac{1}{x_3} + \ldots + \frac{1}{x_n}.$$

Now by AM/GM on the variables $1/x_1, 1/x_2, \ldots, 1/x_n$ we have

$$\frac{1}{\text{HM}} = \frac{1}{h} = \frac{1}{n} \left(\frac{1}{x_1} + \frac{1}{x_2} + \ldots + \frac{1}{x_n} \right) \geq \left(\frac{1}{x_1 x_2 \ldots x_n} \right)^{\frac{1}{n}} = \frac{1}{\text{GM}}.$$

It follows that for n variables also

$$\text{HM} \leq \text{GM} \leq \text{AM} \leq \text{RMS}.$$

the relation $\text{HM} \leq \text{AM}$ is worth quoting as a theorem, because of its significance.

Theorem 5 If $x_1, x_2, \ldots, x_n$ are n positive variables then

$$1/x_1 + 1/x_2 + \ldots + 1/x_n \geq n^2/(x_1 + x_2 + \ldots + x_n).$$

In terms of three positive variables a, b, c the inequalities $p_1 \geq p_2 \geq p_3$ may be written as

$$(a^2 + b^2 + c^2)/3 \geq (bc + ca + ab)/3 \geq (abc)^{2/3}$$

The first of these has been met before in Week 1, and the second of these is the AM/GM inequality on the variables bc, ca, ab. In general the inequality $p_{n-1} \geq p_n$ produces the AM/GM inequality on the variables $g^n/x_1, g^n/x_2, \ldots, g^n/x_n$.

We conclude Week 2 by giving numerous illustrative examples of the applications of the AG/GM inequality and a lengthy set of exercises. It is clear that a great deal of ingenuity has been put into devising problems in this area, and it is for this reason we give such a comprehensive selection of problems.

Examples 12.1

1. If $a, b, c > 0$ prove that $(a^2b + b^2c + c^2a + b^2a + c^2b + a^2c) \geq 6abc$. This is an immediate application of AM/GM to the six variables on the left.

2. Find the maximum value of $x^2(6 - x)$ on the interval $0 < x < 6$. If we apply AM/GM to the three variables $\frac{1}{2}x, \frac{1}{2}x, 6 - x$, since their AM=2, we have $2 \geq \{\frac{1}{4}x^2(6 - x)\}^{\frac{1}{3}}$ so the maximum value is 32 with equality when $\frac{1}{2}x = 6 - x$, that is when $x = 4$. Note that in such a problem the maximum becomes an upper bound that is not achieved if the variables used cannot be made equal to one another.

3. Find the minimum value of $x^6 + y^6 + z^6 - 6xyz$. The given expression, by AM/GM, $\geq 3(xyz)^2 - 6xyz$, with equality if, and only if, $x = y = z$. Putting $xyz = u$ this is equal to $3u^2 - 6u = 3\{(u - 1)^2 - 1\} \geq -3$, with equality if, and only if, $u = 1$. So the minimum is -3, when $x = y = z = 1$.

4. $x_1, x_2, x_3 > 0$ and $y_1 = \frac{1}{2}(x_2 + x_3)$, with y_2, y_3 similarly defined. Prove that $y_1 y_2 y_3 \geq x_1 x_2 x_3$. We have

$$y_1 y_2 y_3 = (1/8)(x_2 + x_3)(x_3 + x_1)(x_1 + x_2)$$

$$= \frac{x_1^2(x_2 + x_3) + x_2^2(x_3 + x_1) + x_3^2(x_1 + x_2) + 2x_1 x_2 x_3}{8}$$

$$\geq x_1 x_2 x_3$$

by Example 12.1.1 with $a = x_1, b = x_2, c = x_3$.

5. Prove that for positive integral $n > 2$

$$\{(n + 1)/2\}^n > n! > n^{\frac{1}{2}n}.$$

The left-hand inequality is proved by AM/GM on $1, 2, 3, \ldots, n$. The right-hand inequality is proved by induction, the key step being that $(n + 1)n^{\frac{1}{2}n} > (n + 1)^{\frac{1}{2}(n+1)}$ since

$$n + 1 > e > (1 + 1/n)^n$$

for $n > 2$.

6. If $x, y, z > 0$ and a, b, c are positive integers prove that

$$(x + y + z)^{a+b+c}/(x^a y^b z^c) \geq (a + b + c)^{a+b+c}/(a^a b^b c^c).$$

Is the result true if a, b, c are positive rational numbers? This is AM/GM on x/a a times, y/b b times and z/c c times. Yes, the result is still true, for if $a = a_1/a_2, b = b_1/b_2, c = c_1/c_2$, where $a_1, a_2, b_1, b_2, c_1, c_2$ are integers then the required inequality is identical to that already proved with a replaced by $a_1 b_2 c_2$ etc.

7. Prove that if $0 < x < 1$ then

$$1 - x^n > n(1 - x)x^{\frac{1}{2}(n-1)}$$

This is AG/GM on $1, x, x^2, \ldots x^{n-1}$.

8. Find the maximum value of $(2x + 1)^3(y + 2)^2$ when $x + y = 3$ and $-\frac{1}{2} < x < 5$. Note that $2x+1$ and $y+2$ are positive when $-\frac{1}{2} < x < 5$, since $x < 5 \Rightarrow y > -2$. AM/GM on $2x+1$ three times and $3y + 6$ twice, so the AM is $33/5$. The maximum is attained when $x + y = 3$ and $2x + 1 = 3y + 6$, that is when $x = 14/5, y = 1/5$ and the maximum is $11^5 \times 3^3/5^5$.

9. Find the maximimum value of $y(y+1)(x+1)$ when $x+3y = 4$ and $-1 < x < 4$.
Note that $x + 1$ and y are positive when $-1 < x < 4$, since $y > 0$ when $x < 4$. Care has to be exercised on the choice of the variables for the application of the AM/GM inequality. If $x + 1$ and $y + 1$ are to be chosen, then for equality $x = y = 1$ and $x + 1 = y + 1 = 2$, so $2y$ has to be the third choice. AM/GM on $2y, y+1, x+1$ gives AM $= 2$ and $y(y+1)(x+1) \leq 4$, with equality when $x = y = 1$.

10. Show that for all $n \geq 1$

$$\{1 + 1/(n+1)\}^{n+1} > (1 + 1/n)^n.$$

Use AM/GM with $(n+1)/n$ n times and 1 once to give

$$(n+2)/(n+1) > \{(n+1)/n\}^{n/(n+1)},$$

from which the result follows immediately.
This is a useful result, for it shows that the sequence $(1 + 1/n)^n$ is monotonic increasing. Since it is clearly bounded above by 3, it follows that the sequence tends to a limit. As you probably know this limit is e, and most authors take this as the basic definition of e, the alternative being its series expansion.

11. If $a, b, c, d > 0$ prove that

$$(a + b + c + d)/4 \geq ab/(a+b) + cd/(c+d)$$

$$\geq \frac{16abcd}{(a^2 + b^2 + c^2 + d^2)(a+b+c+d)}.$$

For the left-hand inequality $ab/(a+b) \leq (a+b)/4$ and $cd/(c+d) \leq (c+d)/4$. For the right-hand inequality, since $ab/(a+b) + cd/(c+d) \leq 2\sqrt{(abcd)}/\sqrt{\{(a+b)(c+d)\}}$ it is sufficient to prove $8\sqrt{(abcd)}\sqrt{(a+b)(c+d)} \leq (a^2+b^2+c^2+d^2)(a+b+c+d)$. This is so since by AM/GM, we have $(a+b)+(c+d) \geq 2\sqrt{\{(a+b)(c+d)\}}$ and $(a^2 + b^2 + c^2 + d^2) \geq 4\sqrt{(abcd)}$.

12. Suppose $0 < x_j < 1, j = 1$ to n and $\Sigma x_j = 1$, prove that $\Sigma x_j^2 \geq n^{2n-1}\Pi x_j^2$. A technique that sometimes works, and does here, is to insert something between the left-hand and right-hand sides and to prove the two resulting inequalities. Here one inserts $1/n$. Then $\{\Sigma x_j^2\}/n \geq \{\Sigma x_j/n\}^2$ since RMS $\geq$ AM, and this in turn $= 1/n^2$. Secondly $1/n = \{\Sigma x_j\}/n \geq \{\Pi x_j\}^{1/n} \Rightarrow n^{-2n} \geq \Pi x_j^2$.

13. Show that if a triangle has a fixed perimeter, its area is maximized when it is equilateral. We have for the area $[ABC]^2 = s(s-a)(s-b)(s-c)$, where s is the semi-perimeter. Now by AM/GM we have

$$s/3 = \{(s-a)+(s-b)+(s-c)\}/3 \geq \{(s-a)(s-b)(s-c)\}^{\frac{1}{3}}.$$

From these two relations we have $[ABC]^2 \leq s^4/27$ with equality if, and only if, $s - a = s - b = s - c$, that is if, and only if, the triangle is equilateral.

14. Find all the possible values of $a, b, c, d, \geq 0$ satisfying $a+b+c+d=12$ and

$$abcd = 27 + ab + bc + ca + ad + bd + cd. \text{(BMO)}$$

We have $3 = (a+b+c+d)/4 \geq (abcd)^{\frac{1}{4}}$ so $abcd \leq 81$ with equality if, and only if, $a = b = c = d$. Next $abcd = 27 + ab + bc + ca + ad + bd + cd \geq 27 + 6(abcd)^{\frac{1}{2}}$. Putting $abcd = u^2$ this means $u^2 \geq 27 + 6u$ so $u \geq 9$ and $abcd \geq 81$. Hence $abcd = 81$ and $a = b = c = d = 3$ is the only solution.

15. Find the maximum value of $f(x,y) = \cos x \cos y \sin(x+y)$ for positive x, y and $x+y < 90°$. Using known identities we have $f(x,y) = \frac{1}{4}\{\sin 2x + \sin 2y + \sin 2(x+y)\} = \frac{1}{4}\{2\sin(x+y)\cos(x-y)+\sin 2(x+y)\}$. For fixed $(x+y)$, since $\sin(x+y) > 0$, $f(x,y)$ has its maximum when $\cos(x-y) = 1$, that is when $x = y$. Then $f(x,y) = F(x) = \frac{1}{2}\sin 2x(1+\cos 2x), 0 < 2x < 90°$. Hence $F(x) = \frac{1}{2}(1-c)^{\frac{1}{2}}(1+c)^{\frac{1}{2}}$, where $c = \cos 2x$, so $0 < c < 1$. Now by AM/GM $3/2 = \frac{1}{4}\{3(1-c)+(1+c)+(1+c)+(1+c)\} \geq \{3(1-c)(1+c)^3\}^{\frac{1}{4}}$ with equality when $3(1-c) = (1+c)$, that is $c = \frac{1}{2}$ or $x = 30°$. Squaring gives a maximum value of $f(x,y)$ as $3\sqrt{3}/8$ when $x = y = 30°$.

Exercises 12.1

1. Find the maximum value of xy^2z^3 given $x^2 + y^2 + z^2 = 1$.

2. If $a, b, c > 0$ prove that $ab/(a+b) + bc/(b+c) + ca/(c+a) \leq \frac{1}{2}(a+b+c)$.

3. Find the maximum volume of a right circular cone inscribed in a sphere of radius r.

4. If $a, b, c, d > 0$ prove that

$$4(a^4 + b^4 + c^4 + d^4) \geq (a + b + c + d)(a^3 + b^3 + c^3 + d^3)$$

$$\geq (a^2 + b^2 + c^2 + d^2)^2 \geq 16abcd.$$

5. If $a, b, c > 0$ prove that $1/a + 1/b + 1/c \geq 9/(a + b + c)$.

6. Prove that if $x_j > 0$ and q_j are positive rational numbers, $j = 1$ to n, then

$$\left(\frac{q_1 x_1 + q_2 x_2 + \ldots + q_n x_n}{q_1 + q_2 + \ldots + q_n} \right)^{q_1 + q_2 + \ldots + q_n} \geq x_1^{q_1} x_2^{q_2} \cdots x_n^{q_n}.$$

7. Let $x_j > 0, j = 1$ to n and $\Sigma x_j = s$. Prove that $\Sigma 1/x_j \geq \Sigma(n - 1)/(s - x_j)$.

8. If $x, y, z > 0$ prove that

$$(x + y + z)^3 \geq 27(y + z - x)(z + x - y)(x + y - z).$$

9. Prove that for all positive integers $n > 1, (n + 1)^n > 2^n n!$.

10. Prove that if $a, b, c > 0$ then $(1+a^3)(1+b^3)(1+c^3) \geq (1+abc)^3$. Generalize.

11. Find the maximum value of $(2x + 5)^5 (7 - x)^2$ on the interval $-5/2 < x < 7$.

12. Find the maximum value of $xy^3 z^4$ subject to $x, y, z > 0$ and $x^3 + y^3 + z^3 = 1$.

13. Show that the maximum value of $\sin^{2p} \theta \cos^{2q} \theta$ is

$$\frac{p^p q^q}{(p + q)^{p+q}}.$$

14. Let $x_1, x_2, \ldots, x_n$ be n positive qualities, and define S_r to be the sum of their r^{th} powers and P_r to be the sum of all their products taken r at a time. Prove that

$$(n - 1)! S_r \geq r!(n - r)! P_r.$$

15. If $a, b, c, d > 0$ and $abcd = 2$ prove that

$$a^2 + b^2 + c^2 + d^2 + ab + bc + ca + ad + bd + cd > 14.$$

16. If $x, y, z > 0$ and $1/3 \leq xy + yz + zx \leq 3$ determine the ranges for xyz and $(x + y + z)$. (BMO)

17. If $a, b, c, x, y, z > 0$ and $ax + by + cz = N$ find the maximum value of xyz and the corresponding values of x, y, z.

18. If $a, b, c, x, y, z > 0$ and $ax^2/y + by^2/z + cz^2/x = N$ find the maximum value of xyz.

19. $a, b, c, x, y, z > 0$ and $ax + by + cz = N$ find the maximum value of $x^p y^q z^r$ and the corresponding values of x, y, z.

20. Prove that if n is any positive integer

$$n^{1/n} + n^{1/(n+1)} + \ldots + n^{1/(2n-1)} \geq n^k, \quad \text{where} \quad k = 2^{1/n}.$$

21. If a, b, c are positive real numbers satisfying $a + b + c \geq 3abc$ prove
$$a^2 + b^2 + c^2 \geq 3abc.$$

22. If a, b, c are positive real numbers prove that
$$(a^2 + b^2 + c^2)(bc + ca + ab) \geq 3(a + b + c)abc.$$

23. Given that $x, y, z > 0$ and $xyz = 32$, find the minimum value of $x^2 + 4xy + 4y^2 + 2z^2$. (BMO)

24. Prove that if $x_j > 0, j = 0, 1, 2, \ldots, n$, then
$$x_0^n + x_1^n + \ldots + x_n^n \geq x_0 x_1 \ldots x_n(1/x_0 + 1/x_1 + \ldots + 1/x_n).$$

25. Let n, x be positive integers. Prove that $\{1 + x/(n+x)\}^{n+x} > (1 + x/n)^n$.

26. Suppose that $p, q, r > 0$ and $1/p + 1/q + 1/r = 1$. Prove that $7(p + q + r) \leq 2pqr + 9$. (Adapted from BMO)

27. Given $x^2 + y^2 + z^2 + 2xyz = 1$ prove that $x^2 + y^2 + z^2 \geq \frac{3}{4}$.

28. Prove that if $w, x, y, z > 0$ and $wxyz = 1$ then $w^3 + x^3 + y^3 + z^3 \geq 1/w + 1/x + 1/y + 1/z$.

29. Prove that if π is any permutation of the numbers $1, 2, \ldots n$ then $\Sigma k/\pi(k) \geq n$.

30. Prove that for all positive integers
$$n\left\{1 + \frac{1}{n+1}\right\}^{n+2} < \left(1 + \frac{1}{n}\right)^{n+1}.$$

31. A farmer wishes to fence a rectangular enclosure cut in half by a fence down the middle. He has 1200 metres of fencing and wants to maximize the area of the enclosure. What dimensions should be used for the enclosure?

32. If $s, t, u, v > 0$ and $1/u + 1/v = 1$ (u and v being rational) prove that $s^u/u + t^v/v \geq st$.

33. Given $|a|, |b|, |c| < 1$ prove that

$$(1 + a)(1 + b)(1 + c) \leq \{1 + \frac{1}{4}(a + b + c)\}^4.$$

12.2 Hints and Answers Week 2

Exercises 12.1

1. Apply AM/GM to x^2 once, $\frac{1}{2}y^2$ twice and $(1/3)z^3$ three times. xy^2z^3 has a maximum of $\sqrt{3}/36$ when $x = 1/\sqrt{6}, y = 1/\sqrt{3}, z = 1/\sqrt{2}$.

2. $ab/(a + b) \leq \frac{1}{2}\sqrt{(ab)} \leq (a + b)/4$.

3. Let h be the distance of the base from the centre of the sphere. Then $V = (1/3)\pi(r + h)^2(r - h)$. Now apply AM/GM to $\frac{1}{2}(r + h)$ twice and $(r - h)$ once. The maximum is attained when $h = r/3$ and is equal to $32\pi r^3/81$.

4. The final inequality is immediate from AM/GM on a^2, b^2, c^2, d^2. For the central inequality use $ab^3 + ba^3 \geq 2a^2b^2$. For the first one use $(a - b)(a^3 - b^3) \geq 0$.

5. This is Theorem 5 with $n = 3$.

6. See Example 12.1.6.

7. Use $1/\text{HM} \geq 1/\text{AM}$ on $x_1, x_2, \ldots, x_{j-1}, x_{j+1}, \ldots, x_n$ to give

$$\frac{1}{n-1}\left(\frac{1}{x_1} + \frac{1}{x_2} + \ldots + \frac{1}{x_{j-1}} + \frac{1}{x_{j+1}} + \ldots + \frac{1}{x_n}\right) \geq \frac{n-1}{s-x_j}.$$

Now sum over j from 1 to n.

8. AM/GM on $y + z - x, z + x - y, x + y - z$.

9. AM/GM on $2, 4, 6, \ldots 2n$.

10. $a^3 + b^3 + c^3 \geq 3abc$ and $b^3 c^3 + c^3 a^3 + a^3 b^3 \geq 3a^2 b^2 c^2$.

11. AM/GM on $(2x + 5)$ five times and $(35 - 5x)$ twice. The maximum is $5^5 \times 19^7/7^7$ when $x = 30/7$.

12. Maximize $x^3 y^9 z^{12}$. The maximum of $xy^3 z^4$ is $3/2^{16/3}$.

13. Use AM/GM with $\sin^2 \theta/p$ p times and $\cos^2 \theta/q$ q times.

14. $a_1^r + a_2^r + \ldots + a_r^r \geq r a_1 a_2 \ldots a_r$. In $^n C_r$ inequalities of this type a_1^r occurs in $^{n-1}C_{r_1}$ of them. So adding all these inequalities together gives $^{n-1}C_{r-1}S_r \geq rP_r$, from which the result follows.

15. $10\sqrt{2} > 14$.

16. Use $xy + yz + zx \geq 3(xyz)^{2/3}$ and $(x+y+z)^2 \geq 3(xy+yz+zx)$, giving $xyz \leq 1$ and $x + y + z \geq 1$.

17. $N^3/(27abc)$ when $x = N/(3a), y = N/(3b), z = N/(3c)$.

18. $N^3/(27abc)$.

19. $\{N/(p+q+r)\}^{p+q+r}(p^p q^q r^r)/(a^p b^q c^r)$ when $x = pN/(p+q+r)$ etc.

20. Write the left-hand side as $(1/n)(n^{(n+1)/n} + n^{(n+2)/(n+1)} + \ldots + n^{2n/(2n-1)})$ and apply AM/GM first to this expression and then to the indices.

21. $(a^2 + b^2 + c^2)/3 \geq \{(a + b + c)/3\}^2 \geq (a + b + c)(abc)^{1/3}/3$ and so $(a^2 + b^2 + c^2)^2 \geq 3(a + b + c)(abc)$.

22. Start from $a^2 + b^2 + c^2 \geq (1/3)(a + b + c)^2$ as in Exercise 11.2.21.

23. Apply AM/GM to $x^2, 2xy$ (twice), $4y^2, z^2$ (twice). The minimum is 96 when $x = 4, y = 2, z = 4$ and this can occur, since then $x^2 = 2xy = 4y^2 = z^2 = 16$.

24. Start with $n = 2, 3$ and see how it goes.

25. Apply AM/GM on n numbers equal to $1/n$ and x numbers equal to $1/(n + x)$.

26. Put $p = 1/u, q = 1/v, r = 1/w$ and use $u + v + w = 1$ to make the inequality homogeneous. Simplify and then use $u^3 + v^3 \geq u^2 v + uv^2$ etc.

27. Suppose $x^2 + y^2 + z^2 < \frac{3}{4}$. Then $\frac{3}{4} > x^2 + y^2 + z^2 \geq 3(xyz)^{2/3}$ and so $|xyz| < \frac{1}{8}$. Hence $x^2 + y^2 + z^2 + 2xyz < 1$. Contradiction.

28. $w^3 + x^3 + y^3 \geq 3wxy$ etc and add together.

29. An immediate application of AM/GM.

30. Apply AM/GM on 1 once and $n/(n + 1)$ $(n + 1)$ times. The sequence decreases monotonically to e.

31. Maximize $2ab$ subject to $4a + 3b = 1200$. The solution is an area of 60000 metres^2 when $a = 150$ metres and $b = 200$ metres.

32. Put $u = r/p, v = r/q$ as fractions in their lowest terms so that $p + q = r$. Then apply AM/GM with s^u p times and t^v q times.

33. Apply AM/GM to $1, a + 1, b + 1, c + 1$.

Chapter 13

Inequalities: Week 3

13.1 An inner product space, the Cauchy-Schwarz and triangle inequalities, applications

13.1.1 An inner product space

Let V be a vector space over the real numbers, enriched with a bilinear functional (f, g) from $V \times V \to \mathbb{R}$ with the following properties:

(i) $(f, g) = (g, f)$ for all $f, g \in V$;

(ii) If $c \in \mathbb{R}$, then $(cf, g) = (f, cg) = c(f, g)$;

(iii) $(f, g + h) = (f, g) + (f, h)$ for all $f, g, h \in V$;

(iv) $(f, f) \geq 0$ with equality if, and only if, $f = 0$, the zero vector.

Then V is called an *inner product space* and (f, g) is said to be the *inner product* of f and g. An example is the 3-dimensional vector space over the reals, with inner product the usual scalar product $(\mathbf{f}, \mathbf{g}) = f_1 g_1 + f_2 g_2 + f_3 g_3$, (f_1, f_2, f_3) being the co-ordinates of $\mathbf{f}$ with respect to some basis. Another example is the infinite-dimensional vector space of functions of one real variable that are square-integrable from x equal $-\infty$ to $+\infty$ with the inner product of $f(x)$ and $g(x)$ defined to be $(f, g) = \int f(x)g(x)dx$.

13.1.2   The Cauchy-Schwarz inequality

Consider $(f + \lambda g, f + \lambda g)$ for $f, g \in V$, where λ is a real variable. By the properties (i) to (iii) above this is equal to

$$(f, f) + 2\lambda(f, g) + \lambda^2(g, g)$$

and by property (iv) above this quantity is ≥ 0 for all real λ. Writing $A = (f, f)$, $B = (f, g)$ and $C = (g, g)$ we have

$$A + 2B\lambda + C\lambda^2 \geq 0 \qquad\qquad (13.1)$$

for all real λ, and again by property (iv) equality holds if and only if λ exists such that $f + \lambda g = 0$. In terms of real 3-dimensional vectors this condition is that the vectors $\mathbf{f}$ and $\mathbf{g}$ are parallel. Since $C > 0$ (we assume f and g are not zero, for if one or both are zero the whole matter is trivial) the condition for the inequality (13.1) to hold is that the discriminant $B^2 - AC \leq 0$. This provides us with the Cauchy-Schwarz inequality, which in future we call the C-S inequality,

$$(f, f)(g, g) \geq (f, g)^2.$$

Using the first example above, if $\mathbf{f}$ and $\mathbf{g}$ are 3-dimensional vectors, then C-S becomes

$$(f_1^2 + f_2^2 + f_3^2)(g_1^2 + g_2^2 + g_3^2) \geq (f_1 g_1 + f_2 g_2 + f_3 g_3)^2$$

with equality if, and only if, **f** and **g** are parallel.

Using the second example above, if $f(x)$ and $g(x)$ are square integrable functions, then C-S becomes

$$\int \{f(x)\}^2 dx \int \{g(x)\}^2 dx \geq \left| \int f(x)g(x)dx \right|^2$$

with equality if, and only if, $f(x)$ is a multiple of $g(x)$ or *vice versa*.

We have proved the following theorem:

Theorem [Cauchy-Schwarz Inequality] If f, g are elements of an inner product space V then $(f, f)(g, g) \geq \{(f, g)\}^2$ with equality if, and only if, a constant λ exists such that $f + \lambda g = 0$ or $g + \lambda f = 0$.

Note that we have not excluded the possibility that either f or g is zero. On a real n-dimensional space this means that if $\mathbf{x} = (x_1, x_2, \ldots, x_n)$ and $\mathbf{y} = (y_1, y_2, \ldots, y_n)$ are two vectors, then

$$(x_1^2 + x_2^2 + \ldots + x_n^2)(y_1^2 + y_2^2 + \ldots + y_n^2) \geq \{(x_1 y_1 + x_2 y_2 + \ldots + x_n y_n)\}^2,$$

with equality if, and only if, $x_1/y_1 = x_2/y_2 = \ldots = x_n/y_n$ (with appropriate indefiniteness conventions when a numerator and denominator vanish simultaneously).

There are other proofs of C-S. One is by induction on the dimension n of the space involved and we leave that as an exercise for the reader. Another proof is to express the product of the squares of the two vectors as the sum of the squares of their inner and outer products. For example when $n = 4$ when $\mathbf{x} = (a, b, c, d)$ and $\mathbf{y} = (e, f, g, h)$ we have $|\mathbf{x}|^2 |\mathbf{y}|^2 = (a^2 + b^2 + c^2 + d^2)(e^2 + f^2 + g^2 + h^2) = (\mathbf{x.y})^2 + (\mathbf{xy})^2 = (ae + bf + cg + dh)^2 + (af - be)^2 + (ag - ce)^2 + (ah - de)^2 + (bg - cf)^2 + (bh - df)^2 + (ch - dg)^2$. Now the last six squares, which comprise the outer product $(\mathbf{xy})^2$ are non-negative, thereby providing C-S in four dimensions. Equality holds if, and only if, the outer product vanishes, which is when $a/e = b/f = c/g = d/h$. In 2 and 3 dimensions the inner and outer products are known respectively as the scalar and vector products, and the reader may well be familiar with the identity $\mathbf{x}.\mathbf{y} = |\mathbf{x}||\mathbf{y}|\cos\theta$. If this equation is now taken to define the angle between two vectors in n dimensions then the C-S inequality says nothing more than $|\cos\theta| \leq 1$.

13.1.3 The triangle inequality

Theorem 7 In any dimension this states that

$$|\mathbf{x} + \mathbf{y}| \leq |\mathbf{x}| + |\mathbf{y}|.$$

Convex function $f(t)$

$$AP = \tfrac{1}{3}\{f(x) + f(y) + f(z)\} \qquad BP = f\left(\frac{x+y+x}{3}\right)$$

Proof From C-S we have $|\mathbf{x}|^2 + |\mathbf{y}|^2 + 2|\mathbf{x}||\mathbf{y}| \geq |\mathbf{x}|^2 + |\mathbf{y}|^2 + 2\mathbf{x}.\mathbf{y}$ and the triangle inequality follows by taking positive square roots. It is also the case, by writing $-\mathbf{y}$ for $\mathbf{y}$ that $|\mathbf{x}| + |\mathbf{y}| \geq |\mathbf{x} - \mathbf{y}|$. ∎

We now give a collection of examples and exercises. Once again there is a very wide range of applications for such a simple idea.

Examples 13.1

1. Find the minimum value of $2x^2 + y^2 + z^2$ subject to $x + y + z = 10$. We take $\mathbf{u} = (x\sqrt{2}, y, z)$ and $\mathbf{v} = (1, \sqrt{2}, \sqrt{2})$, then $(\mathbf{u}.\mathbf{v})^2 \leq |\mathbf{u}|^2 |v|^2$ gives $2(x+y+z)^2 \leq 5(2x^2+y^2+z^2)$, and so $2x^2+y^2+z^2 \geq 40$ with equality if, and only if, $2x = y = z = 4$.

2. Prove that if $a, b, c > 0$ then

$$\frac{a}{b+c} + \frac{b}{c+a} + \frac{c}{a+b} \geq \frac{3}{2}.$$

We take $\mathbf{x} = (\sqrt{\{a/(b+c)\}}, \sqrt{\{b/(c+a)\}}, \sqrt{\{c/(a+b)\}},)$ and $\mathbf{y} = (\sqrt{\{a(b+c)\}}, \sqrt{\{b(c+a)\}}, \sqrt{\{c(a+b)\}})$. Then C-S gives $2\{a/(b+c) + b/(c+a) + c/(a+b)\}(ab+bc+ca) \geq (a+b+c)^2 \geq 3(ab+bc+ca)$, from which the result follows.

3. For finite sequences of n terms $(a_r), (b_r), (c_r), (d_r)$ prove that $(\Sigma a_r b_r c_r d_r)^4 \leq \Sigma a_r^4 \Sigma b_r^4 \Sigma c_r^4 \Sigma d_r^4$ and deduce that for sequences $(x_r), (y_r)$ we have $(\Sigma x_r y_r)^3 \leq n\Sigma x_r^3 \Sigma y_r^3$.
   We have the left-hand side

$$= (\Sigma a_r b_r c_r d_r)^2 (\Sigma a_r b_r c_r d_r)^2 \leq \{\Sigma a_r^2 b_r^2 \Sigma c_r^2 d_r^2\}^2$$

by C-S and this in turn is $\leq \Sigma a_r^4 \Sigma b_r^4 \Sigma c_r^4 \Sigma d_r^4$. For the second part put $a_r = x_r^{3/4}$, $b_r = y_r^{3/4}$, $c_r = (x_r y_r)^{1/4}$ and $d_r = 1$.

4. *ABC* are the vertices of a fixed triangle and P, Q, R lie on the line segments BC, CA, AB respectively. If $[XYZ]$ denotes the area of triangle XYZ prove that

$$\sqrt{[AQR]} + \sqrt{[BRP]} + \sqrt{[CPQ]} \leq \frac{3}{2}\sqrt{[ABC]}.$$

Let the areal co-ordinates of P, Q, R be $(0, l, 1 - l)$, $(1 - m, 0, m)$, $(n, 1 - n, 0)$ respectively. Then $[AQR]/[ABC] =$

$m(1 - n)$ etc. Hence the inequality to be proved is

$$\sqrt{m(1 - n)} + \sqrt{n(1 - l)} + \sqrt{l(1 - m)} \leq 3/2.$$

Now use C-S with

$$\mathbf{x} = (\sqrt{m}, \sqrt{n}, \sqrt{l}),$$

$$\mathbf{y} = (\sqrt{(1 - n)}, \sqrt{(1 - l)}, \sqrt{(1 - m)})$$

and then the left-hand side $= \mathbf{x}.\mathbf{y} \leq c(3 - c)$, where $c = l + m + n$ and $c(3 - c) = 9/4 - (3/2 - c)^2 \leq 9/4$. Equality holds when P, Q, R are the midpoints of the sides.

5. If $0 \leq x_j \leq 1, j = 1$ to 6, and $x_1 x_2 + x_2 x_3 + \ldots + x_6 x_1 = 1$ find the minimum value of $x_1^2 + x_2^2 + \ldots + x_6^2$. Apply C-S to the 6-dimensional vectors $(x_1, x_2, \ldots, x_6)$ and $(x_2, x_3, \ldots, x_1)$ and it is immediate that the minimum value is 1 when $x_1 = x_2 = \ldots = x_6 = 1/\sqrt{6}$.

6. Prove that $|x| + |y| + |z| \leq |y + z - x| + |z + x - y| + |x + y - z|$. By the triangle inequality $|2x| = |(x + y - z) + (x - y + z)| \leq |x + y - z| + |z + x - y|$. Now add together three such inequalities.

7. Given $a + b + c + d = 6$ and $a^2 + b^2 + c^2 + d^2 = 12$ find the range of values of each of the variables. If we apply C-S to the vectors $(1, 1, 1)$ and (a, b, c) we get $(a + b + c)^2 \leq 3(a^2 + b^2 + c^2)$ and so $(6 - d)^2 \leq 3(12 - d^2)$ from which $0 \leq d \leq 3$. When $d = 0, a = b = c = 2$ and when $d = 3, a = b = c = 1$. The other variables also lie between 0 and 3 inclusive.

Exercises 13.1

1. Let P be a point in the interior of triangle ABC, and let d, e, f be the distances from P to the sides a, b, c of the triangle. Show that the minimum value of $a/d + b/e + c/f$ occurs when P is the incentre of the triangle.

2. For n a positive integer, let $(a_1, a_2, \ldots, a_n)$ and $(b_1, b_2, \ldots, b_n)$ be two (not necessarily distinct permutations of $(1, 2, \ldots, n)$. Find sharp lower and upper bounds for

$$a_1 b_1 + a_2 b_2 + \ldots + a_n b_n.$$

3. Prove that for finite sequences of n terms

$$(\Sigma a_r b_r c_r d_r e_r f_r g_r h_r)^8 \leq \Sigma a_r^8 \Sigma b_r^8 \Sigma c_r^8 \Sigma d_r^8 \Sigma e_r^8 \Sigma f_r^8 \Sigma g_r^8 \Sigma h_r^8$$

and deduce that for positive sequences $(x_r), (y_r)$ we have $(\Sigma x_r y_r)^7 \leq n^5 \Sigma x_r^7 \Sigma y_r^7$.

4. Suppose $x, y, z > 1$ and $1/x + 1/y + 1/z = 2$. Prove that

$$\sqrt{(x+y+z)} \geq \sqrt{(x-1)} + \sqrt{(y-1)} + \sqrt{(z-1)}.$$

5. Given that $x, y, z > 0$ and $1/x + 1/y + 1/z = 1$, prove that

$$\sqrt{(x+1)} + \sqrt{(y+1)} + \sqrt{(z+1)} \leq 2\sqrt{(x+y+z)}.$$

6. Minimize $x^2 + y^2 + z^2$ subject to $x + 2y + 3z = 4$.

7. Prove that $(a_1 + a_2 + \ldots + a_k)^2 \leq k(a_1^2 + a_2^2 + \ldots + a_k^2)$. Hence show that if $a_1, a_2, \ldots, a_n$ satisfy the inequality $(a_1 + a_2 + \ldots + a_n \geq \sqrt{\{(n-1)(a_1^2 + a_2^2 + \ldots + a_n^2)\}}$ then $a_j \geq 0$ for all $j = 1$ to n.

8. If $a, b, c > 0$ prove that $abc(a + b + c) \le a^3b + b^3c + c^3a$.

9. If a, b, c and x, y, z are the sides of two triangles, prove that

$$\sqrt{(ax)} + \sqrt{(by)} + \sqrt{(cz)} \le \sqrt{\{(a + b + c)(x + y + z)\}}$$

   with equality if, and only if, the triangles are similar.

10. Minimize $x_1^2 + x_2^2 + \ldots + x_n^2$ subject to $a_1x_1 + a_2x_2 + \ldots + a_nx_n = 1$.

11. Find the minimum of $2x + 3y + 6z$ if $x^2 + y^2 + z^2 = 1$.

12. If a, b, c are the sides of a triangle and $ab + bc + ca = 27$, between what bounds does $p = a + b + c$ lie?

13. If $a, b, c > -1$ and $a + b + c = 1$ prove that $\sqrt{(1 + a)} + \sqrt{(1 + b)} + \sqrt{(1 + c)} \le 2\sqrt{3}$.

14. If $a, b, c > 0$ and $abc = 1$ prove that

$$1/\{a^3(b+c)\} + 1/\{b^3(c+a)\} + 1/\{c^3(a+b)\} \ge 3/2. \quad \text{(IMO 1995)}$$

15. If $a, b, c > 0$ and $a\cos^2\theta + b\sin^2\theta < c$, prove that $\sqrt{a}\cos^2\theta + \sqrt{b}\sin^2\theta < \sqrt{c}$.

16. If $a_j, x_j > 0, j = 1$ to n, prove that

$$\frac{a_1^2}{x_1} + \frac{a_2^2}{x_2} + \ldots + \frac{a_n^2}{x_n} \ge \frac{(a_1 + a_2 + \ldots + a_n)^2}{x_1 + x_2 + \ldots + x_n}.$$

13.2 Hints and Answers Week 3

Exercises 13.1

1. Take
$$\mathbf{u} = (\sqrt{(a/d)}, \sqrt{(b/e)}, \sqrt{(c/f)})$$
and
$$\mathbf{v} = (\sqrt{(ad)}, \sqrt{(be)}, \sqrt{(cf)}),$$
then C-S gives $(a+b+c)^2 \leq (ad+be+cf)(a/d+b/e+c/f)$. But $ad+be+cf = 2[ABC]$ so $a/d+b/e+c/f \geq (a+b+c)^2/\{2[ABC]\}$ with equality if, and only if, $d = e = f$, that is when P is at the incentre.

2. The maximum is
$$|\mathbf{a}||\mathbf{b}| = 1^2 + 2^2 + \ldots + n^2 = n(n+1)(2n+1)/6.$$

Now define $c_j = n + 1 - b_j, j = 1$ to n. Then $(c_1, c_2, \ldots, c_n)$ is also a permutation and $\Sigma a_j b_j = (n+1)\Sigma a_j - \Sigma a_j c_j = \frac{1}{2}n(n+1)^2 - \Sigma a_j c_j$. Hence the minimum is $\frac{1}{2}n(n+1)^2 - n(n+1)(2n+1)/6 = n(n+1)(n+2)/6$.

3. The first part is similar to Example 13.1.3. Then put $a_r = x_r^{7/8}, b_r = y_r^{7/8}, c_r = (x_r y_r)^{1/8}$ and other variables equal to 1.

4. Apply C-S to the vectors $(\sqrt{x}, \sqrt{y}, \sqrt{z})$ and
$$(\sqrt{\{(x-1)/x\}}, \sqrt{\{(y-1)/y\}}, \sqrt{\{(z-1)/z\}}).$$

5. This is almost the same as in Exercise 13.1.4.

6. Apply C-S with (x, y, z) and $(1, 2, 3)$. The minimum value is $8/7$ when $x = 2/7, y = 4/7, z = 6/7$.

7. Apply C-S with $(a_1, a_2, \ldots, a_k)$ and $(1, 1, \ldots 1)$. For the second part use

$$\sqrt{(n-1)(a_1^2 + a_2^2 + \ldots + a_n^2)}$$

$$\geq \sqrt{(n-1)(a_1^2 + a_2^2 + \ldots + a_{n-1}^2)}$$

$$\geq |a_1 + a_2 + \ldots + a_{n-1}| \geq a_1 + a_2 + \ldots + a_{n-1}.$$

8. Apply C-S with $(a/\sqrt{c}, b/\sqrt{a}, c/\sqrt{b})$ and $(\sqrt{c}, \sqrt{a}, \sqrt{b})$.

9. Apply C-S with $(\sqrt{a}, \sqrt{b}, \sqrt{c})$ and $(\sqrt{x}, \sqrt{y}, \sqrt{z})$.

10. The minimum is $m = 1/(a_1^2 + a_2^2 + \ldots + a_n^2)$ when $x_k = a_k m, k = 1$ to n.

11. The minimum is -7 when $x = -2/7, y = -3/7, z = -6/7$.

12. $9 \leq p \leq 6\sqrt{3}$.

13. Apply C-S with $(1, 1, 1)$ and $(\sqrt{(1+a)}, \sqrt{(1+b)}, \sqrt{(1+c)})$.

14. Put $a = 1/x, b = 1/y, c = 1/z$ and apply C-S with

$$(x/\sqrt{(y+z)}, y/\sqrt{(z+x)}, z/\sqrt{(x+y)})$$

and
$$(\sqrt{(y+z)}, \sqrt{(z+x)}, \sqrt{(x+y)}).$$

Then there is a final application of AM/GM using $xyz = 1$.

15. Apply C-S with $(\cos\theta, \sin\theta)$ and $(\sqrt{a}\cos\theta, \sqrt{b}\sin\theta)$.

16. Apply C-S with $(a_1/\sqrt{x_1}, a_2/\sqrt{x_2}, \ldots, a_n/\sqrt{x_n})$ and $(\sqrt{x_1}, \sqrt{x_2}, \ldots, \sqrt{x_n})$.

Chapter 14

Inequalities: Week 4

14.1 The rearrangement lemma, Tchebychef's inequality, the power means inequality

We start with a very simple idea, which you probably have encountered before.

Theorem 8 Suppose $a_1 \geq a_2$ and $b_1 \geq b_2$ then $a_1 b_1 + a_2 b_2 \geq a_1 b_2 + a_2 b_1$.

Proof The left-hand side minus the right-hand side is equal to $(a_1 - a_2)(b_1 - b_2) \geq 0$. ∎

Exercises 14.1

1. Prove that if $a, b > 0$ then $(a^2 + b^2)(a^3 + b^3) \leq 2(a^5 + b^5)$.

2. Prove that if $a_1 \geq a_2 \geq a_3$ and $b_1 \geq b_2 \geq b_3$, then $a_1 b_1 + a_2 b_2 + a_3 b_3 \geq a_1 b_2 + a_2 b_3 + a_3 b_1$.

Theorem 9 (The rearrangement lemma) Suppose that (a_k) and (b_k) are two finite sequences of n terms that are ordered so that $a_j \geq a_k$ and $b_j \geq b_k$ whenever $j \leq k$. In future we shall say that two such sequences *are ordered in the same way*. Let (B_k) be a sequence, which is a permutation of (b_k). Then

$$a_1 b_1 + a_2 b_2 + \ldots + a_n b_n \geq a_1 B_1 + a_2 B_2 + \ldots + a_n B_n.$$

Observe that this theorem is a generalisation of Exercise 14.1.2. If $B_k = b_k$ for all $k = 1$ to n, there is nothing to prove. Otherwise there must be two subscripts, say p and q such that $p > q$ and $B_p \geq B_q$, then $(a_1 B_1 + a_2 B_2 + \ldots + a_q B_p + \ldots + a_p B_q + \ldots + a_n B_n) - (a_1 B_1 + a_2 B_2 + \ldots + a_q B_q + \ldots + a_p B_p + \ldots + a_n B_n) = a_q B_p + a_p B_q - a_q B_q - a_p B_b = (a_q - a_p)(B_p - B_q) \geq 0$. In other words any step towards restoring the correct order amongst the B_k, that is permuting them back towards the b_k, increases the product. ∎

If on the other hand the sequences (a_k) and (b_k) are ordered in the opposite way, then the direction of the inequality is reversed.

Corollary to Theorem 9 It is important to appreciate that if we do not know the precise ordering of the sequence (a_k), but know for certain that the sequence (b_k) is sorted in the opposite way, then it is certainly true that $a_1 b_1 + a_2 b_2 + \ldots a_n b_n \leq a_1 B_1 + a_2 B_2 \ldots + a_n B_n$, where (B_k) is a permutation of (b_k). This is because the labels of the two sequences can be adjusted in the same manner, so that both sequences are ordered, and ordered oppositely.

Examples 14.1

1. We show how to prove AM/GM using the Corollary to Theorem 9. Let $a_k > 0$. Define $g = (a_1 a_2 \ldots a_n)^{1/n}$ to be their geometric mean. Define $c_1 = a_1/g, c_2 = a_1 a_2/g^2, c_3 = a_1 a_2 a_3/g^3, \ldots, c_n = a_1 a_2 \ldots a_n/g^n = 1$ and $d_k = 1/c_k, k = 1$

to n. Clearly the sequences (c_k) and (d_k) are oppositely sorted, and on using the Corollary in the form $c_1 d_1 + c_2 d_2 + \ldots + c_n d_n \leq c_1 d_n + c_2 d_1 + \ldots + c_n d_{n-1}$ we obtain $(1 + 1 + \ldots + 1) \leq a_1/g + a_2/g + \ldots + a_n/g$, that is, $m \geq g$, where m is the arithmetic mean.

2. If $a, b, c > 0$ prove that $a^3 + b^3 + c^3 \geq a^2 c + b^2 a + c^2 b$. Suppose that without loss of generality $a \geq b \geq c$. Consider the sequences (a^2, b^2, c^2) and (a, b, c). These are ordered in the same way. But (c, a, b) is a permutation of (a, b, c). The result now follows immediately from Theorem 9.

Theorem 10 [Tchebychef] If (a_k) and (b_k) are two finite sequences that are ordered in the same way then

$$n(\Sigma a_k b_k) \geq (\Sigma a_k)(\Sigma b_k).$$

Proof The result follows by repeated application of Theorem 9. Details are left to the reader. ∎

We provide a proof independent of Theorem 9, but which uses the same idea, that of Theorem 8. For any pair of suffices p and q, because the sequences are ordered in the same way, we have $(a_p - a_q)(b_p - b_q) \geq 0$. It follows that

$$a_p b_p + a_q b_q \geq a_p b_q + a_q b_p.$$

Summing over p we get $\Sigma a_p b_p + n a_q b_q \geq b_q \Sigma a_p + a_q \Sigma b_p$. Summing over q we get $2n \Sigma a_k b_k \geq 2 \Sigma a_k \Sigma b_k$. If the sequences are ordered in the opposite way, then the inequality's direction is reversed. ∎

As an immediate consequence of Theorem 10 we have

Theorem 11 (Power means inequality for positive powers)

If $a_1, a_2, \ldots, a_n > 0$ and $s, t \geq 0$ then (a_k^s) and (a_k^t) are ordered in the same way and so

$$(\Sigma a_k^{s+t})/n \geq (\Sigma a_k^s)/n \times (\Sigma a_k^t)/n.$$

For example, if $a, b, c > 0$ then

$$3(a^5 + b^5 + c^5) \geq (a^2 + b^2 + c^2)(a^3 + b^3 + c^3).$$

Corollary to Theorem 11 If $a_1, a_2, \ldots, a_n > 0$ and s is a positive integer then

$$(\Sigma a_k^s/n) \geq (\Sigma a_k/n)^s$$

Proof Proof is by induction. The corollary is clearly true for $s = 1$. If now, as an inductive hypothesis, it is true for some integer $s \geq 1$, then Theorem 11 with $t = 1$ shows that it is true for $s + 1$. ■

Theorem 12 (Power means inequality for one positive power and one negative power) If $a_1, a_2, \ldots a_n > 0$ and $s > 0, t < 0$ then (a_k^s) and (a_k^t) are ordered in the opposite way and so

$$\frac{\Sigma a_k^{s+t}}{n} \leq \frac{\Sigma a_k^s}{n} \times \frac{\Sigma a_k^t}{n}.$$

For example, if $a, b, c > 0$ then $3(a^2 + b^2 + c^2) \leq (a^3 + b^3 + c^3)(1/a + 1/b + 1/c)$.

Corollary to Theorem 12 Putting $t = -s$ we obtain

$$\Sigma a_k^s \times \Sigma a_k^{-s} \geq n^2.$$

Theorem 13 (Power means inequality for negative powers)
If $a_1, a_2, \ldots a_n > 0$ and $s, t \leq 0$ then (a_k^s) and (a_k^t) are ordered in
the same way and so

$$(\Sigma a_k^{s+t})/n \geq (\Sigma a_k^s)/n \times (\Sigma a_k^t)/n.$$

For example, if $a, b, c > 0$, then

$$3 \left(\frac{1}{a^4} + \frac{1}{b^4} + \frac{1}{c^4} \right) \geq \left(\frac{1}{a^3} + \frac{1}{b^3} + \frac{1}{c^3} \right) \left(\frac{1}{a} + \frac{1}{b} + \frac{1}{c} \right).$$

We are now in a position to give the result, which compares the
mean of integral powers of n positive quantities with their arithmetic mean. In Week 6 we consider the case of fractional powers
such as $s = \frac{1}{2}$.

Theorem 14 If $a_1, a_2, \ldots, a_n > 0$ and s is a positive integer then

(i) $(a_1^s + a_2^s + \ldots + a_n^s)/n \geq \{(a_1 + a_2 + \ldots + a_n)/n\}^s;$

(ii) $(a_1^{-s} + a_2^{-s} + \ldots + a_n^{-s})/n \geq \{(a_1 + a_2 + \ldots + a_n)/n\}^{-s}.$

Proof Part (i) is the Corollary to Theorem 11, which has already
been proved. For part (ii), we have from part (i) that

$$(a_1^{-s} + a_2^{-s} + \ldots + a_n^{-s})/n \geq \{(1/a_1 + 1/a_2 + \ldots + 1/a_n)/n\}^s,$$

so it is sufficient to prove that $\{(1/a_1 + 1/a_2 + \ldots + 1/a_n)/n\}^s \geq \{(a_1 + a_2 + \ldots + a_n)/n\}^{-s}$. But this result has already been established as the Corollary to Theorem 12. ∎

The reader should review the above theorems and should check
that equality holds in each case if, and only if, certain obvious
conditions hold, such as $a_1 = a_2 = \ldots = a_n$.

Examples 14.2

1. If $a, b, c > 0$ prove that $a/(b + c) + b/(c + a) + c/(a + b) \geq 3/2$. This inequality has already been established using the Cauchy-Schwarz inequality, but it can also be established by rearrangement. If we assume, without loss of generality, that $a \geq b \geq c$, then (a, b, c) and $(1/(b + c), 1/(c + a), 1/(a + b))$ are ordered in the same way. Hence we have

$$a/(b+c)+b/(c+a)+c/(a+b) \geq a/(c+a)+b/(a+b)+c/(b+c)$$

and $a/(b+c) + b/(c+a) + c/(a+b) \geq a/(a+b) + b/(b+c) + c/(c+a)$. Now add.

2. If $a, b, c, d > 0$ prove that $(a^4 + b^4)(a + b)^2 \geq (a^2 + b^2)^3$. The left-hand side minus the right-hand side comes to $2(a^5b + b^5a) - 2(a^4b^2 + b^4a^2)$, so the inequality holds provided $a^4 + b^4 \geq a^3b + b^3a$. Now consider the sequences (a^3, b^3) and (a, b), which are ordered in the same way, and apply Theorem 9.

3. Let $(a_k), (b_k), (c_k), \ldots$ be a collection of sequences all ordered in the same way, and let $p, q, r, \ldots$ be positive integers. Prove that

$$(\Sigma a_k^p b_k^q c_k^r \ldots)/n \geq (\Sigma a_k/n)^p (\Sigma b_k/n)^q (\Sigma c_k/n)^r \ldots.$$

This is proved by a repeated application of Theorem 10 (Tchebychef).

4. Let $(a_k), (b_k)$ be two sequences ordered in the same way. Prove that $(\Sigma a_k)^2 (\Sigma b_k)^2 (\Sigma a_k b_k)^2 \leq n^4 \Sigma a_k^4 \Sigma b_k^4$. From Tchebychef we have $\Sigma a_k \Sigma b_k \leq n\Sigma a_k b_k$. Multiplying by $\Sigma a_k b_k$ we get $\Sigma a_k \Sigma b_k \Sigma a_k b_k \leq n\Sigma a_k b_k \Sigma a_k b_k \leq n^2 \Sigma a_k^2 b_k^2$. Squaring provides the required result, since by C-S $(\Sigma a_k^2 b_k^2)^2 \leq \Sigma a_k^4 \Sigma b_k^4$.

5. Let $a, b, c, d > 0$ and $1/a + 1/b + 1/c + 1/d = 1$. Minimize $a^2 + b^2 + c^2 + d^2$. Put $1/a = u, 1/b = v, 1/c = w, 1/d = x$ then $u + v + w + x = 1$ and we are required to minimize $1/u^2 + 1/v^2 + 1/w^2 + 1/x^2$. Now, by Theorem 14 we have $\frac{1}{4}(1/u^2 + 1/v^2 + 1/w^2 + 1/x^2) \geq \{(u + v + w + x)/4\}^{-2} = 16$. The minimum is therefore 64 with equality if, and only if, $a = b = c = d$.

6. Let $a, b, c > 0$ and $abc = 2$. Prove that

$$(1 + a^4(1 + b^4)(1 + c^4) \geq (1 + 2a)(1 + 2b)(1 + 2c).$$

Is it true (DM) that if $a, b, c, d > 0$ and $abcd = 2$ that

$$(1+a^4)(1+b^4)(1+c^4)(1+d^4) \geq (1+2a)(1+2b)(1+2c)(1+2d)?$$

The answer to the second part is 'No' and can be seen by taking $a = \sqrt{2}, b = \sqrt{2}, c = 1, d = 1$. For the first part the key is to see how to use the condition $abc = 2$, and the trick is to prove the equivalent inequality $(1 + a^4)(1 + b^4)(1 + c^4) \geq (1 + a^2bc)(1 + ab^2c)(1 + abc^2)$. We expand both sides and prove first that $a^4 + b^4 + c^4 \geq abc(a + b + c)$. In fact, by Theorem 12, we have $(1/3)(a^4 + b^4 + c^4) \geq \{(a+b+c)/3\}^4$ so that $a^4+b^4+c^4 \geq (a+b+c)\{(a+b+c)/3\}^3 \geq (a + b + c)abc$, by AM/GM. It remains to prove that $a^4b^4 + b^4c^4 + c^4a^4 \geq a^2b^2c^2(ab + bc + ca)$. But this is the same inequality with bc replacing a etc.

14.1.1   Exercises 14.2

1. Prove that, if $a, b > 0$, then $16(a^5 + b^5) \geq (a + b)^5$.

2. Prove that if $a, b, c, d > 0$ then $(a^3+b^3+c^3+d^3)(a+b+c+d) \geq (a^2 + b^2 + c^2 + d^2)^2$.

3. Prove that if $a, b, c, d > 0$ then $4(a^4 + b^4 + c^4 + d^4) \geq (a^3 + b^3 + c^3 + d^3)(a + b + c + d)$.

4. Prove that if $(a_k), (b_k), (c_k)$ are sequences ordered in the same way, then

$$\Sigma a_k \Sigma b_k \Sigma c_k \Sigma a_k b_k c_k \leq n^3 \Sigma a_k^2 b_k^2 c_k^2.$$

5. (i) Prove that if $t > 0, t \neq 1, x > y > 0$ then $t^x + 1/t^x > t^y + 1/t^y$.

   (ii) Deduce that, if $t > 0, t \neq 1, t^p + t^q > t^r + t^s$ when $p, q, r, s \geq 0, p + q = r + s$ and $p - q > r - s \geq 0$.

   (iii) Prove that when $p, q, r, s \geq 0$ and $p + q = r + s, p - q > r - s \geq 0$ and $a_k > 0$ for $k = 1$ to n then $(\Sigma a_k^p)(\Sigma a_k^q) \geq (\Sigma a_k^r)(\Sigma a_k^s)$.

6. Prove that, if $a, b, c, d > 0$, then

$$(a^4 + b^4 + c^4 + d^4)(a + b + c + d)^2 \geq (a^2 + b^2 + c^2 + d^2)^3.$$

7. Prove that, if $a, b, c > 0$ then $9(a^6 + b^6 + c^6) \geq (a^2 + b^2 + c^2)^3$.

8. If $a_1, a_2, \ldots, a_n > 0$ and $a_1 + a_2 + \ldots + a_n = 1$ find the minimum of $\Sigma(a_k + 1/a_k)^2$.

9. Prove that if a, b, c are positive real numbers and $a + b + c \geq 3abc$ then $a^2 + b^2 + c^2 \geq 3abc$.

10. Let $(x_k), (y_k)$ be sequences of n terms that are ordered in the same way, and let (z_k) be a sequence that is a permutation of (y_k). Prove that $\Sigma(x_k - y_k)^2 \leq \Sigma(x_k - z_k)^2$. (IMO 1975)

11. Let $x, y, z > 0$. Prove that

    (i) $x^2/y^2 + y^2/z^2 + z^2/x^2 \geq y/x + z/y + x/z$;

(ii) $x^2/y^2 + y^2/z^2 + z^2/x^2 \geq x/y + y/z + z/\text{x}$.

12. Establish the following homogeneous quadratic inequalities when $a, b, c > 0$:

(i) $a^4 + b^4 + c^4 \geq b^2c^2 + c^2a^2 + a^2b^2$;

(ii) $2(a^4 + b^4 + c^4) \geq a^3(b + c) + b^3(c + a) + c^3(a + b)$;

(iii) $a^4 + b^4 + c^4 \geq abc(a + b + c)$;

(iv) $a^2/(b + c) + b^2/(c + a) + c^2/(a + b) \geq (a + b + c)/2$.

14.1.2   More on power means

We summarize the results so far, and make certain generalizations, indicating with examples how they are proved. First we introduce some notation. If (a_k) is a sequence of n positive terms and t is any non-zero integer, we define $m_t = (a_1^t + a_2^t + \ldots + a_n^t)/n$ and $M_t = m_t^{1/t}$. It is actually M_t that is called the tth *order mean* of $a_1, a_2, \ldots, a_n$.

Note that M_1 is the arithmetic mean, M_2 is the root mean square, and M_{-1} is the harmonic mean. Now if t is allowed to be any non-zero number then it can be shown that $M_t \to g$ as $t \to 0$, where g is the geometric mean, (though the proof is beyond the scope of this book). So if we define $M_0 = g$, then from the work in Week 2 we have

Result 1 $M_{-1} \leq M_0 \leq M_1 \leq M_2$. Theorem 11 provides
Result 2   If s, t are non-negative integers $m_{s+t} \geq m_s m_t$. The Corollary to Theorem 11 provides
Result 3   If s is a positive integer then $M_s \geq M_1$ or, what is the same thing, $m_s \geq m_1^s$. Theorem 12 provides
Result 4   If s, t are positive integers $m_{s-t} \leq m_s m_{-t}$.

The Corollary to Theorem 12 provides

Result 5 If s is a non-zero integer $m_s m_{-s} \geq 1$.

Theorem 13 provides

Result 6 If s, t are non-negative integers then $m_{-s-t} \geq m_{-s} m_{-t}$.

Theorem 14 repeats Result 3 and also provides

Result 7 If s is a positive integer then $M_{-s} \leq M_1$.

In fact we can do better than Result 7 and (prompted by Results 1 and 3) we find

Result 8 If s is a positive integer then $M_{-s} \leq M_0 = g$.

Proof $m_{-s} = (1/n)(1/a_1^s + 1/a_2^s + \ldots + 1/a_n^s) \geq (a_1 a_2 \ldots a_n)^{s/n} = M_0^s$ by AM/GM. Hence $M_{-s} = m_{-s}^{-s} \leq M_0$. ∎

We now review Exercise 14.2.5 and note that part (i) is true not only if $x > y > 0$, but more generally if $|x| > |y|$. This means that part (ii) is true for all p, q, r, s satisfying $p + q = r + s$ and $p - q > r - s \geq 0$. Thus, for example, if $t > 0, t^3 + t^{-5} \geq t^2 + t^{-4}$, with equality if, and only if, $t = 1$. As a second example, if $t > 0, t^{-3} + t^{-8} \geq t^{-4} + t^{-7}$ with equality if, and only if, $t = 1$. The upshot of this is

Result 9 If p, q, r, s are integers such that $p + q = r + s$ and $p - q > r - s \geq 0$ then

$$m_p m_q \geq m_r m_s.$$

Now observe that Result 1 looks as if it should generalize as

Theorem 15 (General power means inequality)

$$\ldots \leq M_{-5} \leq M_{-4} \leq M_{-3} \leq M_{-2} \leq M_{-1} \leq M_0$$

$$\leq M_1 \leq M_2 \leq M_3 \leq M_4 \leq M_5 \ldots$$

Proof We first give an example on which the proof of the general result is based. We prove $M_5 \geq M_4$ or what is the same thing that $m_5^4 \geq m_4^5$. It follows by repeated use of Result 9.

We have $m_5^4 \geq m_5^3 m_4 m_1 \geq m_5^2 m_4^2 m_2 \geq m_5 m_4^3 m_3 \geq m_4^5$.

In general we prove $M_{s+1} \geq M_s$, or what is the same thing that $m_{s+1}^s \geq m_s^{s+1}$. We have, for positive $s \geq 2$,

$$m_{s+1}^s \geq m_{s+1}^{s-1} m_s m_1 \geq m_{s+1}^{s-2} m_s^2 m_2 \geq m_{s+1}^{s-3} m_s^3 m_3 \geq \ldots$$

$$\geq m_{s+1} m_s^{s-1} m_{s-1} \geq m_s^{s+1},$$

where some steps have to be omitted if $s = 2$ or 3. Note that Result 1 takes care of $s = 0, 1$. For negative values of s care has to be taken at the initial stage; for example, to prove $M_{-2} \geq M_{-3}$ the equivalent statement is $m_{-3}^2 \geq m_{-2}^3$ and the proof then goes as follows: $m_{-3}^2 \geq m_{-1} m_{-2} m_{-3} \geq m_{-2}^3$. The general proof for $s \leq -2$ follows the same pattern. Result 1 takes care of $s = -1$. As you may imagine the general power means inequality is true if s is any real number, but the proof is beyond the scope of this book. ∎

Exercise 14.3

1. Prove in detail, without quoting Theorem 15 that $M_{-5} \leq M_{-4}$.

14.1.3 Hölder's Inequality

Examples 14.3

1. Prove that if s, t are positive integers and $x, y > 0$ then
   $x^s y^t \leq \{(sx + ty)/(s + t)\}^{s+t}$.
   This is just AM/GM with x appearing s times and y appearing t times.

2. Prove that if α, β are rational numbers such that $\alpha + \beta = 1$,
   then $x^\alpha y^\beta \leq \alpha x + \beta y$. Use the result of Example 14.3.1 with
   $\alpha = s/(s + t)$ and $\beta = t/(s + t)$.

Theorem 16 [Hölder's Inequality] Let (x_k) and (y_k) be two sequences of n terms all of which are positive, and let p and q be rational numbers such that $1/p + 1/q = 1$, then

$$(x_1y_1+x_2y_2+\ldots+x_ny_n) \le (x_1^p+x_2^p+\ldots+x_n^p)^{1/p}(y_1^q+y_2^q+\ldots+y_n^q)^{1/q}.$$

Proof Let (a_k) and (b_k) be two sequences of n positive terms. In Example 14.3.2 put $x = a_k/\Sigma a_k$ and $y = b_k/\Sigma b_k$ and sum over k from 1 to n. Since $\alpha + \beta = 1$ we get

$$a_1^\alpha b_1^\beta + a_2^\alpha b_2^\beta + \ldots + a_n^\alpha b_n^\beta \le (a_1 + a_2 + \ldots + a_n)^\alpha (b_1 + b_2 + \ldots + b_n)^\beta.$$

Now put $\alpha = 1/p$ and $\beta = 1/q$ so that $1/p + 1/q = 1$. Also put $a_k = x_k^p$ and $b_k = y_k^p$ and we get

$$(x_1y_1+x_2y_2+\ldots+x_ny_n) \le (x_1^p+x_2^p+\ldots+x_n^p)^{1/p}(y_1^q+y_2+q+\ldots+y_n^q)^{1/q}.$$

If $p = q = 2$, then Hölder's inequality becomes the same as the Cauchy-Schwarz inequality and is therefore a generalization of it. If you write $\mathbf{x} = (x_1, x_2, \ldots, x_n)$ and $\mathbf{y} = (y_1, y_2, \ldots, y_n)$ and divide both sides by $n = n^{(1/p+1/q)}$ we may think of the inequality as saying that the mean of $\mathbf{x}.\mathbf{y} \le M_p(x)M_q(y)$. If $\mathbf{x} = \mathbf{y}$ this reduces to $M_2^2 \le M_p M_q$, which one might have anticipated from Result 9 and Theorem 15. ∎

Exercises 14.4

1. Generalize Examples 14.3 and Theorem 16 to cover more than two sequences.

2. Prove that if $a_1, a_2, \ldots, a_n > 0$, then

$$(1 + a_1)(1 + a_2) \ldots (1 + a_n) \ge (1 + g)^n,$$

where $g = (a_1 a_2 \ldots a_n)^{1/n}$.

3. Prove that if x, y, z, w are positive quantities such that $x + y + z + w = 1$, then

$$(1 + 1/x)(1 + 1/y)(1 + 1/z)(1 + 1/w) \geq 625.$$

4. **(A particular case of Minkowski's inequality)**
   Let $(a_k), (b_k), \ldots, (t_k)$ be sequences of n terms of positive quantities. Prove that

$$(a_1^2 + a_2^2 + \ldots + a_n^2)^{1/2} + (b_1^2 + b_2^2 + \ldots + b_n^2)^{1/2} + \ldots$$

$$+(t_1^2 + t_2^2 + \ldots + t_n^2)^{1/2}$$

$$\geq \{(a_1 + b_1 + \ldots + t_1)^2 + (a_2 + b_2 + \ldots + t_2)^2 + \ldots$$

$$+(a_n + b_n + \ldots + t_n)^2\}^{1/2}.$$

The inequalities of Hölder and Minkowski are important in advanced analysis and are included in this book for that reason.

14.2   Hints and Answers   Week 4

Exercises 14.1

1. We may assume, without loss of generality, that $a \geq b$. Then
   RHS $-$ LHS $= a^5 + b^5 - a^3b^2 - b^3a^2 = (a^3 - b^3)(a^2 - b^2) \geq 0$,
   since $a^3 \geq b^3$ and $a^2 \geq b^2$.

2. Two applications of Theorem 8 give
   $$a_1b_1 + a_2b_2 + a_3b_3 \geq a_1b_2 + a_2b_1 + a_3b_3 \geq a_1b_2 + a_2b_3 + a_3b_1.$$

Exercises 14.2

1. Use the Corollary to Theorem 11 with $n = 2, s = 5, a_1 = a, a_2 = b$.

2. Multiply out and use $a^3b + b^3a \geq 2a^2b^2$ etc.

3. This is a direct application of Theorem 11 with $n = 4, s = 3, t = 1$.

4. From Tchebychef we have
   $$\Sigma a_k \Sigma b_k \Sigma c_k \Sigma a_k b_k c_k \leq n^2 (\Sigma a_k b_k c_k)^2 \leq n^3 \Sigma a_k^2 b_k^2 c_k^2.$$

5. For part (i) consider the sequences $(t^x, t^y), (t^{x+y}, 1)$. For part
   (ii) use $t^{k+x} + t^{k-x} > t^{k+y} + t^{k-y}$ with $k + x = p, k - x = q, k + y = r, k - y = s$. For part (iii) put $t = a/b$, multiply up
   by $b^{p+q} = b^{r+s}$ to get $(a^pb^q + a^qb^p) \geq (a^rb^s + a^sb^r)$. Then put
   $a = a_j, b = a_k$ and perform a summation over all pairs (j, k).

6. By two applications of Exercise 14.2.5 part (iii)
   $$(a^4 + b^4 + c^4 + d^4)(a + b + c + d)^2$$
   $$\geq (a^3 + b^3 + c^3 + d^3)(a^2 + b^2 + c^2 + d^2)(a + b + c + d)$$
   $$\geq (a^2 + b^2 + c^2 + d^2)^3.$$

7. By two applications of Exercise 14.2.5 part (iii)

$$9(a^6 + b^6 + c^6) \geq 3(a^3 + b^3 + c^3)^2$$
$$\geq (a^3 + b^3 + c^3)(a^2 + b^2 + c^2)(a + b + c)$$
$$\geq 9(a^2 + b^2 + c^2)^3.$$

8. $\Sigma(a_k + 1/a_k)^2 = 2n + \Sigma a_k^2 + \Sigma a_k^{-2}$. By Theorem 14 $\Sigma a_k^2 \geq n(\Sigma a_k/n)^2 = 1/n$ and $\Sigma a_k^{-2} \geq n(\Sigma a_k/n)^{-2} = n^3$. Hence the minimum is $n^3 + 1/n + 2n = (1 + n^2)^2/n$.

9. $(a^2 + b^2 + c^2)/3 \geq \{(a + b + c)/3\}^2 \geq (a + b + c)/3 \times (abc)^{1/3}$. Hence $(a^2 + b^2 + c^2)^2 \geq (a + b + c)^2 \geq 3(a + b + c)(abc)$.

10. The squares cancel and what remains is a statement of the rearrangement lemma. IMOs have got harder since 1975!

11. (i) Apply the rearrangement lemma to the sequence $(x/y, y/z, z/x)$. Note that $y/x = y/z \times z/x$ etc.

   (ii) Put $y/z = a, z/x = b, x/y = c$ then the inequality to be proved is $a^2 + b^2 + c^2 \geq a + b + c$ given $abc = 1$. In fact, by the power means inequality, $a^2 + b^2 + c^2 \geq (a+b+c)(a+b+c)/3 \geq (a+b+c)(abc)^{1/3}$ by AM/GM.

12. (i) $(a^2 - b^2)^2 + (b^2 - c^2)^2 + (c^2 - a^2)^2 \geq 0.$

   (ii) By the rearrangement lemma $a^4 + b^4 \geq a^3 b + b^3 a$ etc.

   (iii) By the power means inequality
   $a^4 + b^4 + c^4 \geq (a^3 + b^3 + c^3)/3 \times (a + b + c) \geq abc(a + b + c).$

   (iv) Suppose without loss of generality that $a \geq b \geq c$ then (a^2, b^2, c^2) and $(1/(b+c), 1/(c+a), 1/(a+b))$ are ordered in the same way. Hence $a^2/(b+c) + b^2/(c+a) + c^2/(a+b) \geq a^2/(c+a) + b^2/(a+b) + c^2/(b+c)$ and it is also $\geq a^2/(a+b) + b^2/(b+c) + c^2/(c+a)$. Now add and use $(b^2 + c^2)/(b+c) \geq (b+c)/2$ etc.

Exercises 14.3

1. We have to prove that $m^4_{-5} \geq m^5_{-4}$. Now $m^4_{-5} \geq m_{-4}m_{-1}m^3_{-5} \geq m^2_{-4}m_{-2}m^2_{-5} \geq m^3_{-4}m_{-3}m_{-5} \geq m^5_{-4}$.

Exercises 14.4

1. The generalizations are as follows:

   (i) Suppose there are t sequences of n positive terms (a_k), $(b_k), \ldots, (t_k)$, and that $\alpha, \beta \ldots, \tau$ are t positive rational numbers such that $\alpha + \beta, \ldots + \tau = 1$ then

   $$a^\alpha_1 b^\beta_1 \ldots t^\tau_1 + a^\alpha_2 b^\beta_2 \ldots t^\tau_2 + \ldots + a^\alpha_n b^\beta_n \ldots t^\tau_n$$
   $$\leq (a_1 + \ldots + a_n)^\alpha (b_1 + \ldots + b_n)^\beta \ldots (t_1 + \ldots + t_n)^\tau.$$

   (ii) Suppose $(x_k), (y_k), \ldots, (w_k)$ are t sequences of n positive terms and $p, q, \ldots, s$ are t positive quantities such that $1/p + 1/q + \ldots + 1/s = 1$, then

   $$x_1 y_1 \ldots w_1 + \ldots + x_n y_n \ldots w_n \leq$$
   $$(x^p_1 + \ldots + x^p_n)^{1/p} (y^q_1 \ldots + y^q_n))^{1/q} \ldots (w^s_1 + \ldots + w^s_n)^{1/s}.$$

   The proof in each case is the same as in Examples 14.3 and Theorem 16 except that there are t sequences rather than two.

2. Use the result of Exercise 14.4.1(i) with $n = 2$ and $t = n$, the n sequences being $(1, a_1), (1, a_2), \ldots, (1, a_n)$ and $\alpha = \beta = \ldots = \tau = 1/n$. We then have

   $$(1 + a_1)^{1/n} (1 + a_2)^{1/n} \ldots (1 + a_n)^{1/n}$$
   $$\geq 1 + (a_1 a_2 \ldots a_n)^{1/n} = (1 + g),$$

   which on taking n^{th} powers is what is required to prove.

3. Use the result of Exercise 14.4.1(i) with $n = 2, t = 4, \alpha = \beta = \gamma = \delta = \frac{1}{4}$ and the following four sequences $(1, 1/x)$, $(1, 1/y)$, $(1, 1/z)$, $(1, 1/w)$. We then have $\{(1 + 1/x)(1 + 1/y)(1 + 1/z)(1 + 1/w)\}^{1/4} \geq 1 + 1/(xyzw)^{1/4}$. Now by AM/GM, since $x + y + z + w = 1$, we have $(xyzw)^{1/4} \leq \frac{1}{4}$ so that $1 + 1/(xyzw)^{1/4} \geq 5$.

4. Let $T^2 =$

$$(a_1+b_1+\ldots+t_1)^2+(a_2+b_2+\ldots+t_2)^2+\ldots+(a_n+b_n+\ldots+t_n)^2 =$$

$$a_1(a_1+b_1+\ldots+t_1)+a_2(a_2+b_2+\ldots+t_2)+\ldots+a_n(a_n+b_n+\ldots+t_n)$$

$$+b_1(a_1+b_1+\ldots+t_1)+b_2(a_2+b_2+\ldots+t_2)+\ldots b_n(a_n+b_n+\ldots+t_n)$$

$$+\ldots+$$

$$t_1(a_1+b_1+\ldots+t_1)+t_2(a_2+b_2+\ldots+t_2)+\ldots+t_n(a_n+b_n+\ldots+t_n).$$

Applying the C-S inequality (or Hölder's inequality with $p = q = 2$) in many places we obtain

$$T^2 \leq (a_1^2 + a_2^2 + \ldots + a_n^2)^{1/2}T + (b_1^2 + b_2^2 + \ldots + b_n^2)^{1/2}T + \ldots$$

$$+(t_1^2 + t_2^2 + \ldots + t_n^2)^{1/2}T,$$

which provides the required result. What happens if you apply Hölder's inequality with p, q satisfying $1/p + 1/q = 1$?

Chapter 15

Inequalities: Week 5

15.1 Necessary and sufficient conditions for polynomial equations to have positive roots

15.1.1 Introduction

We now consider inequalities involving positive real numbers, in which the inequalities arise naturally from supposing the positive real numbers are the roots of a polynomial equation. If there are three such positive numbers we denote them by a, b, c and if there are four we denote them by a, b, c, d. If there are n positive roots they are denoted by $a_1, a_2, \ldots, a_n$.

We refer back to Week 2, where it was shown that if the equation

$$x^n - {}^nC_1 p_1 x^{n-1} + {}^nC_2 p_2^2 x^{n-2} + \ldots + (-1)^k \, {}^nC_k p_k^k x^{n-k} \ldots + (-1)^n p_n^n = 0$$

has n positive roots, then

$$p_1 \geq p_2 \geq \ldots \geq p_n.$$

These are necessary but not sufficient conditions for n positive roots. During the course of proving this, it was shown that

$$p_{l+1}^{2(l+1)} \geq p_l^l p_{l+2}^{l+2}, \text{ for } l = 0, 1, 2, \ldots, n - 2,$$

where we defined $p_0 = 1$. Equality holds if, and only if,

$$a_1 = a_2 = \ldots = a_n.$$

Exercises 15.1

1. If $a, b, c, d > 0$ and $ab + bc + ca + ad + bd + cd = 54$, find the least value of $a + b + c + d$ and the greatest value of $abcd$.

2. Given the same data as in Exercise 15.1.1 prove that

$$(a + b + c + d)(bcd + acd + abd + abc) \leq 1296.$$

   If $a, b > 0$ are the roots of the equation $x^2 - 2p_1 x + p_2^2 = 0$, find the equation whose roots are $\sqrt{a}$ and $\sqrt{b}$. Deduce that $\{(\sqrt{a} + \sqrt{b})/2\}^2 \leq (a + b)/2$ or in the terminology of Week 4, that $M_{1/2} \leq M_1$.

3. Prove that for the quadratic equation $x^2 - 2p_1 x + p_2^2 = 0$ where $p_2 > 0$, the condition $p_1 \geq p_2$ is both necessary and sufficient for it to have two positive real roots, with equality if, and only if, the roots are coincident.

4. Prove that for all integers n

$$\cosh^n\{(n + 1)\theta\} \geq \cosh^{n+1}(n\theta).$$

The cubic equation

All cubic equations may be transformed into one or other of the standard forms

$$f_{\pm}(x) \equiv x^3 \pm 3Q^2 x + R^3 = 0,$$

where we may suppose $Q > 0$. (If $Q = 0$ then there is only one real root, $x = -R$, unless $R = 0$ also, when there are three coincident real roots $x = 0$). Now there cannot be three distinct real roots unless there are two real turning points on the graph. Since these are given by $df_{\pm}/dx = 3x^2 \pm 3Q^2 = 0$, we must reject the function f_+. So we may restrict consideration to

$$f(x) \equiv x^3 - 3Q^2 + R^3 = 0.$$

For there to be three real roots it is clear from graphical considerations that $x = -Q$ must be a maximum with $f(-Q) \geq 0$ and $x = Q$ must be a minimum with $f(Q) \leq 0$. For the roots to be distinct equality cannot hold in either case.

Now $f(-Q) = 2Q^3 + R^3 \geq 0$ and $f(Q) = -2Q^3 + R^3 \leq 0$. The two conditions may be combined into the single condition $2^{1/3}Q \geq |R|$. To summarize there are three coincident roots if, and only if, $Q = R = 0$ and there are three real distinct roots if, and only if, $2^{1/3}Q - |R| > 0$. For example when $q = 4, R = 5$ the equation $x^3 - 48x - 125 = 0$ has 3 real distinct roots, which to 4 decimal places are $-3.4890, -4.4901$ and 7.9791.

We now consider the equation

$$f(x) \equiv x^3 - 3px^2 + 3q^2 - r^3 = 0 \qquad (3)$$

where we may take $q > 0$ and where the signs of the various coefficients must alternate for there to be any possibility of three positive real roots. In fact we know from above that a necessary condition is that $p \geq q \geq r \geq 0$. If indeed there are three co-incident roots then since their sum is $3p$, they must each equal p and then $p = q = r$. Conversely if $p = q = r$ then the cubic is equivalent to $(x - p)^3 = 0$ and there are 3 coincident roots $x = p$. However the relations $p \geq q \geq r \geq 0$ are not sufficient for there to be 3 positive real roots. For example, if $p = 5, q = 4$ and $r = 3.6$ we have $p > q > r > 0$, but there is only one real root in the neighbourhood of $x = 11$. With the same values of p and q, if r is a little less at $44^{1/3}$ then there are three real roots $x = 2, 2, 11$. In other words, if we have three positive numbers $\mu_2 \geq \mu_1 \geq \mu_0$ they are not necessarily the $2^{\text{nd}}, 1^{\text{st}}$ and 0th order means of three positive real numbers.

In order to find sufficient conditions for the equation (3) to have three positive real roots not all equal we transform it into standard form by putting $x = y + p$. The resulting equation is

$$y^3 - 3(p^2 - q^2)y + 3q^2p - r^3 - 2p^3 = 0.$$

For example the equation $x^3 - 15x^2 + 48x - 44 = 0$, with 3 positive real roots 2,2,11 is transformed into $y^3 - 27y - 54 = 0$ with roots $y = -3, -3, 6$. The roots have just been translated downwards by $p = 5$ units. Comparison with the equation $x^3 - 3Q^2x + R^3 = 0$ shows that $Q^2 = p^2 - q^2$ and $|R|^3 = |3q^2p - r^3 - 2p^3|$. The sufficient conditions for equation (3) to have three positive real roots, not all equal are $p > q$ and $4(p^2 - q^2)^3 \geq (3q^2p - r^3 - 2p^3)^2$, where two of the roots coincide if, and only if, equality holds. For example when $p = 5, q = 4$ and $r^3 = 44$, both sides come to 2916. The second inequality may be written as

$$q^4(3p^2 - 4q^2) \geq r^3(r^3 - 6pq^2 + 4p^3).$$

Examples 15.1

1. If ABC is an acute-angled triangle and t, s are defined by $t = \tan A + \tan B + \tan C$ and $s = \tan B \tan C + \tan C \tan A + \tan A \tan B$ prove that

$$t \geq 3\sqrt{3}, s \geq 9 \quad \text{and} \quad t^6 + 18t^4 \geq 36s^3 + 729s.$$

A well-known result, when $A + B + C = 180°$, is that

$$\tan A + \tan B + \tan C = \tan A \tan B \tan C,$$

so that $r^3 = 3p$. Since $p \geq r$ it follows that $r^2 \geq 3$. Hence $t = r^3 \geq 3\sqrt{3}$. Also, since $q \geq r$, we have $s = 3q^2 \geq 9$. Now, since $r^3 = 3p$ we have $q^4(3p^2 - 4q^2) \geq 3p(3p - 6pq^2 + 4p^3)$, which simplifies to $3q^4p^2 + 18p^2q^2 \geq 4q^6 + 9p^2 + 12p^4$ and since $p \geq q$ we have $3p^6 + 6p^4 \geq 4q^6 + 9q^2$. Substituting $t = 3p$ and $s = 3q^2$ this means $t^6 + 18t^4 \geq 36s^3 + 729s$.

2. Prove that if $a \geq b \geq c > 0$ and $(a+b+c)(abc)^{1/3} = bc+ca+ab$ then $b^2 = ac$.
$(a+b+c)^3 abc - (bc+ca+ab)^3 = (a^2-bc)(b^2-ac)(c^2-ab)$ from which the result follows because of the ordering of a, b, c.

Exercises 15.2

1. If ABC is a triangle and $u = \tan \frac{1}{2}A + \tan \frac{1}{2}B + \tan \frac{1}{2}C$ and $v = \tan \frac{1}{2}A \tan \frac{1}{2}B \tan \frac{1}{2}C$ prove that $u \geq \sqrt{3}$ and $v \leq 1/(3\sqrt{3})$.

2. If $a, b, c > 0$ and $abc = 1$ and $u = a+b+c$ and $v = bc+ca+ab$ prove that

$$u^6 + 18u^3 \geq 243 + 36v^3.$$

3. If $a, b, c > 0$ and $a + b + c = 3$ prove that

$$(bc + ca + ab + 3abc)^2 \geq 12abc(1 + 2abc).$$

4. If a, b, c are the three positive roots of the equation $x^3 - 3px^2 + 3q^2x - r^3 = 0$ show that they are in arithmetic progression if, and only if, $2p^3 + r^3 = 3pq^2$. What is the condition on p, q, r for a, b, c to form the sides of a triangle?

15.1.2   The quartic equation

The sufficient conditions for the general quartic equation

$$x^4 - 4px^3 + 6q^2x^2 - 4r^3x + s^4 = 0 \quad (p, q, r, s \geq 0) \qquad (15.1)$$

to have four non-negative real roots is too elaborate to be of any real significance in a book on elementary inequalities. However, some of the necessary conditions are worth recording.

First, as shown in Week 2, it is necessary that $p \geq q \geq r \geq s \geq 0$ with equality if, and only if, the four roots a, b, c, d coincide. If we use the notation $S_k = a^k + b^k + c^k + d^k$, $k = 1, 2, 3, 4$, then it is shown by some rather tedious algebra that

$$
\begin{aligned}
S_1 &= 4p, \\
S_2 &= 16p^2 - 12q^2, \\
S_3 &= 64p^3 - 72pq^2 + 12r^3, \\
S_4 &= 256p^4 - 384p^2q^2 + 64pr^3 + 72q^4 - 4s^4.
\end{aligned}
$$

These expressions are all necessarily positive. Power means inequalities produce other necessary conditions. $16S_3 \geq S_1^3 \Leftrightarrow 5p^3 + r^3 \geq 6pq^2$, $4S_2 \geq S_1^2 \Leftrightarrow p \geq q$, $S_1S_3 \geq S_2^2 \Leftrightarrow 2p^2q^2 + pr^3 \geq 3q^4$, and $S_2S_4 \geq S_3^2 \Leftrightarrow 36p^2q^4 + 60pq^2r^3 + 3q^2s^4 \geq 32p^3r^3 + 4p^2s^4 + 9r^6 + 54q^6$.

15.1.3 A new method of solving quartic equations with four positive real roots.

This paragraph is a slight diversion from the main text, but has been included for two reasons. First it shows that a quartic equation may be solved analytically, since an auxiliary cubic equation is bound to have a root. Secondly it points a way towards obtaining sufficient conditions for the quartic to have four positive real roots. We start with Equation (15.1) and show that it may be transformed into the equation $y^4 - 4Py^3 - 6Q^2y^2 - 4R^3y + S^4 = 0$, where it is not obvious that $Q^2 > 0$ and where no requirements are placed on P, Q, R, S except that $PS^2 = R^3$, and that because the transformation used is one of the form $x = y + k$, then Equation (15.1) has four real roots (which are bound to be non-negative because $p, q, r, s \geq 0$) if, and only if, the above equation in y has four real roots. The algebra relating p, q, r, s and P, Q, R, S is straightforward and left to the reader. The result is $P = p - k, Q^2 = -q^2 + 2pk - k^2, R^3 = r^3 - 3q^2k + 3pk^2 - k^3, S^4 = s^4 - 4r^3k + 6q^2k^2 - 4pk^3 + k^4$. The condition $PS^2 = R^3$ produces the auxiliary equation for k, which is

$$k^3(2r^3 - 6pq^2 + 4p^3) + k^2(9q^4 - s^4 - 2pr^3 - 6p^2q^2)$$

$$+k(4p^2r^3 + 2ps^4 - 6q^2r^3) + (r^6 - p^2s^4) = 0.$$

The reason for the transformation is that the equation in y can now be solved by factorization into the form $(y^2 - 2P_1y + S^2)(y^2 - 2P_2y + S^2) = 0$ provided P_1 and P_2 can be found such that $P_1 + P_2 = 2P, 2S^2 + 4P_1P_2 = -6Q^2$ and $2R^3 = S^2(P_1 + P_2)$, the compatibility condition on these equations being precisely $PS^2 = R^3$. There is, of course, the necessary and sufficient condition on the reality of P_1 and P_2, which is that $(P_1 + P_2)^2 \geq 4P_1P_2$ or $2P^2 + S^2 + 3Q^2 \geq 0$. Assuming, without loss of generality, that $P_1 \geq P_2$ the values of P_1 and P_2 are given by $P_1 = P + \frac{1}{2}\sqrt{(4P^2 + 6Q^2 + 2S^2)}$ and $P_2 =$

$P - \frac{1}{2}\sqrt{(4P^2 + 6Q^2 + 2S^2)}$. The solutions of the quartic equation in y are $y = P_1 \pm \sqrt{(P_1^2 - S^2)}$ and $y = P_2 \pm \sqrt{(P_2^2 - S^2)}$. There are two necessary and sufficient condition on the reality of the roots, which are that $P_1^2 \geq S^2$ and $P_2^2 \geq S^2$. These inequalities make the first condition superfluous. In theory these conditions may be expressed in terms of p, q, r, s, k to give a further necessary and sufficient condition along with $p \geq q \geq r \geq s \geq 0$ for Equation (15.1) to have four non-negative real roots.

Exercise 15.3

1. Show that the equation $x^4 - 10x^3 + 35x^2 - 50x + 24 = 0$ is transformed by the substitution $y = x + 5/2$ into the equation $16y^4 - 40y^2 + 9 = 0$. Hence show that the solutions for x of the original equation are $x = 1, 2, 3, 4$.

A miscellany of inequalities related to the theory of equations.

We give a number of examples in which the values of the roots of an equation depend on the form of the equation. Some, like the first example, are rather contrived, others are more general and therefore more interesting.

Examples 15.2

1. Suppose that a, b, c, d, e are real numbers satisfying $a < b < c < d < e$ and $\Sigma a = 10, \Sigma ab = 35, \Sigma abc = 50, \Sigma abcd = 25$, and $0 < abcde < 4$. Here the sums are over all possible such products.
   Prove that $0 < a < \frac{1}{2}(3 - \sqrt{5}) < b < \frac{1}{2}(5 - \sqrt{5}) < c <$

$\frac{1}{2}(3 + \sqrt{5}) < d < \frac{1}{2}(5 + \sqrt{5}) < e < 4$. The clue to this rather cunning exercise is that the sequence of inequalities may be rewritten as $0 < a < 4\sin^2 18^\circ < b < 4\sin^2 36^\circ < c < 4\sin^2 54^\circ < d < 4\sin^2 72^\circ < e < 4$. In fact if we solve $x^5 - 10x^4 + 35x^3 - 50x^2 + 25x - 4\sin^2\psi = 0$, with roots a, b, c, d, e then the initial equations are satisfied. Furthermore if we solve the equation by putting $x = 4\sin^2\theta$ it reduces to $\sin^2 5\theta = \sin^2\psi$ with 5 real solutions in the ranges indicated. Here we have used the relation $\sin 5\theta = 16\sin^5\theta - 20\sin^3\theta + 5\sin\theta$.

2. Let a, b, c be real numbers satisfying $a < b < c$ and $a + b + c = 3$, $abc = 1$ prove that $c > 4$, $-\frac{1}{2} < b < 0$ and $c - a > 9/2$. Putting $a = 3 - b - c$ then $(3 - b - c)bc = 1$, with solution $b = 3/2 - c/2 + \{1/(2c)\}\sqrt{\{c(c-1)^2(c-4)\}}$, $a = 3/2 - c/2 - \{1/(2c)\}\sqrt{\{c(c-1)^2(c-4)\}}$. Since $abc > 0$ and $a < b < c$ we cannot have $c < 0$, hence $c > 4$ and then it follows that $-\frac{1}{2} < b < 0$ and $-\infty < a < -\frac{1}{2}$ so that $c - a > 9/2$.

3. Let a, b, c be distinct integers satisfying $a/b + b/c + c/a = 3$. Find the maximum value of $b/a + c/b + a/c$.
   Let $a/b, b/c, c/a$ be the roots of a cubic equation. These are rational roots whose sum is 3 and whose product is 1. Also the sum of the product of roots taken two at a time is equal to $(a/b)(b/c) + (b/c)(c/a) + (c/a)(a/b) = a/c + b/a + c/b$ which is precisely the quantity whose maximum value is required. Let its value be $3q^2$, where q^2 is rational. The cubic equation may therefore be written as $x^3 - 3x^2 + 3q^2x - 1 = 0$ and we observe that in terms of the notation for cubic equations (see the paragraphs subsequent to Exercises 15.1) $p = 1$ and $r = 1$. The sufficient condition for real roots from the text above is given by $q^4(3 - 4q^2) \geq (5 - 6q^2)$, and this simplifies to $(q^2 - 1)^2(4q^2 + 5) \leq 0$. Now $q \neq 1$, since $a = b = c = $

1 is excluded. Hence $3q^2 \leq -15/4$. The upper bound of $-15/4$ is actually attained when $a = 2, b = -4, c = 8$. (It can actually be shown that whenever a, b, c are integers and $a/b + b/c + c/a = 3$ then abc is a perfect cube.)

Exercises 15.4

1. Consider the theory prior to Exercises 15.3. Show that if $0 < a \leq b \leq c \leq d$ (and not all a, b, c, d are equal) then a suitable value of k is given by $k = (cd - ab)/(c + d - a - b)$ and that the roots of the equation in y are $A = -(c - a)(d - a)/(c + d - a - b), B = -(c - b)(d - b)/(c + d - a - b), C = (c - a)(c - b)/(c + d - a - b), D = (d - a)(d - b)/(c + d - a - b)$.

2. Let a, b, c, d be distinct real numbers such that $a/b + b/c + c/d + d/a = 4$ and $ac = bd$. Find the maximum value of $a/c + b/d + c/a + d/b$.

3. Let a, b, c be real numbers satisfying $a < b < c, a + b + c = 6$ and $ab + bc + ca = 9$. Prove that $0 < a < 1 < b < 3 < c < 4$.

4. Find the range of values of $a + b + c$ for which a solution exists of the simultaneous equations $bc + ca + ab = 12$ and $abc = 2 + a + b + c$.

5. Suppose that a, b, c, d are real and that the quartic equation $x^4 + ax^3 + bx^2 + cx + d = 0$ has four positive roots. Prove $abc \geq a^2d + 5c^2$.

15.2 Hints and Answers Week 5

Exercise 15.1

1. $6p_2^2 = 54$, so $p_2 = 3$. Now $p_1 = (a + b + c + d)/4 \geq p_2 = 3$. Hence the minimum value of $a + b + c + D$ is 12, when $a = b = c = d = 3$. Also $3 = p_2 \geq p_4 = (abcd)^{1/4}$. Hence the maximum value of $abcd$ is 81, when $a = b = c = d = 3$.

2. $p_1 = (a + b + c + d)/4$, $p_2^2 = (ab + bc + ca + ad + bd + cd)/6 = 9$, $p_3^3 = (bcd + acd + abd + abc)/4$. Now $p_2^4 \geq p_1 p_3$. Hence $81 \geq (1/16)(a + b + c + d)(bcd + acd + abd + abc)$ from which the result follows.

3. $(\sqrt{a} + \sqrt{b})^2 = a + b + 2\sqrt{(ab)} = 2(p_1 + p_2)$ and $\sqrt{(ab)} = p_2$, so the equation is $x^2 - \sqrt{\{2(p_1 + p_2)\}}x + p_2 = 0$. Hence $\{(\sqrt{a} + \sqrt{b})/2\}^2 = (p_1 + p_2)/2 \leq p_1 = (a + b)/2$, since $p_1 \geq p_2$.

4. The necessity is proved in Week 2. The sufficiency is school algebra and is a result of the formula for solving quadratic equations $x = p_1 \pm \sqrt{(p_1^2 - p_2^2)}$. Clearly the roots coincide if, and only if, $p_1 = p_2$.

5. Consider the quadratic equation whose roots are $a = e^\theta$ and $b = e^{-\theta}$. Then $m_n = (a^n + b^n)/2 = \cosh(n\theta)$. The result follows from the power means inequality $m_{n+1}^n \geq m_n^{n+1}$.

Exercise 15.2

1. A result from trigonometry is that if $A + B + C = 180°$ then

$$\tan\frac{A}{2}\tan\frac{B}{2} + \tan\frac{B}{2}\tan\frac{C}{2} + \tan\frac{C}{2}\tan\frac{A}{2} = 1,$$

which means that $3q^2 = 1$, when the tangents (which are all positive) are taken as the roots of a cubic. Now $p \geq q =$

$1/\sqrt{3}$, so $u = 3p \geq \sqrt{3}$. Also $q \geq r$, so that $r \leq 1/\sqrt{3}$ and $v = r^3 \leq 1/(3\sqrt{3})$.

2. Take a, b, c to be the roots of a cubic, so that $r^3 = abc = 1$. The sufficiency condition is that $q^4(3p^2 - 4q^2) \geq (1 - 6pq^2 + 4p^3)$. Since $p \geq q$ we have $3p^6 + 2p^3 \geq 1 + 4q^6$. Since $p = (a + b + c)/3$ and $q^2 = (bc + ca + ab)/3$ this reduces to $u^6 + 18u^3 \geq 243 + 36v^2$.

3. Take a, b, c to be the roots of a cubic, so that $p = (a + b + c)/3 = 1$. The sufficiency condition is therefore $q^4(3 - 4q^2) \geq r^3(r^3 - 6q^2 + 4)$ or $3q^4 + 6q^2r^3 \geq r^6 + 4r^3 + 4q^6$. Hence $9q^4 + 18q^2r^3 \geq 3abc(4 + 5abc)$ and so $(3q^2 + 3r^3)^2 \geq 12abc + 24(abc)^2$. This finally gives $(ab + bc + ca + 3abc)^2 \geq 12abc(1 + 2abc)$.

4. $(a+b-2c)(b+c-2a)(c+a-2b) = 0$ gives $2(a^3+b^3+c^3)-3(a^2b+ab^2+b^2c+bc^2+c^2a+ca^2)+12abc = 0$. After some algebra this reduces to $2p^3 + r^3 = 3pq^2$. The condition for a, b, c to form the sides of a triangle is that $(a+b-c)(b+c-a)(c+a-b) > 0$, which reduces to $36pq^2 > 27p^3 + 8r^3$.

Exercise 15.3

1. $y = \pm 3/2$ or $\pm 5/2$.

Exercise 15.4

1. Put $A = a - k, B = b - k, C = c - k, D = d - k$ (where k is going to be negative) and then the condition $AB = CD$ gives $k = (cd - ab)(c+d-a-b)$. Substituting this value of k into the formulae $A = a-k$ gives $A = -(c-a)(d-a)/(c+d-a-b)$ etc.

2. The maximum value is -12 attained, for example, when $a = 3+2\sqrt{2}, b = 1, c = -1, d = -3-2\sqrt{2}$. The proof is as follows: Suppose $a/b, b/c, c/d, d/a$ are the roots of the of the quartic equation

$$y^4 - 4py^3 + qy^2 - 4r^3y + s^4 = 0.$$

Note that q in this equation may be negative, since the roots may not all be positive. Then we are given $p = 1$ and clearly $s = 1$. Now it is also given that $ac = bd$, so $(a/b)(c/d) = (b/c)(d/a) = 1$, hence from the theory given above on the quartic equation $ps^2 = r^3 = 1$, so the quartic becomes $y^4 - 4y^3 + qy^2 - 4y + 1 = 0$. Now we have $q = a/c + ca/bd + d/b + b/d + bd/ca + c/a = a/c + b/d + c/a + d/b + 2$. Hence the quantity we wish to maximize $a/c + b/d + c/a + d/b = q - 2$. Now we are told that the roots are distinct. So the case $q = 6$ must be excluded, and hence we know that $q < 6$. We want the condition for the above quartic to have real roots. It may be written in the form $(y-1)^4 = (6-q)y^2$. Putting $6-q = t^2$, where we may take $t > 0$, the quartic becomes $(y-1)^2 = \pm ty$, that is $y^2 - (2 \pm t)y + 1 = 0$. For both these equations to have 2 real roots we have $(2 \pm t)^2 \geq 4 \Rightarrow t \geq 4 \Rightarrow q \leq -10$. It follows that $q - 2 \leq -12$, a value which we have already shown may be obtained.

3. Suppose that a, b, c are the roots of the equation $x^3 - 6x^2 + 9x - r = 0$. Since $df/dx = 0$ when $x = 1$ and $x = 3$ we require for 3 real roots that $f(1) > 0$ and $f(3) < 0$, which imply $0 < r < 4$. Suppose then $r = 4\sin^2 u$, where $0 < u < \pi/2$ then, if we make the substitution $x = 4\sin^2 v$, the equation reduces to $\sin 3v = \sin u$, so the roots are $v = u/3, u/3+\pi/3, u/3+2\pi/3$. Hence $a = 4\sin^2 u/3$ and $0 < a < 1, b = 4\sin^2(u/3 + 2\pi/3)$ and $1 < b < 3, c = 4\sin^2(u/3 + \pi/3)$ and $3 < c < 4$.

4. If a, b, c are all positive then $12 = ab + bc + ca \geq 3(abc)^{2/3}$ that

is $abc \le 8$, with equality if, and only if, $a = b = c = 2$. Also $abc = 2+a+b+c \ge 2+3(abc)^{1/3}$, so putting $abc = u^3$ we have $u^3 \ge 2+3u$, and since $u > 0$ this means $u \ge 2$, that is $abc \ge 8$. Hence $abc = 8$ and $a = b = c = 2$. More generally, let a, b, c be the roots of the equation $u^3 - pu^2 + 12u - (2 + p) = 0$. The condition for real roots is $p = 6$ or $-7.5 < p < -6.5$.

5. Given that the quartic has four positive roots, it must factorize over the reals in the form $(x^2 - Ax + B)(x^2 - Cx + D)$, where $A^2 \ge 4B > 0, C^2 \ge 4D > 0$ and where we may take $A, C > 0$. Comparing coefficients we have $a = -(A + C), b = (B + D + AC), c = -(AD + BC), d = BD$. Evidently $B^2 + D^2 + A^2D + C^2B \ge B^2 + D^2 + 8BD \ge 10BD$. Hence $ACB^2 + ACD^2 + A^3CD + AC^3B \ge 10ABCD$. Also $A^2BC^2 \ge 4B^2C^2$ and $A^2C^2D \ge 4A^2D^2$. Putting these results together

$$ACB^2 + ACD^2 + A^3CD + AC^3B + A^2D^2 + B^2C^2$$

$$+A^2BC^2 + A^2C^2D \ge 5A^2D^2 + 10ABCD + 5B^2C^2.$$

Substituting back, we find, after some elementary algebra, that $abc - a^2d \ge 5c^2$.

Chapter 16

Inequalities: Week 6

16.1 Calculus, Jensen's theorem, series expansions, Lagrange's multipliers

Calculus is not necessary for national or international competitions such as the Olympiads, in the sense that no problem is set that specifically requires its use. It is even the case that no problem would wittingly be set for which the use of calculus would make it rather easier than if solved by other methods. However, calculus is a useful tool in dealing with inequalities, and for that reason it seems desirable to include a short account of the methods available at an elementary level. On the other hand we quote a number of theorems, rather than prove them, and the reader will either have met the ideas involved already or will do so as an undergraduate, when the study of inequalities becomes much more analytic. For the above reasons only a few illustrative examples and exercises are given. For the purposes of competitions the student is advised to learn Jensen's theorem, as knowledge of convex and concave functions should be known. I also recommend that, as an alternative resource, Lagrange's method of undetermined multipliers should be known for problems with constraints.

16.1.1 Stationary points and tests for local maxima and minima

If $f(x)$ is differentiable then $f(x)$ is said to have a *stationary point* at $x = a$ if $df/dx = 0$ at $x = a$.

Theorem 17 If $f(x)$ is twice differentiable and has a stationary value at $x = a$ then, if $d^2f/dx^2 > 0$ at $x = a$, then the stationary value is a minimum.

Note the conditions are not necessary. The obvious counter-example is $f(x) = x^4$, which has a minimum of zero at $x = 0$, but $d^2f/dx^2 = 0$ at $x = 0$.

Note also that such a minimum or maximum is local. For example if there is a calculus minimum at $x = a$, then $f(a\pm\varepsilon) > f(a)$ for all sufficiently small values of $\varepsilon > 0$, but $f(x)$ may take values lower than $f(a)$ elsewhere.

Examples 16.1

1. Prove that $f(x) \equiv x^4 + 4x^3 - 26x^2 - 60x + 225 \geq 0$.
   We have $df/dx = 4x^3 + 12x^2 - 52x - 60 = 0$ where $x = -5, x = -1, x = 3$.
   Now $f(x) = 0$ at $x = -5$ and $x = 3$ and $f(x) = 256$ at $x = -1$.
   Also $d^2f/dx^2 = 12x^2 + 24x - 52$ and this takes on the value 128 when $x = -5$ and $x = 3$ and the value -64 when $x = -1$.

The values of 0 at $x = -5$ and $x = 3$ are therefore local minima and the value of 256 at $x = -1$ is a local maximum. Since $x^4 \to \infty$ as $x \to \pm\infty$ it follows that $f(x) \geq 0$ for all values of x.

This problem may also be solved by purely algebraic methods. If we put $x = y - 1$ then the function becomes $y^4 - 32y^2 + 256 = (y^2 - 16)^2 \geq 0$, with equality if, and only if, $y = \pm 4$. It is also clear that for very small values of y the function is approximately equal to $256 - 32y^2$, showing $y = 0$ is a local maximum.

2. Prove that $f(x) \equiv 5\cosh x + 3\sinh x \geq 4$, with equality if, and only if, $x = -\log 2$. $f(x) = 4e^x + e^{-x}$, so $df/dx = 4e^x - e^{-x} = 0$ when $e^{2x} = \frac{1}{4}$, that is when $x = -\log 2$. Then $f(x) = 4$. Now $d^2f/dx^2 = f = 4$ when $x = -\log 2$, so 4 is a minimum value. An algebraic method exists. We have $f(x) - 4 = 4e^x - 4 + e^{-x} = (2e^{x/2} - e^{-x/2})^2 \geq 0$, with equality if, and only if, $x = -\log 2$.

Exercises 16.1

1. Prove that $3x^4 + 8x^3 - 66x^2 - 144x + 567 \geq 0$.

2. Let $f(x) = (6x - 10)/(x^2 - 1)$.

   (i) Prove that if $-1 < x < 1$ then $f(x) \geq 9$.
   (ii) Prove that if $x > 1$ then $f(x) \leq 1$.

3. Prove that $0 \leq x^4/(x^2 + 1)^3 \leq 4/27$.

4. Prove that $(1 - x)^5(1 + x)(1 + 2x)^2 \leq 6834375/4194304$ with equality when $x = -7/8$. (This corrects an error in the USSR Olympiad Problem Book, problem 278 in which it is stated that 1 is the maximum when $x = 0$.)

5. Prove that $-1 \leq (6x+8)/(x^2+1) \leq 9$. When does equality hold?

6. Prove that for $0 \leq x \leq \pi, 0 \leq 6\sin x + \sin 3x \leq 3\sqrt{3}$.

7. Prove that $-\sqrt{3} \leq 3\sin x/(2+\cos x) \leq \sqrt{3}$.

16.1.2 The meaning of the derivative and Concave and Convex function

If $df/dx > 0$ then the function $f(x)$ is increasing. This leads to a very simple theorem, which is nonetheless useful for managing some types of inequality.

Theorem 18
If $f(x)$ is differentiable, $f(0) = 0$ and $df/dx > 0$ for $0 < x < a$, then $f(x) > 0$ for $0 < x < a$.

The interval can, of course, begin at a point different from $x = 0$.

Examples 16.2

1. Prove that, for $0 < x < \pi/2, x - x^3/6 < \sin x < x$.
   Consider first the function $f(x) = x - \sin x$. We have $df/dx = 1 - \cos x > 0$ on $0 < x < \pi/2$. But $f(0) = 0$, so by Theorem 18, we have $x - \sin x > 0$ on $0 < x < \pi/2$. Now consider the function $g(x) = \sin x - x + x^3/6$. We have $dg/dx = h(x) = \cos x - 1 + x^2/2$ and $dh/dx = -\sin x + x = f(x)$. Now $h(0) = 0$, and we have proved $dh/dx = f(x) > 0$ on $0 < x < \pi/2$ and hence $h(x) > 0$ on the same interval. Next $g(0) = 0$ and we have shown $dg/dx = h(x) > 0$ on the interval and so $g(x) > 0$ on $0 < x < \pi/2$.

2. Prove Huygen's inequality that, for $0 < x < \pi/2, 2\sin x + \tan x \geq 3x$.

Consider $f(x) = 2\sin x + \tan x - 3x$. We have $f(0) = 0$, and $df/dx = 2\cos x + \sec^2 x - 3 = \sec^2 x(1 - \cos x)^2(1 + 2\cos x) \geq 0$. The result now follows from Theorem 18.

Exercises 16.2

1. Prove that, for $0 < x < \pi, \sin x > x \cos x$.

2. Prove that, for all $x > 0$ and all positive integers $n, e^x > 1 + x + x^2/2! + \ldots + x^n/n!$

3. Prove that the equation $1 + x + x^2/2! + \ldots + x^{2n}/(2n)! = 0$ has no real roots.

4. Prove that, for $0 < u \leq x \leq \pi/2, \tan x/x \geq \tan u/u$.

5. Prove that, for $0 < u \leq x \leq \pi/2, \sin x/x \leq \sin u/u$.

6. Prove that, for $x > 0, x \neq 1, (x \log x)/(x^2 - 1) \leq \frac{1}{2}$.

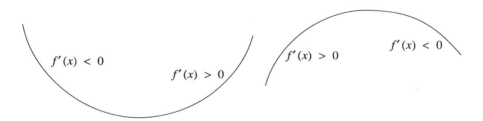

Convex function $f''(x) > 0$ Concave function $f''(x) < 0$

$f'(x) < 0$ $f'(x) > 0$ $f'(x) > 0$ $f'(x) < 0$

The diagrams illustrating convex and concave functions when the functions concerned are twice differentiable are self-explanatory. $f(x) = x^2$ is the simplest example of a convex function, and $f(x) = -x^2$ the simplest example of a concave function. Sometimes the

interval over which a function is convex or concave must be spec-
ified. For example if $f(x) = \sin x$, we have $f''(x) = -\sin x < 0$
for $0 < x < \pi$, so $\sin x$ is concave on the interval $0 < x < \pi$. A
function may pass from being a convex function to being a concave
function, and if it does then at the point $x = a$ where its character changes it must satisfy $f''(a) = 0$. A point where the second
derivative vanishes is called a *point of inflexion*. Thus $\sin x$ has a
point of inflexion at $x = \pi$ and on the interval $\pi < x < 2\pi$ it is
convex. We shall not deal with the more general definition of a
convex or concave function in this book.

Example 16.3

1. Prove that $1 - 2x \leq \cos \pi x$ for $0 \leq x \leq \frac{1}{2}$.
   Consider $g(x) = \cos \pi x + 2x - 1$. We have $g(0) = 0$ and
   $dg/dx = -\pi \sin \pi x + 2$. Over the interval in question this
   function starts at 2 and eventually becomes negative. In
   fact $d^2g/dx^2 = -\pi^2 \cos \pi x < 0$ for $0 \leq x < \frac{1}{2}$, so $g(x)$ is
   concave for $0 < x < \frac{1}{2}$. Since $g(\frac{1}{2}) = 0$ also, it follows that
   $g(x) \geq 0$ over the entire interval and is strictly greater than
   zero for $0 < x < \frac{1}{2}$. Use of Theorem 18 on the function
   $f(x) = (1/\pi) \sin \pi x - x + x^2$, together with the symmetry of
   $f(x)$ about $x = \frac{1}{2}$, implies that $f(x) > 0$ for $0 < x < 1$.

Exercise 16.3

1. Prove that $1 - 4x^2 \geq \cos \pi x$ for $-\frac{1}{2} \leq x \leq \frac{1}{2}$. Deduce that
   $4x(1 - x) \geq \sin \pi x$ for $0 \leq x \leq 1$.

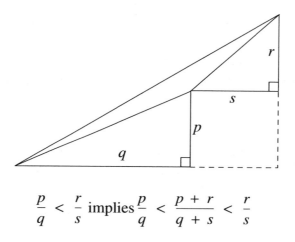

$$\frac{p}{q} < \frac{r}{s} \text{ implies } \frac{p}{q} < \frac{p+r}{q+s} < \frac{r}{s}$$

16.1.3 Jensen's Theorem on Convex and Concave functions

The figure shows a convex function $f(t)$ and illustrates Jensen's theorem for 3 points labelled $t = x, y, z$. It is self-explanatory. the fact that $AP \geq BP$, shows that

$$(1/3)\{f(x) + f(y) + f(z)\} \geq f((x+y+z)/3)$$

with equality if, and only if, $x = y = z$.

More generally we have:

Theorem 19 (Jensen's Theorem) If $f(x)$ is a convex function on (a, b) and $a < x_1 \leq x_2 \leq \ldots \leq x_n < b$ then

$$\frac{f(x_1) + f(x_2) + \ldots + f(x_n)}{n} \geq f\left(\frac{x_1 + x_2 + \ldots + x_n}{n}\right).$$

If $f(x)$ is concave the direction of the inequality is reversed. Equality holds if, and only if, $x_1 = x_2 = \ldots = x_n$.

Jensen's Theorem opens up a whole new set of possibilities, as well
as providing new proofs of known results. This is partly because
of the ease of handling fractional indices. Amongst the examples
we first give yet another proof of the AM/GM inequality.

Examples 16.4

1. Let $f(x) = \log x$ We have $df/dx = 1/x$ and $d^2f/dx^2 = -1/x^2$. It follows that $f(x)$ is concave for $x > 0$. Hence from the second part of Theorem 19, for $x_1, x_2, \ldots, x_n > 0$,

$$\log\left(\frac{x_1 + x_2 + \ldots + x_n}{n}\right) \geq \frac{\log x_1 + \log x_2 + \ldots + \log x_n}{n}$$

and hence

$$\frac{x_1 + x_2 + \ldots x_n}{n} \geq (x_1 x_2 \ldots x_n)^{1/n}.$$

2. We generalize the Corollary to Theorem 11 in Week 4. Let $f(x) = x^m, m \neq 0, 1$ then $d^2f/dx^2 = m(m-1)x^{m-2}$ and so $f(x)$ is convex on $x > 0$ if $m > 1$ or if $m < 0$, but is concave on $x > 0$ if $0 < m < 1$. Suppose now $a_1, a_2, \ldots a_n > 0$, then we have $(1/n)\Sigma a_k^m \geq (\Sigma a_k/n)^m$ for $m > 1$ or for $m < 0$, and $(1/n)\Sigma a_k^m \leq (\Sigma a_k/n)^m$ for $0 < m < 1$. For example, if $a, b, c > 0$, then $(\sqrt{a} + \sqrt{b} + \sqrt{c}) \leq \sqrt{3(a+b+c)}$.

Exercise 16.4

1. Prove that, if $0 < x, y, z < \pi/4$ and $x + y + z = \pi/2$, then $1 \leq \tan^2 + \tan^2 y + \tan^2 z < 2$.

2. Prove that, if $x, y, z > 0$ and $x + y + z = 24$, then $x^{1/3} + y^{1/3} + z^{1/3} \leq 6$.

3. Prove that, if A, B, C are the angles of a triangle, then

$$\sin\frac{A}{2}\sin\frac{B}{2}\sin\frac{C}{2} \leq 1/8.$$

4. Prove that, if $l, m, n > 0$, then $l^3(m+n) + m^3(n+l) + n^3(l+m) \geq 2lmn(l+m+n)$.

5. Prove that amongst all triangles with inradius 1 the equilateral triangle has the shortest perimeter.

16.1.4 Bernoulli's inequality

An alternative method of proving the result of Example 16.4.2, which leads to other interesting consequences, is by means of a fundamental inequality attributed to Bernoulli.

Theorem 20 [Bernoulli] If $x > 0, x \neq 1$, then

$$x^p - 1 > p(x-1) \quad \text{if} \quad p > 1 \quad \text{or} \quad p < 0,$$

but, if $0 < p < 1$, then the direction of the inequality is reversed.

Proof   Let $f(x) = x^p - 1 - p(x-1)$. We have $f(1) = 0$. Now $df/dx = p(x^{p-1} - 1)$. Now if $p > 1$ or $p < 0, df/dx$ is negative for $0 < x < 1$, is zero when $x = 1$ and is positive when $x > 1$. Thus $f(x)$ has a minimum at $x = 1$. But if $0 < p < 1, p - 1 < 0$, and so $x^{p-1} > 1$ for $0 < x < 1$. Hence df/dx is positive for $0 < x < 1$, is zero when $x = 1$ and is negative for $x > 1$. Accordingly $f(x)$ now has a maximum at $x = 1$. ∎

Corollary 1   (Power Means) Let $a_1, a_2, \ldots, a_n > 0$, then, for $m > 1$ or $m < 0, (1/n)\Sigma a_k^m \leq (\Sigma a_k/n)^m$, and if $0 < m < 1$ the direction of the inequality is reversed.

Let $(\Sigma a_k)/n = \mu$. Put $x = a_k/\mu$ then, by Theorem 20 with $p = m$ we have, on multiplying by μ^m,

$$a_k^m - \mu^m \geq m\mu^{m-1}(a_k - \mu).$$

Summing over k gives $\Sigma a_m \geq n\mu^m$, as required. When $0 < m < 1$, the direction of the inequality is reversed, as in the theorem.

Corollary 2 (Weighted Power Means) Let $a_1, a_2, \ldots, a_n > 0$ and let $w_1, w_2, \ldots, w_n > 0, w_1 + w_2 + \ldots + w_n = 1$, then for $m > 1$ or $m < 0, \Sigma w_k a_k^m \geq (\Sigma_k w_k a_k)^m$. If $0 < m < 1$, the direction of the inequality is reversed.

Proof Define $x_k = a_k/(\Sigma w_k a_k)$, so that $\Sigma w_k x_k = 1$. Now from Theorem 20, for $m < 0$ or $m > 1$, we have $w_k x_k^m - w_k \geq m(w_k x_k - w_k)$. Summing over k gives $\Sigma w_k x_k^m \geq 1$, from which the result follows. If $0 < m < 1$ the direction of the inequality is reversed, as in the theorem. ∎

Taylor's Theorem We quote, without proof, the following theorem:

Theorem 21 (Taylor) If $f, f', f'', \ldots, f^{(n-1)}$ are continuous in the interval $a \leq x \leq a + h$, and $f^{(n}$) exists for $a < x < a + h$, then

$$f(a + h) = f(a) + hf'(a) + \frac{h^2}{2!}f''(a) + \ldots + \frac{h^{n-1}}{(n-1)!}f^{(n-1)}(a) + R_n,$$

where $R_n = (h^n/n!)f^{(n)}(a + \theta h)$ with $0 < \theta < 1$. ∎

R_n is a remainder term, which may be thought of as a truncation error if omitted. The form of the remainder term given here is due to Lagrange. In school mathematics the limit of Taylor's theorem as $n \to \infty$ is quoted without much attention being given to the convergence of the resulting Taylor series expansion.

Infinite series expansions may be used to prove certain inequalities.

Examples 16.5

1. Prove that $x < \frac{1}{2}\log\{(1+x)/(1-x)\}$ for $0 < x < 1$. The Taylor series for the function on the right, valid for $0 < x < 1$ is

$$x + x^3/3 + x^5/5 + \ldots + x^{2n+1}/(2n+1) + \ldots > x.$$

2. Generalize Example 16.2.1. We have the Taylor series expansion $\sin x = x - x^3/3! + x^5/5! - \ldots + x^{4n+1}/(4n+1)! - x^{4n+3}(4n+3)! + \ldots$ valid for all x. The derivatives change sign, so for $x > 0$, the remainder term in the finite Taylor series expansions alternate in sign. This means that we have the sequence of inequalities: $\sin x < x - x^3/3! + \ldots + x^{4n+1}/(4n+1)!$ and $\sin x > x - x^3/3! + \ldots - x^{4n+3}/(4n+3)!$.

These are particular cases of the following theorems:

Theorem 22 If the Taylor series expansions for $f(x)$ and $g(x)$ are $f(x) = \Sigma a_n x^n$ and $g(x) = \Sigma b_n x^n$ and if $a_n \leq b_n$ for all $n \geq 0$, then $f(x) \leq g(x)$ for all positive values of x for which the series are both valid.

Theorem 23 If the Taylor series expansions for $f(x)$ is given by $f(x) = \Sigma(-1)^n a_n x^n$, and where $a_n > 0$ for all $n \geq 0$ and if S_n is the sum up to and including the term in x^n, then $S_{2n-1} < f(x) < S_{2n}$ for all positive values of x for which the series expansion is valid.

16.1.5 Functions of two real variables

Let $f(x, y)$ be a function of two real variables with continuous partial derivatives of all orders, then the Taylor series expansion about the point (a, b) is

$$f(a + h, b + k) = f(a, b) + h\frac{\partial f}{\partial x} + k\frac{\partial f}{\partial y}$$

$$+ \frac{1}{2}\left(h^2\frac{\partial^2 f}{\partial x^2} + 2hk\frac{\partial^2 f}{\partial x \partial y} + k^2\frac{\partial^2 f}{\partial y^2}\right) + \dots$$

where the partial derivatives are calculated at (a, b). The point (a, b) is said to be a *stationary point* if the first order terms vanish for all h, k that is if, and only if, $\partial f/dx = 0$ and $\partial f/\partial y = 0$. The stationary point (a, b) is a minimum if the second order terms are positive definite. This is so if $\partial^2 f/\partial x^2 > 0$ and $\partial^2 f/\partial x^2 \partial^2 f/\partial y^2 > (\partial^2 f/\partial x \partial y)^2$. Likewise the stationary point (a, b) is a maximum if the second order terms are negative definite. This is so if the second condition holds but $\partial^2 f/\partial x^2 < 0$.

Example 16.6

1. Find all the stationary points of the function $f(x, y) = x^3 + 2xy - 3y^2 + 1$ and determine whether any of them are maxima or minima. We have $\partial f/\partial x = 0 = 3x^2 + 2y$ and $\partial f/\partial y = 0 = 2x - 6y$ so $x = 3y$ and $27y^2 + 2y = 0$.
   Hence $y = 0, x = 0$ and $y = -2/27, x = -2/9$ are the two stationary points. Now $\partial^2 f/\partial x^2 = 6x$, $\partial^2 f/\partial y^2 = -6$, $\partial^2 f/\partial x \partial y = 2$. Hence the point $(0, 0)$ is neither a maximum nor a minimum. But at $(-2/9, -2/27)$ the second order terms are negative definite and there is a maximum.

Exercise 16.5

1. Find the maximum and minimum values of the function

$$f(x, y) = (x + y - 1)/(2x^2 + y^2 + 2).$$

Sometimes when there are two or more variables and the stationary point is known it is more effective to use purely algebraic methods, rather than calculus methods, to determine whether a maximum or a minimum is involved.

Example 16.7

1. Let $x, y, z > 0$. Prove that there exists a neighbourhood of $x = y = z = m > 0$ for which

$$f(x, y, z) \equiv 2(xy^2 + yz^2 + zx^2) - 3xyz - (x^2y + y^2z + z^2x) \geq 0.$$

Make the substitutions $x = m + u, y = m + v, z = m + w$ where u, v, w are small quantities. After some lengthy algebra it emerges that

$$f(x, y, z) = f(u, v, w) + m(u^2 + v^2 + w^2 - vw - wu - uv).$$

In this expression the quadratic term is known to be positive semi-definite, since $(v - w)^2 + (w - u)^2 + (u - v)^2 \geq 0$. Since $f(u, v, w)$ is cubic, it follows for all sufficiently small u, v, w that $f(m + u, m + v, m + w) \geq 0$ with equality if, and only if, $u = v = w$.

16.1.6 Lagrange's method of undetermined multipliers

This is a method for determining the stationary values of a function of several variables subject to a number of *constraints* (or *side conditions*, as they are sometimes called). We describe the method by giving some examples.

Examples 16.8

1. Find the minimum value of $f(x, y, z) = x^2 + 2y^2 + 3z^2$ subject to $x + y + z = 1$. We consider the function $F(x, y, z) = f(x, y, z) - \lambda(x + y + z - 1)$ where λ is the multiplier. Any minimum of f will give a minimum of F. So a necessary condition is that $dF = \partial F/\partial x\, dx + \partial F/\partial y\, dy + \partial F/\partial z\, dz = 0$. Hence $(2x - \lambda)dx + (4y - \lambda)dy + (6z - \lambda)dz = 0$. We now choose λ so that $\lambda = 2x$. Now f is a function of three variables subject to a single constraint. Hence dy and dz may be varied independently. It follows that $\lambda = 4y$ and $\lambda = 6z$. Since $x + y + z = 1$, we therefore have four equations for the four unknowns λ, x, y, z. It follows that $\lambda/2 + \lambda/4 + \lambda/6 = 1$ and hence $\lambda = 12/11$ and $x = 6/11, y = 3/11, z = 2/11$. Then $f(x, y, z) = 6/11$. To show this is a minimum put $x = 6/11 + u, y = 3/11 + v, z = 2/11 + w$. Since $x + y + z = 1$, we have $u + v + w = 0$. Also $x^2 + 2y^2 + 3z^2 = 6/11 + (12/11)(u + v + w) + u^2 + 2v^2 + 3w^2 = 6/11 + (u^2 + 2v^2 + 3w^2) \geq 6/11$.

2. Find the minimum distance from the origin to the plane with equation $2x + 3y + 6z = 7$. In a similar fashion to Example 16.8.1 we construct the function $F(x, y, z) = x^2 + y^2 + z^2 - \lambda(2x + 3y + 6z - 7)$ and set its three partial derivatives to zero, giving $2x - 2\lambda = 2y - 3\lambda = 2z - 6\lambda = 0$, from which $\lambda = 2/7, x = 2/7, y = 3/7, z = 6/7$ and $\sqrt{(x^2 + y^2 + z^2)} = \sqrt{7}$. The fact that this is a minimum is evident from geometrical considerations.

Both the above examples may be solved using the Cauchy-Schwarz inequality. In general if there is a function of n variables $x_1, x_2, \ldots x_n$ subject to m constraints, we have to use m multipliers $\lambda_1, \lambda_2, \ldots, \lambda_m$. The m constraints together with n partial derivatives put equal to zero produces $m+n$ equations for the $m+n$ unknowns $x_1, x_2, \ldots, x_n,$

$\lambda_1, \lambda_2, \ldots, \lambda_m$.

3. Find the lengths of the axes of the conic in which the ellipsoid $x^2 + y^2/2 + z^2/5 = 1$ meets the plane with equation $x + y + z = 0$. Since the squares of these lengths are $x^2 + y^2 + z^2$ we want to find its stationary values subject to the above two side conditions. We therefore form the function $F(x, y, z) = x^2 + y^2 + z^2 + l(x^2 + y^2/2 + z^2/5 - 1) + 2m(x + y + z)$, where l and $2m$ are the multipliers. The solution to the problem arises therefore from the five equations

$$\begin{aligned}
x^2 + y^2/2 + z^2/5 &= 1, \\
x + y + z &= 0, \\
x + lx + m &= 0, \\
y + ly/2 + m &= 0, \\
z + lz/5 + m &= 0.
\end{aligned}$$

Multiplying the last three equations by x, y, z respectively and adding gives

$$f = x^2 + y^2 + z^2 = -l(x^2 + y^2/2 + z^2/5) - m(x + y + z) = -l.$$

Hence the stationary values of f are given by

$$\begin{aligned}
(1 - 1/f)x - m/f &= 0, \\
(1/2 - 1/f)y - m/f &= 0, \\
(1/5 - 1/f)z - m/f &= 0, \\
x + y + z &= 0.
\end{aligned}$$

Eliminating the ratios $x : y : z : -m/f$ we obtain

$$1/(f - 1) + 2/(f - 2) + 5/(f - 5) = 0$$

from which $f = 3$ or $5/4$, which are the squares of the axes.

The reason for the adjective 'undetermined' can be seen from this example, as m does not need to be evaluated.

Exercise 16.6

1. Let $x, y, z > 0$ and $x + 4y + 9z = 1$. Find the stationary value of $1/x + 1/y + 1/z$ deciding whether it is a maximum or a minimum.

2. Find the maximum value of xy^2z^3 subject to $x^2 + y^2 + z^2 = 1$.

3. Let $a, b, c, x, y, z > 0$. Find the minimum value of $a/x + b/y + c/z$ given $ax + by + cz = 1$.

4. If $a, b, c \geq 0$ and $ab + bc + ca = 3$ find the minimum of $a + b + c$.

5. Find the minimum value of $x^2 + 5y^2 + 8z^2$ given $xy + yz + zx = -1$.

6. Find the maximum and minimum values of xy subject to $3x^2 + 4xy + 3y^2 = 10$.

7. Let x, y, z be positive real numbers such that $xyz = 32$. Find the minimum value of $x^2 + 4xy + 4y^2 + 2z^2$. (BMO)

8. If x, y, z are non-zero $x + y + z = 1$, $x^2 + y^2 + z^2 = 1$ find the stationary values of $x^3 + y^3 + z^3$, and decide whether they are maxima or minima.

16.2 Hints and Answers Week 6

Exercises 16.1

1. $df/dx = 12x^3 + 24x^2 - 132x - 144 = 0$ when $x = -4, -1, 3$ and $d^2f/dx^2 = 36x^2 + 48x - 132$. At $x = -4, f = 343$ and $d^2f/dx^2 = 252$ so this is a local minimum. When $x = -1, f = 640$ and $d^2f/dx^2 = -144$, so this is a local maximum. When $x = 3, f = 0$ and $d^2f/dx^2 = 336$, so this is a local minimum. If we put $x = y + 3$, $f(x)$ becomes $g(y) = 3y^2\{(y + 22/3)^2 + 20/9\}$ showing that $y = 0$, that is $x = 3$ produces an absolute minimum, and hence $f \geq 0$ for all x, with equality if, and only if, $x = 3$.

2. $df/dx = -2(3x^2 - 10x + 3)/(x^2 - 1)^2 = 0$ when $x = 1/3$ or $x = 3$. Now $d^2f/dx^2 = 4(3x^3 - 15x^2 + 9x - 5)/(x^2 - 1)^3$. When $x = 1/3, f(x) = 9$ and $d^2f/dx^2 = 81/4$ showing that this is a minimum. And as $f(x) \to +\infty$ on $-1 < x < 1$ as $x \to \pm 1$, it follows that $f(x) \geq 9$ for $-1 < x < 1$. When $x = 3, f(x) = 1$ and $d^2f/dx^2 = -\frac{1}{4}$ showing that this is a maximum. As $f(x) \to -\infty$ as $x \to 1$ from above and as $f(x) \to 0$ as $x \to \infty$ it follows that $f(x) \leq 1$ for $x \geq 1$.

3. $x^4/(x^2 + 1)^3 \to 0$ as $x \to \pm\infty$ and as $x \to 0$. Now $df/dx = -2x^3(x^2 - 2)/(x^2 + 1)^4 = 0$ at $x = \pm\sqrt{2}$. Then $f(x) = 4/27$, which from graphical considerations is a maximum. At $x = 0$ there is a minimum of $f(x) = 0$.

4. $dy/dx = -2x(x - 1)^4(2x + 1)(8x + 7) = 0$ when $x = -7/8$, $-\frac{1}{2}, 0, 1$. $d^2y/dx^2 = -2(x-1)^3(112x^3 + 84x^2 - 9x - 7)$. At $x = -7/8, y = 6834375/4194304$ and $d^2y/dx^2 = -1063125/8192$ so this is a maximum. At $x = -\frac{1}{2}, y = 0$ and $d^2y/dx^2 = 243/8$, so this is a minimum. At $x = 0, y = 1$ and $d^2y/dx^2 = -14$, so this is a maximum. At $x = 1, y = 0$ and $d^2y/dx^2 =$

0. Near $x = 1, y \approx 18(1 - x)^5$, so $x = 1$ is a point of inflexion. Since $y \to \infty$ as $x \to \pm\infty$, it follows that $y \le 6834375/4194304$ for all values of x.

5. $dy/dx = -2(3x^2 + 8x - 3)/(x^2 + 1)^2 = 0$ when $x = -3$ or $x = 1/3$. $d^2y/dx^2 = 4(3x^3 + 12x^2 - 9x - 4)/(x^2 + 1)^3$. At $x = -3, y = -1$ and $d^2y/dx^2 = 1/5$, so this is a minimum. At $x = 1/3, y = 9$ and $d^2y/dx^2 = -8/5$ so this is a maximum. As $y \to 0$ as $x \to \pm\infty$, it follows that $-1 \le y \le 9$.

6. There is a maximum of $3\sqrt{3}$ at $x = \pi/3, x = 2\pi/3$. There is a minimum of 0 at $x = 0, \pi$. And there is a local minimum of 5 at $x = \pi/2$.

7. y is obviously bounded. $dy/dx = 3(2\cos x + 1)/(2 + \cos x)^2 = 0$ when $x = -2\pi/3, 2\pi/3$.
   At these points $y = -\sqrt{3}, \sqrt{3}$ respectively, which are therefore absolute minimum and maximum values.

Exercise 16.2

1. Let $f(x) = \sin x - x \cos x$. Then $f(0) = 0$ and $df/dx = \cos x - \cos x + x \sin x > 0$ for $0 < x < \pi$. Hence $\sin x > x \cos x$ for $0 < x < \pi$.

2. Let $f_n(x) = e^x - (1 + x + x^2/2! + \ldots + x^n/n!)$. We have $df_n/dx = f_{n-1}$, so since $f_0(x) = e^x - 1 > 0$ for $x > 0$, it follows by induction that $f_n(x) > 0$ for all $x > 0$.

3. Clearly $f(x) = 1 + x + x^2/2! + \ldots + x^{2n}/(2n)! \ge 1$ for all $x > 0$.
   Also $1 - x + x^2/2! + \ldots + x^{2n}/(2n)! > e^{-x}$ for all $x > 0$, so that $1 + x + x^2/2! + \ldots + x^{2n}/(2n)! > e^x > 0$ for all $x < 0$.
   Hence $f(x) > 0$ for all x.

4. Let $f(x) = \tan x/x$. We have

$$\frac{df}{dx} = \frac{x - \sin x \cos x}{x^2 \cos^2 x}$$

and since $2x > \sin 2x$ for $x > 0$ it follows that $df/dx > 0$ for $0 < x < \pi/2$. Hence $\tan x/x > \tan u/u$ for $0 < u \le x < \pi/2$.

5. Let $f(x) = \sin x/x$. We have $df/dx = (x \cos x - \sin x)x^2 < 0$ for $0 < x < \pi/2$ by Exercise 16.2.1 It follows that $\sin x/x \le \sin u/u$ for $0 < u \le x < \pi/2$.

6. Consider the function $f(x) = 2x \log x - (x^2 - 1)$. We have $df/dx = 2 \log x + 2 - 2x$ and $d^2f/dx^2 = 2/x - 2$. We have $df/dx = 0$ at $x = 1$ and $d^2f/dx^2 > 0$ for $0 < x < 1$ and $d^2f/dx^2 < 0$ for $x > 1$. It follows that $df/dx < 0$ for $0 < x < 1$ and for $x > 1$. Hence $f(x) \ge 0$ for $0 < x < 1$ and $f(x) \le 0$ for $x > 1$. Hence $x \log x/(x^2 - 1) \le \frac{1}{2}$ for $x > 0, x \ne 1$.

Exercise 16.3

1. Consider the function $h(y) = \sin \pi y/2 - \sqrt{2y}, 0 \le y \le \frac{1}{2}$. Now $h(0) = h(1/2) = 0$. Also $dh/dy = (\pi/2) \cos \pi y/2 - \sqrt{2} > 0$ at $y = 0$. Also $d^2h/dy^2 = -\pi^2 \sin \pi y/2 < 0$ for $0 < y < \frac{1}{2}$. Hence $h(y)$ is concave and so $h(y) \ge 0$ for $0 \le y \le \frac{1}{2}$, with equality if, and only if, $y = 0$ or $y = \frac{1}{2}$. Squaring, we obtain $\sin^2 \pi y/2 \ge 2y^2$ for $-\frac{1}{2} \le y \le \frac{1}{2}$ or $1 - 4y^2 \ge \cos \pi y$ for $-\frac{1}{2} \le y \le \frac{1}{2}$, with equality if (and only if) $y = -\frac{1}{2}, 0, \frac{1}{2}$. Now put $x = y + \frac{1}{2}$ and one obtains $4x(1 - x) \ge \sin \pi x$ for $0 \le x \le 1$, with equality if, and only if, $x = 0, \frac{1}{2}, 1$.

Exercise 16.4

1. $f(x) = \tan^2 x$ is convex on $0 < x < \pi/2$, hence by Jensen's theorem. $T = (\tan^2 x + \tan^2 y + \tan^2 z \ge 3 \tan^2((x + y +$

$z)/3) = 3\tan^2 \pi/6 = 1$. Now, since $x+y+z = \pi/2$, $\tan x \tan y + \tan y \tan z + \tan z \tan x = 1$. Hence $(\tan x + \tan y + \tan z)^2 = T+2$. Now, since $0 < x, y, z < \pi/4$, $\tan x + \tan y + \tan z > T$. Therefore $T + 2 < T^2$ and so $T < 2$.

2. By the power means inequality for fractional indices we have $(x^{1/3} + y^{1/3} + z^{1/3})/3 \le \{(x + y + z)/3\}^{1/3} = 2$.

3. $y = \sin x$ is concave on $0 < x < \pi/2$ and $A/2, B/2, C/2$ are all in this range, so $(1/3)(\sin \frac{1}{2}A + \sin \frac{1}{2}B + \sin \frac{1}{2}C) \le \sin\{(A+B+C)/6\} = \frac{1}{2}$. Now, by AM/GM, the left-hand side $\ge (\sin \frac{1}{2}A \sin \frac{1}{2}B \sin \frac{1}{2}C)^{1/3}$, from which the result follows.

4. From the power means inequality for fractional indices $(1/3)(l^{5/2} + m^{5/2} + n^{5/2}) \ge \{(l + m + n)/3\}^{5/2}$ and hence

$$3^{3/2}(l^{5/2}+m^{5/2}+n^{5/2}) \ge (l+m+n)^{5/2} \ge (l+m+n)(l+m+n)^{3/2}$$

$$\ge 3^{3/2}(l + m + n)(lmn)^{1/2}.$$

Now $l^3(m + n) + m^3(n + l) + n^3(l + m) \ge 2l^3\sqrt{(mn)} + 2m^3\sqrt{(nl)} + 2n^3\sqrt{(lm)} = 2(lmn)^{1/2}(l^{5/2} + m^{5/2} + n^{5/2}) \ge 2lmn(l + m + n)$.

5. Let I be the incentre and L, M, N the feet of the perpendiculars from I on to the sides BC, CA, AB respectively. Let $BL = y, LC = z, CM = z, MA = x, AN = x, NB = y$. Let $\angle AIN = u, \angle BIL = v, \angle CIM = w$. Then since AI bisects $\angle BAC$ etc., we have $0 < u, v, w < \pi/2$ and $u + v + w = \pi$. Let s be the semi-perimeter of triangle ABC, then $s/3 = (x + y + z)/3 = (\tan u + \tan v + \tan w)/3$, since the inradius $=1$. But $\tan x$ is convex on $0 < x < \pi/2$ so the right-hand side $\ge \tan\{(u + v + w)/3\} = \tan \pi/3 = \sqrt{3}$. Thus $s \ge 3\sqrt{3}$, with equality if and only if $u = v = w$, which is when the triangle is equilateral.

Exercise 16.5

1. There is a maximum of $\frac{1}{4}$ at $(1,2)$ and a minimum of $-\frac{3}{4}$ at $(-1/3, -2/3)$.

Exercise 16.6

1. Form $F(x, y, z) = 1/x + 1/y + 1/z + \lambda(x + 4y + 9z)$. Setting its partial derivatives to zero we get $\lambda = 1/x^2, 4\lambda = 1/y^2, 9\lambda = 1/z^2$. Since $x, y, z > 0$ and $x + 4y + 9z = 1$ we obtain $x = 1/6, y = 1/12, z = 1/18$. Put $x = 1/6 + u, y = 1/12 + v, z = 1/18 + w$, then $u + 4v + 9w = 0$ and $F(x, y, z) = 36 + 36u^2 + 1728v^2 + 5832w^2 + \ldots$, showing that 36 is a minimum.

2. The maximum is $(1/36)\sqrt{3}$ when $x = 1/\sqrt{6}, y = 1/\sqrt{3}, z = 1/\sqrt{2}$.

3. Form the function $F(x, y, z) = a/x + b/y + c/z + \lambda(ax + by + cz - 1)$. Setting its partial derivatives equal to zero gives $\lambda = 1/x^2 = 1/y^2 = 1/z^2$. Since $x, y, z > 0$ this means $x = y = z = 1/(a + b + c)$ and so the minimum value of $a/x + b/y + c/z$ is 1. See also Exercise 16.6.1.

4. Form the function $F(a, b, c) = a + b + c - \lambda(ab + bc + ca - 1)$. Setting its partial derivatives equal to zero we obtain $1 - \lambda(b + c) = 1 - \lambda(c + a) = 1 - \lambda(a + b) = 0$. It follows, since $a, b, c > 0$ and $ab + bc + ca = 1$, that $a = b = c = 1/\sqrt{3}$. Now put $a = 1/\sqrt{3} + u, b = 1/\sqrt{3} + v, c = 1/\sqrt{3} + w$, then the side condition gives $2(u + v + w) + \sqrt{3}(uv + vw + wu) = 0$. Then $a + b + c = \sqrt{3} + (u + v + w) = \sqrt{3} - \frac{1}{2}\sqrt{3}(uv + vw + wu) = \sqrt{3} - \frac{1}{4}\sqrt{3}\{(u + v + w)^2 - (u^2 + v^2 + w^2)\} \geq \sqrt{3}$, since $u + v + w$ is second order small.

5. Consider the function $F(x, y, z) = x^2 + 5y^2 + 8z^2 - \lambda(xy + yz + zx - 1)$. Setting its partial derivatives equal to zero we

obtain

$$2x - \lambda(y + z) = 10y - \lambda(z + x) = 16z - \lambda(x + y) = 0.$$

Multiplying these equations by x, y, z and adding we get $\lambda = -F$. Putting this value back into the equations and eliminating the ratios $x : y : z$ we obtain $(F - 4)(F^2 - 10F - 40) = 0$. Since $F > 0$, it follows that the minimum value of $F = 4$.

6. $-5 \le xy \le 1$.

7. The minimum value us 96 when $x = 4, y = 2, z = 4$.

8. Form the function $F(x, y, z) = x^3 + y^3 + z^3 - \lambda(x^2 + y^2 + z^2 - 1) - \mu(x + y + z - 1)$. Setting the partial derivatives to zero we get $3x^2 - 2x\lambda - \mu = 0$, $3y^2 - 2y\lambda - \mu = 0$, $3z^2 - 2z\lambda - \mu = 0$. Subtracting these equations one from another gives $y = x$ or $3(y+x) = 2\lambda$ and two similar equations. Since $x = y = z$ is impossible, it follows that the three stationary points are $(2/3, 2/3, -1/3), (2/3, -1/3, 2/3), (-1/3, 2/3, 2/3)$ and then $x^3 + y^3 + z^3 = 5/9$. This value is a minimum.

Chapter 17

Inequalities: Week 7

17.1 Geometrical inequalities, geometrical, trigonometrical and algebraic forms

17.1.1 Three equivalent forms

It is often the case that a geometrical inequality may appear in three different forms, which at first sight bear no obvious relationship to one another, but which are, in fact, equivalent. These forms are (i) a relationship concerning a geometrical figure, (ii) a relationship involving angles and (iii) a relationship involving side lengths. We refer to these three presentations as respectively the *geometrical, trigonometrical* and *algebraic* versions of the inequality.

To illustrate this, consider perhaps the best known geometrical inequality of all. This, in its geometrical form, is $R \geq 2r$, where R is the circumradius and r is the inradius of a triangle. In its trigonometrical form this is equivalent to $8 \sin \frac{1}{2}A \sin \frac{1}{2}B \sin \frac{1}{2}C \leq 1$, where, of course, A, B, C are the angles of the triangle. That the two problems are the same follows from the formula

$$r = 4R \sin \frac{1}{2}A \sin \frac{1}{2}B \sin \frac{1}{2}C.$$

In terms of the side lengths of the triangle the same geometrical problem is equivalent to $abc \geq (b + c - a)(c + a - b)(a + b - c)$, as may be checked using the formulae $abc/4R = [ABC] = rs$ and $[ABC]^2 = s(s - a)(s - b)(s - c)$, where $s = \frac{1}{2}(a + b + c)$ (Heron's formula) . Of course it may be not be feasible to transfer a problem from one form to another, but when this is possible it is always worth considering which is the best framework for solving the problem. We illustrate some of the methods available for solving geometrical inequalities by treating the above problem in its three forms.

17.1.2   Method 1

We prove $OI^2 = R^2 - 2Rr$ where O and I are the circumcentre and incentre respectively of triangle ABC, by purely geometrical means. Since a square is non-negative it follows at once that $R \geq 2r$ (due to Euler). We also show that equality holds if, and only if, triangle ABC is equilateral.

Let AI meet the circumcircle at P and let POQ be a diameter of the circumcircle. We have $(AI)(IP) = R^2 - OI^2$, by the intersecting chord theorem. Now extend AIP to I_1, the excentre opposite A. Since triangle ABC is the nine-point circle of the triangle of excentres and I is its orthocentre, we have $IP = PI_1$. But $\angle IBI_1 = 90^o$ and so II_1 is a diameter of circle IBI_1 and hence $IP = PB = 2R \sin \frac{1}{2}A$, since $\angle BAP = \frac{1}{2}A$. Also $AI = r \mathrm{cosec} \frac{1}{2}A$ and it follows that $(AI)(IP) = 2Rr$ and hence $OI^2 = R^2 - 2Rr$. Also if ABC is equilateral we have $r/R = \sin 30^o = \frac{1}{2}$ so $R = 2r$. And finally if $R = 2r$, I and O coincide, so $AI = r \mathrm{cosec} \frac{1}{2}A = R =$

$2r$ so $\angle A = 60^o$ or 120°. Similarly for $\angle B$ and $\angle C$ and hence triangle ABC is equilateral.

17.1.3   Method 2

To prove $\sin \frac{1}{2}A \sin \frac{1}{2}B \sin \frac{1}{2}C \leq 1/8$ there are two standard ways of proceeding. The more elementary way is to fix the angle C, then maximize $\sin \frac{1}{2}A \sin \frac{1}{2}B$ and finally vary angle C to obtain the overall maximum. We have

$$2 \sin \frac{1}{2}A \sin \frac{1}{2}B = \cos \frac{1}{2}(A - B) - \cos \frac{1}{2}(A + B) \leq 1 - \sin \frac{1}{2}C$$

since $A + B + C = 180^o$. Hence $\sin \frac{1}{2}A \sin \frac{1}{2}B \sin \frac{1}{2}C \leq \frac{1}{2}s(1 - s)$, where $s = \sin \frac{1}{2}C$. Now by the AM/GM inequality $1 = s + 1 - s \geq 2\sqrt{\{s(1 - s)\}}$ from which $s(1 - s) \leq \frac{1}{4}$, and the result follows. Furthermore equality holds if, and only if, $A = B$ and $s = \frac{1}{2}$, that is, if, and only if, $A = B = C = 60^o$. The second way uses a more advanced concept, that of a property of concave functions. The graph of the sine curve for acute angles is certainly concave, since its second derivative is negative. One then argues that if X, Y, Z are three points on the curve representing angles x, y, z such that $x + y + z = 90^o$, then the point P representing $\sin 30^o = \frac{1}{2} = \sin\{(x + y + z)/3\}$ lies not below the centroid of triangle XYZ representing $(1/3)(\sin x + \sin y + \sin z)$, with coincidence if, and only if, X, Y, Z are the same point. Putting $x = \frac{1}{2}A, y = \frac{1}{2}B, z = \frac{1}{2}C$ this means that $(1/3)(\sin \frac{1}{2}A + \sin \frac{1}{2}B + \sin \frac{1}{2}C) \leq \frac{1}{2}$. But by the AM/GM inequality $(1/3)(\sin \frac{1}{2}A + \sin \frac{1}{2}B + \sin \frac{1}{2}C) \geq (\sin \frac{1}{2}A \sin \frac{1}{2}B \sin \frac{1}{2}C)^{1/3}$ from which the inequality follows, with equality if, and only if, $A = B = C = 60^o$.

Note that the second way has actually given us more than we needed, and has yielded a second result that $\sin \frac{1}{2}A + \sin \frac{1}{2}B + \sin \frac{1}{2}C \leq 3/2$, a sharper result than the one involving their product. It is not always immediately obvious what the geometrical significance of a trigonometrical inequality is.

17.1.4   Method 3

There is a difficulty when trying to establish an inequality involving the lengths of a geometrical figure, which is easy to overcome. The difficulty is that certain triangle inequalities have to be satisfied as constraints. Thus, for a triangle, we have $b + c > a, c + a > b, a + b > c$. The usual method of proceeding is to set $a = m+n, b = n+l, c = l+m$, and then the triangle inequalities become replaced by $l, m, n > 0$ for which standard techniques may be used. In the present instance, the inequality $abc \geq (b+c-a)(c+a-b)(a+b-c)$ becomes $(m + n)(n + l)(l + m) \geq 8lmn$, which follows at once from multiplying together three inequalities of the form $m + n \geq 2\sqrt{(mn)}$. Equality holds if, and only if, $l = m = n$, that is if, and only if, $a = b = c$ and the triangle is equilateral.

17.1.5   Some results

In my experience it is unusual for any but the simplest inequalities to be needed in dealing with elementary geometrical inequalities. These are

(1) The AM/GM inequality, which states that if $x_1, x_2, x_3, \ldots x_n$ are positive then

$$(1/n)(x_1 + x_2 + \ldots + x_n) \geq (x_1 x_2 \ldots x_n)^{1/n},$$

with equality if, and only if, $x_1 = x_2 = \ldots = x_n$. See Week 2.

(2) The Cauchy-Schwarz inequality, which states that the n-dimensional vectors $(a_1, a_2, \ldots, a_n)$ and $(b_1, b_2, \ldots, b_n)$ have the property that $(\mathbf{a.b})^2 \leq |\mathbf{a}|^2 |\mathbf{b}|^2$, with equality if, and only

if, $\mathbf{a} = k\mathbf{b}$, for some constant k. This may also be expressed as $-1 \leq \cos\theta \leq 1$ for any angle θ. See Week 3.

(3) If $a_1, a_2, \ldots, a_n$ and $b_1, b_2, \ldots b_n$ are two n-tuples and they are sorted so that they are both in increasing order (or both in decreasing order) then

$$a_1 b_1 + a_2 b_2 + \ldots + a_n b_n \geq a_1 b_{\pi 1} + a_2 b_{\pi 2} + \ldots + a_n b_{\pi n},$$

where π is any permutation of $1, 2, \ldots, n$. Similarly, if the n-tuples are sorted in reverse order to one another then the direction of the inequality is reversed. See Week 4.

(4) Tchebychef's inequality, which states that if the n-tuples in (3) are sorted in the same way, then $a^* b^* \geq (ab)^*$, where $a^* = (1/n)(a_1 + a_2 + \ldots + a_n)$ etc., and $(ab)^* = (1/n)(a_1 b_1 + a_2 b_2 + \ldots + a_n b_n)$ and again if the n-tuples are sorted in reverse order then the direction of the inequality is reversed. See Week 4.

(5) If ABC is a triangle and if K is a point with areal co-ordinates (l, m, n) and P is any point in the plane of ABC, then

$$lAP^2 + mBP^2 + nCP^2 = lAK^2 + mBK^2 + nCK^2 + PK^2,$$

so that when PK^2 is omitted on the right we have an inequality. This inequality is equivalent to the theorem in Statistics that $\Sigma f_k(x_k - a)^2$ is minimized when $a = m$, the mean of the readings x_k, appearing with frequency f_k.

(6) Jensen's theorem, that if $f(x)$ is a convex function on the interval $a < x < b$ (i.e. with a graph like $y = x^2$), then with $a < x_1 < x_2 < \ldots < x_n < b$ we have

$$f\left(\frac{x_1 + x_2 + \ldots + x_n}{n}\right) < \frac{f(x_1) + f(x_2) + \ldots + f(x_n)}{n}.$$

For a concave function the direction of the inequality is reversed. See Week 6.

Exercise 17.1

1. If ABC is a triangle of incentre I and inradius r, prove that

$$\frac{1}{AI} + \frac{1}{BI} + \frac{1}{CI} \leq \frac{3}{2r}.$$

2. Find the trigonometrical and algebraic versions of the geometrical inequality $OH^2 \geq 0$ where O is the circumcentre and H the orthocentre of triangle ABC.

17.1.6   Trigonometrical and algebraic forms

In addition to the above inequalities, when dealing with trigonometrical inequalities, we often need the aid of certain trigonometrical identities. In particular we have:

(1) $\cos A + \cos B = 2 \cos \frac{1}{2}(A + B) \cos \frac{1}{2}(A - B)$. If A and B are both acute, then the right hand side is $\leq 2 \cos \frac{1}{2}(A + B)$.

(2) Similarly, if A and B are both acute, then $\sin A + \sin B \leq 2 \sin \frac{1}{2}(A + B)$.

(3) If A, B and C are the angles of a triangle, then

$$\tan A + \tan B + \tan C = \tan A \tan B \tan C.$$

Coupled with the AM/GM inequality this immediately implies both quantities are $\geq 3\sqrt{3}$ for an acute-angled triangle. The identity is a direct consequence of the fact that $\tan(A + B) = -\tan C$.

(4) If A, B, C are the angles of a triangle then

$$\cos^2 A + \cos^2 B + \cos^2 C + 2\cos A \cos B \cos C = 1$$

This identity is a consequence of the fact that the three equations in a, b, c $\quad a = b\cos C + c\cos B, b = c\cos A + a\cos C, c = a\cos B + b\cos A$ have non-zero solutions, so that their determinant of coefficients vanishes.

(5) If $A + B + C = 360°$, then $\cos^2 A + \cos^2 B + \cos^2 C = 1 + 2\cos A \cos B \cos C$. In fact if $VABC$ is a tetrahedron and the angles of the plane faces at V are A, B, C and $VA = d, VB = e, VC = f$, then the volume of the tetrahedron is given by $[VABC] =$

$$\frac{d^2 e^2 f^2 (1 + 2\cos A \cos B \cos C - \cos^2 A - \cos^2 B - \cos^2 C)}{36}$$

which is positive unless the tetrahedron flattens out into a plane with zero volume. Trigonometrical identities cannot be regarded as being entirely distinct from algebraic inequalities, since they are connected by the sine rule

$$\frac{a}{\sin A} = \frac{b}{\sin B} = \frac{c}{\sin C} = 2R$$

and the cosine rule

$$c^2 = a^2 + b^2 - 2ab\cos C$$

and similar formulas by cyclic change of letters.

We now give a number of Examples, followed by a collection of problems in Exercises 17.2. These are numerous so that only hints, rather than full solutions, are given.

Examples 17.1

1. Prove that $\cos^2 A + \cos^2 B + \cos^2 C \geq \frac{3}{4}$ and $\cos A \cos B \cos C \leq 1/8$. See Exercise 17.1.2. It is equivalent to the first of these, by using $\cos 2A = 2\cos^2 A - 1$ etc. The second follows from it by identity (4) p. 261. A method independent of Exercise 17.1.2 is to prove the second inequality by means of the cosine rule. It amounts to proving $a^2 b^2 c^2 \geq (b^2 + c^2 - a^2)(c^2 + a^2 - b^2)(a^2 + b^2 - c^2)$. As the inequality is trivial for obtuse or right-angled triangles we may suppose the triangle acute, and then setting $b^2 + c^2 - a^2 = x^2$ etc. the inequality reduces to the product of three inequalities of the form $2a^2 = y^2 + z^2 \geq 2yz$. Identity (4) may now be used to establish the first inequality.

2. Prove that if a, b, c are the side lengths of a triangle, then

$$3/2 \leq a/(b+c) + b/(c+a) + c/(a+b) < 2.$$

For the left-hand inequality multiply up and one is left to prove

$$2(a^3 + b^3 + c^3) \geq b^2 c + c^2 b + c^2 a + a^2 c + a^2 b + b^2 a.$$

This follows from adding together three inequalities of the form $(b-c)(b^2 - c^2) \geq 0$. For the right-hand inequality, since $a < b + c$, it follows that $a/(b+c) < 2a/(a+b+c)$. Adding two similar inequalities completes the proof. This inequality is best possible, as can be seen by letting $a \to b$ and $c \to 0$.

3. Prove that if x, y, z are real numbers and A, B, C are the angles of a triangle, then

$$x^2 + y^2 + z^2 \geq 2yz \cos A + 2zx \cos B + 2xy \cos C.$$

The difference between the left-hand side and right-hand side is equal to $(x - z \cos B - y \cos C)^2 + (y \sin C - z \sin B)^2 \geq 0$ with equality if, and only if, $x \operatorname{cosec} A = y \operatorname{cosec} B = z \operatorname{cosec} C$.

4. Prove that if G is the centroid of an acute-angled triangle, whose circumradius is R, then $AG^2 + BG^2 + CG^2 > 8R^2/3$. Using Apollonius's theorem, this is equivalent to the inequality $\sin^2 A + \sin^2 B + \sin^2 C > 2$. Now ABC is acute-angled so $\tan(A+B) = -\tan C$ is negative, and hence $\tan A \tan B > 1$. This means $\sin^2(A + B) > \cos^2 A + \cos^2 B$, from which the result follows.

5. Prove that if a, b, c are the sides of the triangle and $[ABC]$ its area then

$$a^2 + b^2 + c^2 \geq 4\sqrt{3}[ABC].$$

Let $s = \frac{1}{2}(a+b+c)$ then by the AM/GM inequality, we have

$$\{(s - a) + (s - b) + (s - c)\} \geq 3\{(s - a)(s - b)(s - c)\}^{1/3}.$$

Cubing, multiplying by s and using Heron's formula we obtain $\frac{1}{2}(a + b + c)^2 \geq 6\sqrt{3}[ABC]$. Adding in the known inequality $a^2 + b^2 + c^2 \geq ab + bc + ca$ we get the desired result.

6. Prove that if A, B, C are the sides of a triangle,

$$\sin 2A + \sin 2B + \sin 2C \leq \sin A + \sin B + \sin C$$

$$\leq \cos \frac{1}{2}A + \cos \frac{1}{2}B + \cos \frac{1}{2}C.$$

For the left-hand inequality start from $2r \leq R$, which by using $\frac{1}{2}r(a+b+c) = abc/(4R)$, gives $abc/(4R) \leq \frac{1}{4}R(a+b+c)$ and hence $8R \sin A \sin B \sin C \leq a+b+c$. The inequality now follows from the sine rule and the identity

$$\sin 2A + \sin 2B + \sin 2C = 4 \sin A \sin B \sin C.$$

For the right-hand inequality, use the identity

$$\sin A + \sin B + \sin C = 4\cos\frac{1}{2}A\cos\frac{1}{2}B\cos\frac{1}{2}C,$$

so that it is sufficient to prove $4P \le S$, where P and S are respectively the product and the sum of the three cosines of half-angles. Now all the terms of S are positive, so by the AM/GM inequality we have $S^3 \ge 27P$. Also, by Jensen's theorem, since $y = \cos x$ is concave for acute angles we have $S \le 3\sqrt{3}/2$. Putting these two results together gives the result.

7. Prove that if A, B, C are the angles of a triangle then

$$\sin 2A \sin^2 A + \sin 2B \sin^2 B + \sin 2C \sin^2 C$$

$$- \sin 2A \sin 2B \sin 2C \le \frac{3}{4}\sqrt{3}.$$

Using $\sin A = a/(2R)$ etc., and $\cos A = (b^2 + c^2 - a^2)(2bc)$ etc, there is massive cancellation leading to the equivalent inequality, $abc \le 3\sqrt{3}R^3$, which in turn is equivalent to $\sin A \sin B \sin C \le 3\sqrt{3}/8$. Now the left-hand side is equal to $\frac{1}{2}(\cos(A-B) + \cos C)\sin C \le \frac{1}{2}(1 + \cos C)\sin C = \frac{1}{2}(1 + \cos C)^{3/2}(1 - \cos C)^{1/2} \le 3\sqrt{3}/8$, by the AM/GM inequality.

8. Prove that if ABC is an acute-angled triangle with sides a, b, c then

$$(b^2 + c^2 - a^2)^{1/2} + (c^2 + a^2 - b^2)^{1/2} + (c^2 + a^2 - b^2)^{1/2} \le a + b + c.$$

Put $(b^2 + c^2 - a^2) = x^2$ with y^2 and z^2 similarly defined. The inequality now follows from adding together three inequalities of the form $\frac{1}{2}(x + y) \le \{\frac{1}{2}(x^2 + y^2)\}^{1/2}$.

9. Prove that if AL, BM, CN are the medians of triangle ABC and $AL + BM + CN = k$ and $AB + BC + CA = p$, then $3p/2 > k > 3p/4$. From triangle LAC we have $LC + CA > AL$ from which $a+2b > 2l$. Adding in two similar inequalities $3(a+b+c) > 2(l+m+n)$ and hence $3p/2 > k$. From triangle GAC we have $AG + GC > CA$ from which $2(n + l) > 3b$. Adding in two similar inequalities we get $4(l + m + n) > 3(a + b + c)$ and hence $k > 3p/4$.

Exercise 17.2

1. If a, b, c are the sides of a triangle prove that

$$\frac{1}{b+c-a} + \frac{1}{c+a-b} + \frac{1}{a+b-c}$$

$$\geq \frac{1}{a} + \frac{1}{b} + \frac{1}{c} \geq \frac{9}{a+b+c}.$$

2. H is the orthocentre of triangle ABC. Prove that

$$BC/AH + CA/BH + AB/CH \geq 3\sqrt{3}.$$

3. If a, b, c are the sides of a triangle, prove that

$$\frac{1}{2} < (bc + ca + ab)/(a^2 + b^2 + c^2) \leq 1.$$

4. If A, B, C are the angles of a triangle prove that

$$(1 - \cos A)(1 - \cos B)(1 - \cos C) \geq \cos A \cos B \cos C.$$

5. Prove that if x, y, z are real numbers satisfying $x + y + z = 0$, and a, b, c are the sides of a triangle, then $x^2(b^2 + c^2 - a^2) + y^2(c^2 + a^2 - b^2) + z^2(a^2 + b^2 - c^2) \geq 0$ with equality if, and only if $x = y = z = 0$.

6. In triangle $ABC, AB = 2AC$. Find the minimum value of $\cot B - \cot C$. (DM)

7. Let a, b, c be the sides of a triangle. Find the smallest number k such that

$$k(ab + bc + ca) > a^2 + b^2 + c^2.$$

8. If A, B, C are the angles of a triangle prove that

$$\frac{\cos A}{\cos B \cos C} + \frac{\cos B}{\cos C \cos A} + \frac{\cos C}{\cos A \cos B} \geq 6.$$

9. If a, b, c are the sides of a triangle, prove that

$$2(a^2b + b^2c + c^2a + ab^2 + bc^2 + ca^2) \geq a^3 + b^3 + c^3 + 9abc.$$

10. In triangle ABC let the radii of the circumcircle and incircle be R and r respectively. Prove that (i) $(abc)^{2/3} \geq 6Rr$, (ii) $[ABC]^2 \geq 27Rr^3/2$, (iii) $(a + b + c)^2 \geq 54Rr$.

11. For $0 < a, b, c < 1$ and $a + b + c = 2$, prove that

$$8(a + b - c)(b + c - a)(c + a - b) \leq 27a^2b^2c^2.$$

12. If A, B, C are the angles of a triangle, prove that $\cos^2 A + \cos^2 B + \cos^2 C$ is greater than, equal to, or less than 1 according as to whether triangle ABC is obtuse, right-angled or acute.

13. Triangle ABC has circumradius R. Prove that $R^2(a+b+c) \geq abc$.

14. A triangle has inradius 1 and semi-perimeter s. Prove that $s > 5$.

15. If a, b, c are the sides of a triangle prove that $abc(a + b + c)$ is at least

$$bc(c+a-b)(a+b-c)+ca(a+b-c)(b+c-a)+ab(b+c-a)(c+a-b).$$

16. Prove that

$$\frac{s}{2R} \leq \cos A \cos \frac{1}{2}A + \cos B \cos \frac{1}{2}B + \cos C \cos \frac{1}{2}C,$$

where s is the semi-perimeter and R the circumradius of triangle ABC.

17. Let a, b, c be the sides of a triangle. Prove that

$$a^3+b^3+c^3+6abc \geq (ab+bc+ca)(a+b+c) > a^3+b^3+c^3+5abc.$$

18. Let x, y, z be angles each lying strictly between 0° and 45° with $x + y + z = 90^o$. Prove that

$$1 \leq \tan^2 x + \tan^2 y + \tan^2 z < 2.$$

19. Prove that if A, B, C are the angles of an acute-angled triangle then

$$\sin A + \sin B + \sin C > \cos A + \cos B + \cos C. \quad \text{(DM)}$$

17.1.7 More Inequalities involving triangles

We now consider inequalities involving properties of triangles, and their associated circles, other than those stated in terms of a, b, c, A, B, C, R, s and r. For some of the problems the use of areal (or barycentric) co-ordinates are used so a brief account of the properties of such co-ordinates is now given.

17.1.8   Areal co-ordinates

If P is a point in the plane of triangle ABC, then the areal co-ordinates of P are given by (l, m, n) where $l = [BPC]/[ABC], m = [CPA]/[ABC], n = [APB]/[ABC]$, with the convention that l is negative if P lies on the other side of BC than A etc. It follows that for all choices of P we have $l + m + n = 1$. It is a remarkable property of such co-ordinates that they behave exactly as vectors do in the sense that the displacement $\mathbf{PQ}$ is represented by the difference of the co-ordinates of Q and P, and proportional vectors represent parallel displacements. There is also a distance function for use with such co-ordinates, which states that the square of the length of the displacement $\mathbf{PQ}$, represented by the vector with co-ordinates (x, y, z), is given by $PQ^2 = -a^2yz - b^2zx - c^2xy$. Such an expression is positive definite, since $x + y + z = 0$. Sometimes the areal co-ordinates are given in unnormalized form, that is with $l + m + n \neq 1$, and care must then be exercised to normalize them before the areal metric is used. The equation of the line joining P_1 and P_2 may be written down in vector form or in co-ordinate form as $(m_1 n_2 - n_1 m_2)x + (n_1 l_2 - l_1 n_2)y + (l_1 m_2 - m_1 l_2)z = 0$. In unnormalized form the co-ordinates of the incentre I are (a, b, c), those of the circumcentre O are $(\sin 2A, \sin 2B, \sin 2C)$ and those of the orthocentre H are $(\tan A, \tan B, \tan C)$. The co-ordinates of A, B, C are, of course, $(1, 0, 0), (0, 1, 0), (0, 0, 1)$ respectively. And those of L, M, N, the midpoints of BC, CA, AB are $(0, \frac{1}{2}, \frac{1}{2}), (\frac{1}{2}, 0, \frac{1}{2}), (\frac{1}{2}, \frac{1}{2}, 0)$ respectively, and those of the centroid G are $(\frac{1}{3}, \frac{1}{3}, \frac{1}{3})$. Also $[P_1 P_2 P_3]/[ABC]$ is equal to the value of the determinant whose rows are the normalized co-ordinates of the points P_1, P_2, P_3.

We now give a number of worked examples, followed by some problems.

Examples 17.2

1. Prove that if a point K is chosen inside triangle ABC and AK meets BC at L, and M and N are similarly defined, then $[LMN]/[ABC] \leq \frac{1}{4}$, with equality if, and only if, K is the centroid.

   It is easy to show that, with $K(l, m, n)$, we have

   $$\frac{[LMN]}{[ABC]} = \frac{2lmn}{(l+m)(m+n)(n+l)},$$

   so the required inequality is $(l+m)(m+n)(n+l) \geq 8lmn$, which follows from three applications of the AM/GM inequality.

2. Prove that, if in triangle ABC the length of the median through A is l and the length of the internal bisector of angle BAC is u, then $l/u \geq (b+c)^2/(4bc)$.

   The following formulae are well known: $l^2 = \frac{1}{4}(2b^2 + 2c^2 - a^2)$ and $u^2 = bc(b+c-a)(a+b+c)/(b+c)^2$. Hence, after some algebra $16l^2b^2c^2 - (b+c)^4u^2 = bc(b-c)^2(a-b+c)(a+b-c)$. By the triangle inequalities this expression is positive or zero when $b = c$.

3. Work out the range of values of the expression $S = pAO/AD + qBO/BE + rCO/OF$, where AOD, BOE, COF are three cevians of triangle ABC, with D, E, F on BC, CA, AB respectively, and $p > q > r$, and O is any point internal to ABC.

   We show $p + q > S > q + r$. In fact, if (l, m, n) are the areal co-ordinates of O, we have $p + q - S = (p+q)(l+m+n) - p(m+n) - q(n+l) - r(l+m)$, since $AO/AD = m+n$ etc., and this is equal to $(p-r)l + (q-r)m > 0$. The right hand inequality is proved in much the same way.

4. In this example P is an internal point of triangle ABC, and
$AP = x, BP = y, CP = z$. Show how to minimize $f(x, y, z)$
as P varies.

Unless $f(x, y, z)$ has some special form such as $x + y + z$,
for which special methods are available, it is best to use
calculus. Suppose that the co-ordinates of the points are
$P(p, q), A(a, d), B(b, e), C(c, f)$. We have $x^2 = (p-a)^2 + (q-d)^2, y^2 = (p-b)^2 + (q-e)^2, z^2 = (p-c)^2 + (q-f)^2$. Now
$x\partial x/\partial p = (p-a), y\partial y/\partial p = (p-b), z\partial z/\partial p = (p-c)$, with
similar expressions for derivatives with respect to q. Now

$$\frac{\partial f}{\partial p} = \frac{\partial f}{\partial x} \cdot \frac{\partial x}{\partial p} + \frac{\partial f}{\partial y} \cdot \frac{\partial y}{\partial p} + \frac{\partial f}{\partial z} \cdot \frac{\partial z}{\partial p},$$

and at a turning value this must vanish. Hence

$$0 = \frac{\partial f}{\partial x}(p-a)/x + \frac{\partial f}{\partial y}(p-b)/y + \frac{\partial f}{\partial z}(p-c)/z.$$

Similarly

$$0 = \frac{\partial f}{\partial x}(q-d)/x + \frac{\partial f}{\partial y}(q-e)/y + \frac{\partial f}{\partial z}(q-f)/z.$$

Hence

$$\frac{\partial f}{\partial x} : \frac{\partial f}{\partial y} : \frac{\partial f}{\partial z}$$
$$= \{(p-b)(q-f) - (p-c)(q-e)\}/(yz) : \ldots : \ldots .$$

The first term in this ratio is equal to

$$\{(\mathbf{b} \times \mathbf{c}) + (\mathbf{c} \times \mathbf{p}) + (\mathbf{p} \times \mathbf{b}\}/(yz),$$

where $\mathbf{a}, \mathbf{b}, \mathbf{c}, \mathbf{p}$ are the vector positions of A, B, C, P. This
is equal to $2[BPC]/\{(BP)(CP)\} = \sin BPC$. We therefore
have the general result that for a turning value

$$\frac{\partial f}{\partial x} : \frac{\partial f}{\partial y} : \frac{\partial f}{\partial z} = \sin BPC : \sin CPA : \sin APB.$$

For example if $f(x, y, z) = x+y+z$, then the angles are equal, and provided the triangle has all its angles less that 120°, we deduce $AP + BP + CP$ has a minimum at the Steiner point F, where $\angle BFC = \angle CFA = \angle AFB = 120^\circ$.

5. Show that, if O is any point inside triangle ABC of semi-perimeter s, then

$$s < AO + BO + CO < 2s.$$

The left-hand inequality is just three applications of the triangle inequality. For the right hand inequality, consider confocal ellipses, with foci at B and C. Clearly the ellipse through O is contained within the ellipse through A, and hence $BO + CO < BA + CA$. This is because the ellipse through P satisfies $PB + PC = 2k$, where k is the major axis of that ellipse. Adding two similar inequalities produces the result.

6. For a point P varying inside an acute-angled triangle ABC and u, v, w the perpendicular distances of P from BC, CA, AB respectively, find the maximum values of (a) $avw+bwu+cuv$ and (b) uvw, and in each case we determine the position of P that gives the maximum value.

For part (a) we maximize $f(u, v, w) = avw + bwu + cuv$ subject to $au + bv + cw = 2[ABC]$, using a Lagrange multiplier l and obtain $bw+cv = la, cu+aw = lb$ and $av+bu = lc$. These equations and the constraint are satisfied by $l = R$, the circumradius, and $u = R\cos A, v = R\cos B, w = R\cos C$. The point P is therefore the circumcentre and the maximum value is $\frac{1}{4}abc$, where in obtaining this we have used the expansion of $\sin(A + B + C)$. For part (b) we use the AM/GM inequality to give $2[ABC] = au + bv + cw \geq 3(abcuvw)^{\frac{1}{3}}$ so the maximum value of uvw is $(8/27)[ABC]^3/abc$. The point P

is when $au = bv = cw$, which is when P coincides with the centroid G.

7. For a point P varying inside triangle ABC and LMN its pedal triangle, with L, M, N on BC, CA, AB respectively we show (a) $BL^2 + CM^2 + AN^2 \geq \frac{1}{4}(a^2 + b^2 + c^2)$ and (b) $[ABC]^2 \leq (BL^2 + CM^2 + AN^2)(PL^2 + PM^2 + PN^2)$. We use the notation $BL = x, CM = y, AN = z, PL = u, PM = v, PN = w$. A well-known theorem for this configuration, proved by repeated application of Pythagoras's theorem, is that

$$x^2 + y^2 + z^2 = (a - x)^2 + (b - y)^2 + (c - z)^2.$$

This implies $ax + by + cz = \frac{1}{2}(a^2 + b^2 + c^2)$. Now the Cauchy-Schwarz inequality gives $(ax + by + cz)^2 \leq (a^2 + b^2 + c^2)(x^2 + y^2 + z^2)$ from which $x^2 + y^2 + z^2 \geq \frac{1}{4}(a^2 + b^2 + c^2)$, with equality if, and only if, $x = \frac{1}{2}a, y = \frac{1}{2}b, z = \frac{1}{2}c$ and P is the circumcentre. We also have, by the Cauchy-Schwarz inequality, $4[ABC]^2 = (au + bv + cw)^2 \leq (a^2 + b^2 + c^2)(u^2 + v^2 + w^2)$, with equality if, and only if, $u : v : w = a : b : c$, that is when P is the symmedian point. Putting the two inequalities together we get $[ABC]^2 \leq (x^2 + y^2 + z^2)(u^2 + v^2 + w^2)$, with equality if, and only if, the triangle is equilateral and P is its circumcentre.

8. Show that if ABC is an acute-angled triangle with orthocentre H and AH meets circle BHC at D, BH meets circle CHA at E and CH meets circle AHB at F, then

$$(HD)(HE)(HF) \leq 8R^3.$$

In fact it is easy to see that triangles DBC and ABC are congruent and so have the same circumradius. Now $\angle CBH =$

$90° − C$ so $\angle DBH = 90° + B − C$ and we have $HD = 2R\sin(90° + B − C) = 2R\cos(C − B) \le 2R$, with equality if, and only if, $B = C$. Similar results hold for HE and HF and so the inequality holds, with equality if, and only if, ABC is equilateral.

9. Show that if ABC is a triangle, centroid G and AG, BG, CG meet the circumcircle again at D, E, F respectively, then $[DEF] \ge [ABC]$.

The equation of the circumcircle, using areal co-ordinates is $a^2yz + b^2zx + c^2xy = 0$ and the equation of AG is $y = z$. Solving these with the side condition $x + y + z = 1$, we find the co-ordinates of D to be $(-a^2, b^2 + c^2, b^2 + c^2)/(2b^2 + 2c^2 − a^2)$, with similar expressions for those of E and F by cyclic change of a, b, c. The ratio of areas $[DEF]/[ABC]$ is given by the determinant of co-ordinates with those of D, E, F forming rows 1,2,3 respectively. After evaluation we find this ratio to be

$$(u + v + w)^3/\{(2u + 2v − w)(2v + 2w − u)(2w + 2u − v)\},$$

where $u = a^2, v = b^2, w = c^2$. Now each term in the denominator is positive, and by the AM/GM inequality on the three terms in the denominator, whose average is $(u + v + w)$ we see that this ratio is ≥ 1.

10. Prove that, if I is the incentre of triangle ABC, circumradius R, and I_1, I_2, I_3 are the excentres opposite A, B, C respectively, then $(II_1)(II_2)(II_3) \le 8R^3$ and $[I_1I_2I_3]/[ABC] \ge 4$.

Let AI meet the circcmumcircle again at P. The following angles are easily deduced: $\angle PBC = \frac{1}{2}A, \angle I_1BC = \frac{1}{2}C, \angle BPI = C, \angle BI_1C = \frac{1}{2}C$. It follows that $PB = PC = PI_1$ so P is the centre of circle BIC and II_1 is a diameter of this circle. Now by the sine rule for triangle PAC we have $PC =$

$2R \sin \frac{1}{2}A$ and so $II_1 = 4R \sin \frac{1}{2}A$. Hence $(II_1)(II_2)(II_3) = 64R^3 \sin \frac{1}{2}A \sin \frac{1}{2}B \sin \frac{1}{2}C \le 8R^3$, by the result of Method 2.

Furthermore, since ABC is the pedal triangle of triangle $I_1 I_2 I_3$, the latter triangle has circumradius $2R$ and hence $I_1 C = 4R \sin \frac{1}{2}A \cos \frac{1}{2}B$. Similarly $I_2 C = 4R \sin \frac{1}{2}B \cos \frac{1}{2}A$. Adding we get $I_1 I_2 = 4R \cos \frac{1}{2}C$. It follows that $[I_1 I_2 I_3] = 8R^2 \cos \frac{1}{2}A \cos \frac{1}{2}B \cos \frac{1}{2}C$. But $[ABC] = 2R^2 \sin A \sin B \sin C$ and the result follows since $\sin \frac{1}{2}A \sin \frac{1}{2}B \sin \frac{1}{2}C \le \frac{1}{8}$.

11. Prove that if H is the orthocentre and N is the nine-point centre of triangle ABC and R is the circumradius, then $AN^2 + BN^2 + CN^2 \le 3R^2 \le AH^2 + BH^2 + CH^2$. From result (5) with $l = m = n = \frac{1}{3}$ we have $AP^2 + BP^2 + CP^2 = AG^2 + BG^2 + CG^2 + 3PG^2$ for any point P in the plane ABC. Let $NG = d$, then $OG = 2d$ and $HG = 4d$, where O is the circumcentre. Taking P to be successively O, N, H and writing $AG^2 + BG^2 + CG^2 = D^2$ we have $3R^2 = D^2 + 12d^2$, $AN^2 + BN^2 + CN^2 = D^2 + d^2$, $AH^2 + BH^2 + CH^2 = D^2 + 48d^2$, from which the result follows.

12. Suppose that ABC is a triangle with incircle S and radius r, and that circles S_A, S_B, S_C of radii r_A, r_B, r_C respectively are drawn, each touching two sides of ABC and touching S externally, with S_A touching AB, AC and S externally etc. Prove that

$$r \le r_A + r_B + r_C < 2r.$$

Let I_B be the centre of S_B, and let L_B and L be the feet of the perpendiculars from I_B and I on to BC. $BI_B I$ is a straight line, the internal bisector of $\angle ABC$. Now $\angle I_B L_B B = \angle ILB = 90°$, so triangles $BI_B L_B$ and BIL are similar. Let $I_B B = x$, then we have $r_B/x = r/(r + r_B + x)$. But $x = r_B \operatorname{cosec} \frac{1}{2}B$. Eliminating x we find $r_B = r(1 - \sin \frac{1}{2}B)/(1 + \sin \frac{1}{2}B) = r\{-1 + 2/(1 + \sin \frac{1}{2}B)\}$, with similar expressions for r_C, r_A. To prove that $r_A + r_B + r_C \geq r$, it is sufficient to prove that

$$1/(1+\sin\tfrac{1}{2}A) + 1/(1+\sin\tfrac{1}{2}B) + 1/(1+\sin\tfrac{1}{2}C) \geq 2. \quad (17.1)$$

Now by the Cauchy-Schwarz inequality we have 9 is less than or equal to the product of

$$3 + \sin\frac{A}{2} + \sin\frac{B}{2} + \sin\frac{C}{2}$$

and

$$\frac{1}{1+\sin\frac{A}{2}} + \frac{1}{1+\sin\frac{B}{2}} + \frac{1}{1+\sin\frac{C}{2}}.$$

Using Jensen's inequality that $\sin\frac{A}{2} + \sin\frac{B}{2} + \sin\frac{C}{2} \leq 3/2$ we deduce that Equation (17.1) holds. To prove that $r_A + r_B + r_C < 2r$ it is sufficient to show that $1 < \sin\frac{A}{2} + \sin\frac{B}{2} + \sin\frac{C}{2}$. Now the right-hand side $= 2\sin\frac{A+B}{4}\cos\frac{A-B}{4} + 1 - 2\sin^2\frac{A+B}{4} = 1 + 2\sin\frac{A+B}{4}(\cos\frac{A}{4} - \sin\frac{A}{4})(\cos\frac{B}{4} - \sin\frac{B}{4}) > 1$ since $\frac{A}{4}, \frac{B}{4} < 45^o$.

13. ABC is a triangle and P an internal point. $AP = x$, $BP = y$, $CP = z$ and the perpendicular distances of P from BC, CA, AB are p, q, r respectively. Prove (i) $ax < by + cz$; (ii) $ax \geq bq + cr$; (iii) $px + qy + rz \geq 2(qr + rp + pq)$ (iv) $xyz \geq 8pqr$.
For part (i) we have

$$az/\sin(\angle BPC - \angle BAC)$$

$$= by/\sin(\angle CPA - \angle CBA)$$

$$= cz/\sin(\angle APB - \angle ACB)$$

and since the three angles add to 180° it follows that ax, by, cz form the sides of a triangle, and so $ax < by + cz$ etc. For part

(ii) let P have areal co-ordinates (l, m, n) and suppose that $[ABC] = 1$. Then $bq + cr = 2\{[APB] + [APC]\} = 2(m + n)$. Suppose that AP meets BC at L, then $ax = a(m + n)AD \geq 2(m + n) \geq bq + cr$. For part (iii) we have from part (i) $px \geq (bpq + cpr)/a$, with similar inequalities for qy and rz. Adding these together provides the result. For part (iv), we have from part (i)

$$axbycz \geq (bq + cr)(cr + ap)(ap + bq) \geq 8abcpqr.$$

Dividing through by abc produces the result.

Exercises 17.3

1. Prove that if K has areal co-ordinates (l, m, n), then AK meets BC in the point D which has normalized co-ordinates $\frac{1}{m+n}(0, m, n)$ so that $BD/DC = n/m$.

2. Prove that the length of the internal bisector of the angle A of triangle ABC does not exceed $\frac{1}{2}(b + c)$.

3. Prove that in an obtuse or acute angled triangle

$$\tan A(PA)^2 + \tan B(PB)^2 + \tan C(PC)^2$$

is a maximum or minimum respectively when P is at H, the orthocentre, and then the stationary value is

$$8R^2 \sin A \sin B \sin C.$$

4. Use the result of Example 17.2.4 to show that $AP^2 + BP^2 + CP^2$ is a minimum as P varies over the inside of triangle ABC when P lies at the centroid G.

5. Use the result of Example 17.2.4 to show that $a(AP)+b(BP)+c(CP)$ is a minimum as P varies over the inside of the acute-angled triangle ABC when P lies at the orthocentre H.

6. $ABCDEF$ is a hexagon in which AB is equal and parallel to FA. Prove that

$$AC^2 + BD^2 + CE^2 \leq 3AB^2 + 3BC^2 + 3CD^2$$

7. A point P is at distance 3,4,5 from the vertices A, B, C of a triangle. What are the maximum and minimum possible values of the sums of the squares of the sides of the triangle?

8. Let AP be the internal bisector of $\angle BAC$ and suppose Q is the point on BC such that $BQ = PC$. Prove that $AQ \geq AP$.

9. ABC is an acute-angled triangle, circumcentre O and circumradius R. AO meets circle BOC again at D. BO meets circle COA again at E. CO meets circle AOB again at F. Prove that $(OD)(OE)(OF) \geq 8R^3$.

10. ABC is an acute-angled triangle. D is the reflection of A in the side BC, with E and F similarly defined. Prove that $[DEF]/[ABC] \leq 4$.

11. ABC is a triangle . Locate, with proof, the point P in the plane of the triangle for which $(AP)\cos\frac{1}{2}A + (BP)\cos\frac{1}{2}B + (CP)\cos\frac{1}{2}C$ is a minimum, and find the minimum value of the expression.

12. ABC is a triangle. Its incircle touches the sides BC, CA, AB at X, Y, Z respectively. The points P, Q, R are the feet of the perpendiculars from X to YZ, from Y to ZX and from Z to XY respectively. Prove that $[ABC] \geq 16[PQR]$.

13. Circles S_A, S_B, S_C, S are drawn with equal radius p, so that all four circles lie inside a triangle ABC that has no angle less than $30°$. S_A touches AB, AC and S and S_B, S_C are similarly defined. Prove that $p \leq \frac{1}{4}R$, where R is the circumradius of ABC.

14. ABC is a triangle with incentre I. AI, BI, CI meet the circumcircle of ABC at D, E, F. Prove that $(AI)(BI)(CI) \leq (ID)(IE)(IF)$.

15. ABC is a triangle with centroid G and symmedian point S Prove that

$$AS/AG + BS/BG + CS/CG \leq 3.$$

16. ABC is a triangle with circumradius R. The circle through A touching BC at its midpoint has radius R_1. The radii R_2, R_3 are similarly defined. Prove that

$$R_1^2 + R_2^2 + R_3^2 \geq 27R^2/16.$$

17. Locate the points P on the circumcircle of the (non-equilateral) triangle ABC such that $PA^2 + PB^2 + PC^2$ is a maximum or a minimum.

17.2 Hints and Answers Week 7

Exercises 17.1

1. See the text, from which the solution follows at once, since $AI = r\operatorname{cosec}\frac{1}{2}A$ etc.

2. The trigonometrical version is $\cos 2A + \cos 2B + \cos 2C \geq -3/2$ and the algebraic version is $a^2 + b^2 + c^2 \leq 9R^2$.

Exercises 17.2

1. For the left-hand inequality put $a = m+n, b = n+l, c = l+m$, with $l, m, n > 0$. The inequality transforms to the sum of three inequalities like $1/m + 1/n \geq 4/(m + n)$. For the the right-hand inequality just clear fractions and apply AM/GM to six terms of the form a^2b, b^2a.

2. This follows immediately from trigonometrical identity (3) on p. 260.

3. The right-hand inequality, after multiplying up, follows from $(a - b)^2 + (b - c)^2 + (c - a)^2 \geq 0$, which is obviously true.

4. Use the cosine rule and after multiplying up the inequality is equivalent to
$$(b + c - a)^2(c + a - b)^2(a + b - c)^2$$
$$\geq (b^2 + c^2 - a^2)(c^2 + a^2 - b^2)(a^2 + b^2 - c^2).$$
In fact $\{(a - b + c)(a + b - c)\}^2 \geq (c^2 + a^2 - b^2)(a^2 + b^2 - c^2)$, since on expansion and factorization the difference of these expressions is $2(b - c)^2(b^2 + c^2 - a^2)$, and this is positive for acute-angled triangles. Multiplying three such results shows the inequality is true for acute-angled triangles. The inequality is trivial when the triangle is not acute.

5. In the given expression replace z by $-x - y$ and collect like terms, then use the cosine rule to obtain $2\{(bx + ay \cos C)^2 + (ay \sin C)^2\} \geq 0$.

6. $3/2$ when $\cot B = 2$ and $\cot C = 0.5$

7. $k = 2$. Put $a = m + n$ etc., so the triangle inequalities become $l, m, n > 0$. Then the difference between the two sides is $4(lm + mn + nl)$, and this can be made arbitrarily small by letting, say, m and n tend to zero, but keeping l large. This would correspond to $b = c$ and a very small.

8. Let $x = \tan A, y = \tan B, z = \tan C$ then from identity (3) on p. 260 we have $1/yz + 1/zx + 1/xy = 1$. Hence by the Cauchy-Schwarz inequality $(yz + zx + xy) \geq 9$. Now $\cos A = -\cos(B + C) = \sin B \sin C - \cos B \cos C$ so that $\cos A/(\cos B \cos C) = yz - 1$ etc.

9. Using the standard substitution, as in Problem 7, this reduces to the known inequality

$$l^3 + m^3 + n^3 + 3lmn \geq l^2m + m^2n + n^2l + lm^2 + mn^2 + nl^2.$$

10. Use $[ABC] = abc/(4R) = r(a + b + c)/2$ to give $a + b + c = abc/(2Rr) \geq 3(abc)^{\frac{1}{3}}$ to give $(abc)^{\frac{2}{3}} \geq 6Rr$. Using $4R[ABC] = abc$ gives $[ABC]^2 \geq 27Rr^3/2$. The final part follows from $[ABC] = \frac{1}{2}r(a + b + c)$.

11. The inequality is trivial unless a, b, c are the sides of a triangle. Writing $8 = (a + b + c)^3$ to make the inequality homogeneous, and using formulae for area, we find the inequality reduces to the known one $\sin A + \sin B + \sin C \leq 3\sqrt{3}/2$.

12. This follows at once from identity (4) p. 261.

13. In Example 17.1.7. of the text it is proved that

$$\sin A \sin B \sin C \le 3\sqrt{3}/8. \tag{17.2}$$

Now the given inequality is equivalent to $\sin A + \sin B + \sin C \ge 4 \sin A \sin B \sin C$, and follows from Inequality (17.2) and AM/GM that

$$\sin A + \sin B + \sin C \ge 3(\sin A \sin B \sin C)^{\frac{1}{3}}.$$

14. From Heron's formula $r = 1$ implies $s = (s-a)(s-b)(s-c)$. The AM/GM inequality gives $s/3 = \{(s-a)+(s-b)+(s-c)\}/3 \ge s^{\frac{1}{3}}$ and hence $s \ge 3\sqrt{3} > 5$.

15. Using the usual substitution $a = m+n$ etc. the inequality is equivalent to $l^3(m+n)+m^3(n+l)+n^3(l+m) \ge 2lmn(l+m+n)$. Now by the AM/GM inequality we have both $l^3m+lm^3 \ge 2l^2m^2$ etc., and $(l^2m^2 + l^2n^2) \ge 2l^2mn$ etc.

16. Let H be the orthocentre and D, E, F the feet of the altitudes. Let $\angle ECH = u$. Then $CD + CE = CH \cos u + CH \cos(C - u) \le 2CH \cos \frac{1}{2}C = 4R \cos C \cos \frac{1}{2}C$. Adding together two similar inequalities produces the result.

17. The standard substitution reduces this to proving, for $l, m, n > 0$ that

$$l^2m + m^2n + n^2l + lm^2 + mn^2 + nl^2 + 2lmn \ge 8lmn > 0.$$

18. For the left-hand inequality use Jensen's theorem which gives $(1/3)(\tan^2 x + \tan^2 y + \tan^2 z) \ge \tan^2\{(x + y + z)/3\} = 1/3$. For the right hand-inequality note that $\tan x \tan y + \tan y \tan z + \tan z \tan x = 1$, since $x + y + z = 90°$, so that $(\tan x + \tan y + \tan z)^2 = \tan^2 x + \tan^2 y + \tan^2 z + 2 = T^2 + 2$. Now since $x, y, z < 45°$, we have $T < \tan x + \tan y + \tan z$, and so $T^2 < T + 2$. Hence $T < 2$.

19. Let C be the largest angle, then certainly $45^o < C < 90^o$. The required inequality is equivalent to proving $2\cos(\frac{1}{2}(A - B))(\cos\frac{1}{2}C - \sin\frac{1}{2}C) + (\sin C - \cos C) > 0$. Since $C > 45^o$, we have $\sin C > \cos C$, and since $\frac{1}{2}C < 45^o$, we have $\cos\frac{1}{2}C > \sin\frac{1}{2}C$, and hence the result.

Exercises 17.3

1. –

2. Using the areal distance formula, it is easy to show that the length AU of the internal bisector of angle A is given by $AU^2 = bc(b + c - a)(b + c + a)/(b + c)$. The inequality now follows, using $b + c > a$ and $bc \leq \frac{1}{4}(b + c)^2$.

3. We use the result (5) in the text. Since tha areal co-ordinates of H are $(\tan A, \tan B, \tan C)$ it follows that

$$\tan A(PA)^2 + \tan B(PB)^2 + \tan C(PC)^2$$

$$= \tan A(HA)^2 + \tan B(HB)^2 + \tan C(HC)^2$$

$$+ \tan A \tan B \tan C(PH)^2,$$

The result now follows since all of the tangents are positive when triangle ABC is acute, and precisely one is negative when triangle ABC is obtuse. The stationary value in either case is $8R^2 \sin A \sin B \sin C$ since $AH = 2R\cos A$ etc.

4. Using the notation of Example 17.2.4 we have the minimum when $\sin BPC : \sin CPA : \sin APB = x : y : z$. This means that P must satisfy $[BPC] = [CPA] = [APB]$, and so P coincides with the centroid G .

5. The minimum is when P satisfies

$$\sin BPC : \sin CPA : \sin APB = a : b : c$$

which implies $\angle BPC = 180°{-}A, \angle CPA = 180°{-}B, \angle APB = 180° - C$, so that P coincides with the orthocentre H.

6. Let $AB = p, BC = q, CD = r$. Denote the angles $\angle BCA$, $\angle CDE, \angle ABC$ by x, y, z respectively. Use the cosine formula for triangles ABC, BCD, CDE and add to get $AC^2 + BD^2 + CE^2 = 2p^2 + 2q^2 + 2r^2 - 2qr \cos x - 2rp \cos y - 2pq \cos z$. To prove what is required it is sufficient to show that

$$p^2 + q^2 + r^2 - 2qr \cos x - 2rp \cos y - 2pq \cos z \geq 0$$

But this is so, since the left-hand side is equal to

$$(p + r \cos y + q \cos z)^2 + (r \sin y - q \sin z)^2.$$

Equality holds when $p : q : r = \sin x : \sin y : \sin z$.

7. The maximum is 150 when P is internal and the minimum 50 when P is external.

8. We have $PC = BQ = ba/(b{+}c)$ and $BP = QC = ca/(b{+}c)$. Using the cosine rule on triangles APC and APB we find $bc(b + c) = a^2bc/(b + c) + (b + c)(AP)^2$. Similarly $b^3 + c^3 = a^2bc/(b + c) + (b + c)(AQ)^2$. Subtracting yields the result $(AQ)^2 = (AP)^2 + (b - c)^2$, which shows that $AQ \geq AP$, with equality if, and only if, triangle ABC is isosceles with $b = c$.

9. The radius of circle BOC is easily shown to be $\frac{1}{2}R \sec A$ and as $\angle DBO = 90°{+}C{-}B$ it follows that $OD = R \sec A \cos(B{-}C)$. The required inequality now follows from

$$\cos(A - B) \cos(B - C) \cos(C - A) \geq 8 \cos A \cos B \cos C.$$

To prove this take $A \geq B \geq C$ and $0 < C \leq 60^{\circ}$. If $C = 60^{\circ}$ then the triangle is equilateral and equality holds. If $C < 60^{\circ}$ then $\frac{1}{2} < \cos C < 1$ and the given inequality reduces to $f(\cos(A - B)) \equiv \cos^2(A - B) - \cos C(4\cos^2 C + 5)\cos(A - B) + 8\cos^2 C \geq 0$. Now $\cos C(4\cos^2 C + 5) > 3$, and $f(0) > 0$, $f(1) > 0$, so $f(x) = 0$ does not have two real roots in $0 < x < 1$, and the inequality holds.

10. The areal co-ordinates of D are

$$(-1, 2\sin B \cos C/\sin A, 2\sin C \cos B/\sin A)$$

and those of E and F are found by cyclic change of A, B, C. The ratio $[DEF]/[ABC]$ is given by the determinant whose rows are the co-ordinates of D, E, F. When evaluated this ratio comes to $3 + 8\cos A \cos B \cos C$, where result (4) of section 7.4 has been used. Now from Example 1 of 17.4 we have $\cos A \cos B \cos C \leq \frac{1}{8}$ so $[DEF]/[ABC] \leq \frac{1}{4}$.

11. Recall the theory of Example 17.2.4. The minimum is attained where $\sin BPC : \sin CPA : \sin APB = \cos\frac{1}{2}A : \cos\frac{1}{2}B : \cos\frac{1}{2}C$. It follows that $\angle BPC = 180^{\circ} - \frac{1}{2}B - \frac{1}{2}C$, with similar expressions for $\angle CPA$ and $\angle APB$. It follows that P is the incentre I and the minimum value of the expression is $r(\cot\frac{1}{2}A + \cot\frac{1}{2}B + \cot\frac{1}{2}C) = \frac{1}{2}(a + b + c)$.

12. Note that triangles ABC and PQR are similar and similarly situated so that AP, BQ, CR are concurrent. Let r be the radius of the circumcircle of triangle ABC. Let ρ be the circumradius of triangle PQR, then since circle XYZ is the circumcircle of triangle PQR and since circle PQR is the nine-point circle of triangle XYZ we have $\rho = \frac{1}{2}r \leq \frac{1}{4}R$. Hence, since ABC and PQR are similar, we have $[ABC]/[PQR] = R^2/\rho^2 \geq 16$.

13. Let L, M, N be the centres of S_A, S_B, S_C respectively. Since the circles have equal radius triangle LMN is homothetic with triangle ABC. Let P be the centre of S. Then $LP = MP = NP = 2p$, so P is the circumcentre of triangle LMN and hence of ABC. Thus $\angle MPN = 2A$ and $MN = 4p \sin A$. (That this must exceed $2p$ accounts for the condition that $A < 30^\circ$.) Since S_B touches AB and BC, BM bisects $\angle ABC$ so the projection of BM on BC is $P(\cot\frac{1}{2}B + \cot\frac{1}{2}C) + 4p \sin A = BC = 2R \sin A$. The result now follows since

$$\cot\frac{1}{2}B + \cot\frac{1}{2}C = \frac{\cos\frac{1}{2}A}{(\sin\frac{1}{2}B \sin\frac{1}{2}C)},$$

$$\sin A = 2\sin\frac{1}{2}A \cos\frac{1}{2}A$$

and

$$\sin\frac{1}{2}A \sin\frac{1}{2}B \sin\frac{1}{2}C \leq \frac{1}{8}.$$

14. We have $(AI)(ID) = (BI)(IE) = (CI)(IF) = 2Rr$, since the products all equal the power of I with respect to the circumcircle and $OI^2 = R^2 - 2Rr$. So the required inequality is equivalent to $(AI)^2(BI)^2(CI)^2 \leq 8R^3r^3$. Now $AI = r\operatorname{cosec}\frac{1}{2}A$ etc., and a standard result is

$$r = 4R \sin\frac{1}{2}A \sin\frac{1}{2}B \sin\frac{1}{2}C.$$

The required inequality is therefore reduced to the standard result $\sin\frac{1}{2}A \sin\frac{1}{2}B \sin\frac{1}{2}C \leq \frac{1}{8}$.

15. By Apollonius's theorem $AG^2 = (2b^2 + 2c^2 - a^2)/9$. Now the areal co-ordinates of S are $(a^2, b^2, c^2)/(a^2 + b^2 + c^2)$, so the displacement $\mathbf{AS} = (-(b^2 + c^2), b^2, c^2)/(a^2 + b^2 + c^2)$. Using the areal metric we find that $AS/AG = 3bc/(a^2 + b^2 + c^2)$ and the inequality holds since $ab + bc + ca \leq a^2 + b^2 + c^2$.

16. Let L be the midpoint of BC. By Apollonius's theorem $AL^2 = l^2 = \frac{1}{4}(2b^2 + 2c^2 - a^2)$. Let the centre of the circle through A touching BC at L be O_1. Then if $\angle ALC = \theta$ we have $\angle LO_1A = 2\theta$ and since $O_1L = O_1A$ we have $l = 2R_1 \sin \theta$. Now, using the sine rule for triangle ALC we have

$$l = b \sin C / \sin \theta.$$

It follows that

$$R_1 = \frac{l^2}{2b \sin C}$$

and hence

$$\frac{R_1}{a} = \frac{R(2b^2 + c^2 - a^2)}{4abc}.$$

Adding in similar expressions for R_2/b and R_3/c we have

$$\frac{R_1}{a} + \frac{R_2}{b} + \frac{R_3}{c} = \frac{3R(a^2 + b^2 + c^2)}{4abc}.$$

By the Cauchy-Schwarz inequality the square of this is $\leq (R_1^2 + R_2^2 + R_3^2)(1/a^2 + 1/b^2 + 1/c^2)$. Hence $R_1^2 + R_2^2 + R_3^2 \geq$

$$\frac{9R^2(a^2 + b^2 + c^2)^2}{16(b^2c^2 + c^2a^2 + a^2b^2)} \geq \frac{27R^2}{16}.$$

17. Use result (5) on p. 259 with K at G. The points P are the ends of the diameter containing G, since these are the points where PG is a maximum or a minimum.

Chapter 18

Inequalities: Addendum

18.1 The Muirhead, Schur and Erdös-Mordell inequalities

18.1.1 Schur's Inequality

Muirhead's theorem and Schur's inequality are very powerful theorems which can be used to solve a large number of symmetric inequalities with little thought (although proficiency with algebra is definitely required). First, some notation. Let

$$\sum_{\text{sym}} x_1^{a_1} x_2^{a_2} \ldots x_n^{a_n} = \sum_{\sigma} x_{\sigma(1)}^{a_1} x_{\sigma(2)}^{a_2} \ldots x_{\sigma(n)}^{a_n}$$

where the sum on the right is taken over all permutations of

$$\{1, 2, \ldots, n\}.$$

Note that in the symmetric sum, every permutation is taken, even if the product is unchanged (which will happen if some of the a_i are the same). For example, if our variables are a, b, c, then $\sum_{sym} a^3 b^2 c^2 = a^3 b^2 c^2 + a^3 c^2 b^2 + b^3 a^2 c^2 + b^3 c^2 a^2 + c^3 a^2 b^2 + c^3 b^2 a^2$

We often write $[a_1, a_2, \ldots, a_n]$ for $\sum_{\text{sym}} x_1^{a_1} x_2^{a_2} \ldots x_n^{a_n}$; this is called bracket notation. There is a variation on this notation when we sum over all cyclic permutations of the variables, rather than all permutations. Thus $\sum_{cyc} a^3 b^2 c^2 = a^3 b^2 c^2 + b^3 a^2 c^2 + c^3 a^2 b^2$.

Theorem 24 [Schur's Inequality] Given non-negative real numbers x, y and z, it follows that when t is positive we have

$$x^t(x - y)(x - z) + y^t(y - z)(y - x) + z^t(z - x)(z - y) \geq 0.$$

Equality occurs if and only if either the three variables coincide or two coincide and the third is 0. Let us restate it using the cyclic sum notation:

$$\sum_{cyc} x^t(x - y)(x - z) \geq 0.$$

Proof   We may assume that $x \geq y \geq z$. It is important to understand why we may assume this – it would be clear if we were summing over all permutations of the variables, but we are not!

Now consider the expression

$$x^t(x - y)(x - z) + y^t(y - z)(y - x) + z^t(z - x)(z - y)$$

$$= (x^t(x - y)(x - z) - y^t(x - y)(y - z)) + z^t(z - x)(z - y).$$

The last terms is non-negative. Also $0 \leq y^t \leq x^t$ and $0 \leq y - z \leq x - z$. Thus the expression $x^t(x - y)(x - z) - y^t(x - y)(y - z)$ is non-negative and the inequality is established. Clearly Schur's inequality becomes an equality when the variables coincide or when two coincide and the third vanishes. A detailed analysis shows that this sufficient condition for equality is also necessary.

Exercise 18.1

1 Use bracket notation to express the AM/GM inequality

$$x_1^n + x_2^n + \ldots + x_n^n \geq x_1 x_2 \ldots x_n.$$

18.1.2 Muirhead's Inequality

Muirhead's theorem is a way of showing that one symmetric sum is always greater than or equal to another, subject to a condition on the exponents known as majorization. . It is defined as follows. Let $(a_1, a_2, \ldots, a_n)$ and $(b_1, b_2, \ldots, b_n)$ be sequences of real numbers. Then $(a_1, a_2, \ldots, a_n)$ is said to *majorize* $(b_1, b_2, \ldots, b_n)$ if:

1. (a_i) and (b_i) are decreasing sequences,

2. $a_1 + \ldots + a_n = b_1 + \ldots + b_n$,

3. $a_1 + \ldots + a_i \geq b_1 + \ldots + b_i$ for $1 \leq i \leq n$

This is written $(a_1, a_2, \ldots, a_n) \succ (b_1, b_2, \ldots, b_n)$.

   Now suppose $A = (a_1, \ldots, a_n)$ and $B = (b_1, \ldots, b_n)$ are two sequences with $A \succ B$. If A and B are not the same, then since $a_1 + \ldots + a_n = b_1 + \ldots + b_n$, we must have $a_i < b_i$ for some i. Choose the smallest such i, and let that be k. Since $a_1 \geq b_1$, $k > 1$. We have $a_{k-1} \geq b_{k-1} \geq b_k > a_k$. Consider the sequence $A' = (a'_1, \ldots, a'_n)$ defined as follows:
$a'_i = a_i$ if $i \neq k - 1, k$. If $a_{k-1} - b_{k-1} \geq b_k - a_k$ then $a'_k = b_k$ and $a'_{k-1} = a_{k-1} + a_k - b_k$. Otherwise, set $a'_{k-1} = b_{k-1}$ and $a'_k = a_k + a_{k-1} - b_{k-1}$. In other words, we slide a_k and a_{k-1} closer together, keeping their sum the same, until one of them is equal to the corresponding member of B.

Lemma 25

$$A \succ A' \succ B$$

Proof Since $a_k + a_{k-1} = a'_k + a'_{k-1}$, and aside from these two terms A and A' are identical, we only need show that

1. The sequence A' is still decreasing and,

2. $a_1 + \ldots + a_{k-1} \geq a'_1 + \ldots + a'_{k-1} \geq b_1 + \ldots + b_n$.

Since when we formed A' we decreased a_{k-1} and increased a_k, the only way the sequence can not be decreasing is if $a'_{k-1} < a'_k$. We consider the case $a_{k-1} - b_{k-1} \geq b_k - a_k$; the other case is similar. If $a'_{k-1} < a'_k$, then $a_{k-1} + a_k - b_k < b_k$, so

$$a_{k-1} - b_{k-1} \leq a_{k-1} - b_k < b_k - a_k$$

which is a contradiction. So we have shown 1).

For 2), we note that $a_{k-1} \geq a'_k \geq b_k$ and also $a_1 + \ldots + a_{k-2} = a'_1 + \ldots + a'_{k-2} \geq b_1 + \ldots + b_{k-2}$. ∎

We can now prove

Theorem 26 [Muirhead's Theorem] If $(a_1, \ldots, a_n) \succ (b_1, \ldots, b_n)$, then

$$\sum_{\text{sym}} x_1^{a_1} x_2^{a_2} \ldots x_n^{a_n} \geq \sum_{\text{sym}} x_1^{b_1} x_2^{b_2} \ldots x_n^{b_n} \tag{18.1}$$

for **non-negative** variables $x_1, x_2, \ldots, x_n$.

Proof We use induction on the number n of variables. In case $n = 2$ we have

$$x_1^{b_1} x_2^{b_2} \left(x_1^{a_1 - b_1} - x_2^{b_2 - a_2} \right) \left(x_2^{b_2 - a_1} - x_1^{a_2 - b_1} \right)$$

$$= x_1^{a_1} x_2^{a_2} + x_1^{a_2} x_2^{a_1} - x_1^{b_1} x_2^{b_2} - x_1^{b_2} x_2^{b_1}.$$

This is easily confirmed by expanding the left hand side, remembering that $a_1 + a_2 = b_1 + b_2$. Now, since the left hand side is symmetric in x_1 and x_2, we may assume $x_1 \geq x_2$. Then $\left(x_1^{a_1 - b_1} - x_2^{b_2 - a_2}\right) \geq 0$ since $a_1 - b_1 = b_2 - a_2 \geq 0$ and $\left(x_2^{b_2 - a_1} - x_1^{a_2 - b_1}\right) \geq 0$ as $b_2 - a_1 = a_2 - b_1 \leq 0$.

Induction step Suppose that the result is true for $n = k - 1$. If A is a sequence, then $[A]$ will represent the symmetric sum formed by the elements of A. Let A' be the sequence formed from A and B in Lemma 18.1.2. Let a_i and a_{i+1} be the places where the sequence has been changed. Suppose $j \in \{i, i+1\}$ such that $a'_j = b_j$. Then the sequence $A' \setminus a'_j$ majorizes $B \setminus b_j$. Also, $(a_i, a_{i+1}) \succ (b_i, b_{i+1})$. Now,

$$
\begin{aligned}
[A'] &= \sum_{\text{sym}} \left(x_1^{a_1} \cdots x_{i-1}^{a_{i-1}} x_{i+1}^{a_{i+1}} \cdots x_k^{a_k} \sum_{\text{sym}} x_i^{a'_i} x_{i+1}^{a'_{i+1}} \right) \\
&\leq \sum_{\text{sym}} \left(x_1^{a_1} \cdots x_{i-1}^{a_{i-1}} x_{i+1}^{a_{i+1}} \cdots x_k^{a_k} \sum_{\text{sym}} x_i^{a_i} x_{i+1}^{a_{i+1}} \right) \\
&= [A]
\end{aligned}
$$

by the case $n = 2$.

Also,

$$
\begin{aligned}
[A'] &= \sum_{\text{sym}} \left(x_i^{a'_i} x_{i+1}^{a'_{i+1}} \sum_{\text{sym}} x_1^{a_1} \cdots x_{i-1}^{a_{i-1}} x_{i+1}^{a_{i+1}} \cdots x_k^{a_k} \right) \\
&\geq \sum_{\text{sym}} \left(x_i^{a'_i} x_{i+1}^{a'_{i+1}} \sum_{\text{sym}} x_1^{b_1} \cdots x_{i-1}^{b_{i-1}} x_{i+1}^{b_{i+1}} \cdots x_k^{b_k} \right) \\
&= [B]
\end{aligned}
$$

by the inductive hypothesis.

So

$$[A] \geq [A'] \geq [B]$$

∎

Example 18.1

If a, b, $c \geq 0$ prove that

$$\frac{a}{b+c} + \frac{b}{c+a} + \frac{c}{a+b} \geq \frac{3}{2}$$

Multiply both sides by $(a + b)(b + c)(c + a)$ and expanding brackets we find that the inequality is equivalent to

$$2(a^3 + b^3 + c^3) \geq (a^2b + b^2a + b^2c + c^2b + c^2a + a^2c).$$

In bracket notation, this is $[3, 0, 0] \geq [2, 1, 0]$; since $3 + 0 + 0 = 2 + 1 + 0$, $3 \geq 2$, $3 + 0 \geq 2 + 1$, this is true by Muirhead's Theorem.

Example 18.2

Given that $abc = 1$ and a, b, $c > 0$, show that

$$\frac{b+c}{1+a} + \frac{c+a}{1+b} + \frac{a+b}{1+c} \geq 3.$$

Multiply it all out, it turns out that we want

$$2([2, 1, 0] + [2, 0, 0] + [1, 1, 0] + [1, 0, 0])$$

$$\geq [0, 0, 0] + 3[1, 0, 0] + 3[1, 1, 0] + [1, 1, 1].$$

Now we use the condition $abc = 1$ to homogenize this. We make all the terms degree three by multiplying by $(abc)^k = 1$. This is the same as adding k to each term inside the square brackets. So we have reduced the problem to:

$$2\left([2,1,0] + \left[\frac{7}{3},\frac{1}{3},\frac{1}{3}\right] + \left[\frac{4}{3},\frac{4}{3},\frac{1}{3}\right] + \left[\frac{5}{3},\frac{2}{3},\frac{2}{3}\right]\right) \geq$$

$$\geq [1,1,1] + 3\left[\frac{5}{3},\frac{2}{3},\frac{2}{3}\right] + 3\left[\frac{4}{3},\frac{4}{3},\frac{1}{3}\right] + [1,1,1].$$

This is true by Muirhead's theorem as, each term on the left majorizes each term on the right.

Note that in the last example we multiplied out first and then homogenized; this is generally wise, as it simplifies the algebra.

Exercises 18.2

Unless otherwise stated, all variables are positive reals.

2 Prove that

$$27(x+y)^2(y+z)^2(z+x)^2 \geq 64xyz(x+y+z)^3.$$

3 Show:

$$\left(\frac{a}{b}+\frac{b}{a}\right)\left(\frac{b}{c}+\frac{c}{b}\right)\left(\frac{c}{a}+\frac{a}{c}\right) \geq 2\left(1+\frac{a+b+c}{\sqrt[3]{abc}}\right).$$

4 If a, , b, c are the sides of a triangle, and $a+b+c=6$, show that

$$12(3-a)(3-b)(3-c)\left(\frac{1}{a^2}+\frac{1}{b^2}+\frac{1}{c^2}\right) \leq \frac{7(a^2+b^2+c^2)}{2}.$$

5 Let $xyz = 1$. Prove that

$$\frac{x^3}{(1+y)(1+z)} + \frac{y^3}{(1+z)(1+x)} + \frac{z^3}{(1+x)(1+y)} \geq \frac{3}{4}.$$

6 Let $xyz \geq 1$. Show that

$$\frac{x^5 - x^2}{x^5 + y^2 + z^2} + \frac{y^5 - y^2}{x^2 + y^5 + z^2} + \frac{z^5 - z^2}{x^2 + y^2 + z^5} \geq 0.$$

18.1.3   Erdös-Mordell inequality

Theorem 27 [Erdös-Mordell] Let ABC be a triangle and P a point in its interior. Let the foot of the perpendicular from P to BC be P_A. Define P_B and P_C in similar fashion. Then

$$2(PP_A + PP_B + PP_C) \leq PA + PB + PC$$

with equality if, and only if, the triangle is equilateral.

Proof There are now many proofs known of this result. We refer the reader to *Forum Geometricorum*, a free access geometry journal on the internet in the hope that he or she will explore the articles at leisure. A proof of this theorem can be found in Hojoo Lee's article, pages 7–8 of Volume 1. See `http://forumgeom.fau.edu/`

Index